DARWIN—A Novel

DARWIN—A Novel

S. A. Prio

For Sophia

Novels, those works of the imagination, though not of a very high order, have been for years a wonderful relief to me, so much so that I often bless all novelists. I like any novel well enough if moderately good, and if it does not end unhappily (against which occurrence a law ought to be passed). But those novels that I rank the highest must, according to my tastes, contain some person I can thoroughly love, and if a pretty woman—then all the better.

—The Autobiography of Charles Darwin, *1876*

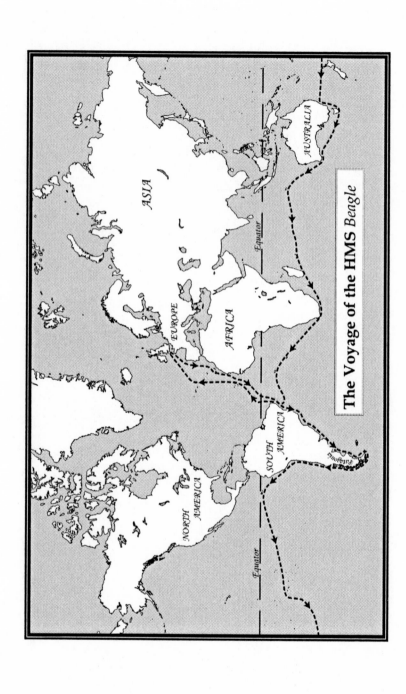

The Voyage of the HMS *Beagle*

1

DARWIN FELT THE HOT BLOOD in his eyes, sensed the hatred of the two women who had smashed his skull with sharp stones from the riverbed, the firelight from the burning village behind them fringing their bodies in the darkness. The blood flooded into his eyes so that he could barely make out the fists, each clenching a stone, dropping toward his face for another blow. The fire flared behind them as the roofs of their houses caught, filling his sight with the redness of flames seen though blood. And then darkness blotted up the light.

A pinpoint of red grew into the glowing tip of Lucy's cigar. Darwin was on his back, flaccid after their first time together, his first with anyone, the night screeches of the Brazilian rainforest all around. Orange smoke curled out of the corners of the beautiful mouth of the ambassador's daughter as she drew so hard on the cigar that its tip burst into flames.

Orange smoke turned into flames leaping among the pieces of dry driftwood and guanaco dung as Old Bernantio, squatting on the other side of the campfire, told the stories of his people. "When Walleechu first created all the animals," he began, "each one knew the place where it properly belonged." But Darwin already knew the story, as if he had heard it before, from the war among the tribes of animals to the truce in which their ambassadors agreed that each tribe must in future keep to its own territory and consort only with its own kind, those with scales together, those with hair together, and so on.

The dancing flames of the campfire became the curly red hair of Captain Fitzroy shaking from side to side in disapproval. Darwin's ideas about the origin of species were wrong. Everything about the voyage of the *Beagle* was wrong Fitzroy's shaking curls insisted until they became the red Phrygian caps of General Rosas's troops encamped beside the Rio Negro. "My plan is to kill every male, whether man or baby, and every female old enough to breed," Rosas proclaimed, standing tall in his tent while he pointed at the maps spread out before him. "The girls will be sold in Buenos Aires. Not a single Indian will be left to interfere with the Argentine nation's settlement of the pampas."

Like drying blood, the redness began to lose its brilliance, becoming the gore-besmirched torso of one of the general's victims. The corpse hung upside down from an ombu tree along the road to Buenos Aires, a dark pile of entrails spilling from the gashed abdomen onto the ground beside a face. First that face belonged to Augustus Earle, Lord Palmerston's secret agent with whom Darwin had crossed the Patagonian desert.

Then, as the face faded into darkness, it became Darwin's own, warmed by the fireplace in the public room at the Devonport Inn. The winter gale that blew up the English Channel out of the Atlantic chilled the town of Plymouth. Darwin consoled himself that while such contrary winds might have kept HMS *Beagle* from sailing for two full weeks, he had at least been able to stay ashore rather than abide the cramped quarters aboard. He was ship's naturalist, but his status as a civilian supernumerary required no set duties and allowed him the freedom to busy himself in town. He had used the time to write long letters, sharing his hopes and trepidations with family and friends he would not see for the next two years. He had made several purchases to fill out his kit. He smiled as he thought of the rifle and two pistols he had bought at a good price in a pawnshop near the dockyard. And he had read another few volumes of von Humboldt's account of a journey through the wilds of South America, not to mention having begun Lyell's iconoclastic *Principles of Geology*.

This Boxing Day morning he sat beside the big fireplace in the inn's public room. His eyes were fixed on the copy of Lyell that lay open on the table. But rather than concentrating on geology, he was yet again dwelling on the wisdom of agreeing to sail on a voyage around the world. The prospect seemed more ominous with every day stuck in port. He had almost no experience with ships. He had never even been out of sight of land, and the *Beagle* seemed so tiny compared to the immensity of the open ocean.

Most worrying of all was the delay in leaving. He feared it would exhaust his resolve. At this rate, the planned voyage of two years could stretch into four or more. Thus far seafaring seemed to consist of waiting in port for favorable winds. And judging by the men who filled the inn's tables, the blue coats of naval officers contrasting with the scarlet of marines, gambling at whist would be the requisite entertainment during much of that time. Such men had learned how to dull the monotony of blockading French ports year after year and, since Waterloo, the monotony of life ashore on half pay while waiting for the next war. This time they had already been waiting an unprecedented decade and a half, with no relief in sight, victims of their own success.

Back home in Shrewsbury, he lamented, the family home would yesterday have been full of Christmas cheer. His father, being a popular doctor and community patriarch, never lacked for company dropping by. Darwin thought of singing around the piano, of warm pies, and of walks in the woods with his sisters and brother.

And Fanny might be visiting. Last autumn, riding in the woods together to hunt pheasants, they had kissed on the lips, and she had let him reach under her skirts to feel a smooth, soft thigh. He blushed a little to relive the rush of excitement while sitting in the public room of an inn.

Here, far from the comfortable familiarity of Shrewsbury, he felt as oddly displaced as a creature from the bottom of the sea he had agreed to sail on—and as lonely. He tried to concentrate on Lyell, but the account so contradicted Scripture that he felt overwhelmed, lost, disoriented. He desperately needed to discuss such ideas among learned company, but Plymouth was not Cambridge, nor even Shrewsbury. If not for the constant clamor of the card players, which provided at least a semblance of company, he might have returned to his room after breakfast.

A loud "Mister Dahwin!" interrupted his gloomy thoughts. Just inside the door stood Captain Fitzroy, a stocky young man with curly red hair and the hawkish, aristocratic features of his Stewart ancestors. "The weather is changing, Dahwin. I believe the wind will veer during the night and we will be able to sail at dawn. The jolly boat will collect you at noon." Fitzroy did not make the slightest gesture of reassurance, not even a grin, before turning to the door and leaving a startled Darwin to dwell on the news.

A glance through the window, revealed the captain in his dripping navy cloak hurrying up the street in the direction of the Admiralty offices. A civilian in unadorned black accompanied him. Darwin could not be sure without seeing the face but thought he recognized the tall figure of Augustus Earle, the artist Fitzroy had engaged for the voyage. The captain no doubt needed to check for final orders before sailing, but Darwin could think of no reason for an artist to report to the admiral.

When he had first met Earle on board two weeks ago, the artist was well spoken and had seemed pleasant enough but also quite guarded, to the point of making the introduction somewhat uncomfortable. Of course all the new shipmates had been somewhat reserved upon first meeting each other, as anyone would expect. Those who would be so closely confined together for month after month had no wish to offend each other from the outset or, worse, reveal minority opinions on sensitive topics. Who knew what might fester only to flare up after months at sea? Even the highest-ranking officers took time to reveal themselves, listening first for idiom and intonation. Navy rank, after all, was one thing and social rank altogether something else. Yet Earle had been a little too reticent, all the more strange since he and Darwin were to be rare civilians aboard a navy ship and might naturally have felt drawn together.

As for Robert Fitzroy, Darwin had know him only since meeting in London in September and had as yet not formed a strong opinion of the young captain, who at twenty-six was only four years his senior. Fitzroy certainly seemed dedicated to duty and expert in it, commendably so. He could not otherwise have been promoted so rapidly, whatever his lineage, especially given the current peace. Yet he was perhaps too preoccupied with duty, to the point of obsession, and exceedingly serious even on social occasions. His family's reputation for lunacy also worried Darwin. He recalled that an uncle, no less than the famous Lord Londonderry who had been the Tory Secretary of War, had slit his own throat with a penknife a few years ago.

Nonetheless, Darwin's professors had all praised Fitzroy as having been an intelligent and likable student. Doctor Henslow had even ventured that the two young men were so similar in inclination and ability that if they had overlapped at Cambridge they would have been close friends. Both also exhibited a strong spirituality. Darwin was entertaining the possibility of becoming a parson, and Fitzroy seemed bent on Christianizing the indigenes of South America. He had returned from his last voyage with four Fuegians. Now, a year later, one of them was dead of smallpox, but the other three had been schooled in English, Christianity, the horticultural and domestic arts, and other diverse aspects of civilized life. Fitzroy planned to return them in that enlightened state to Tierra del Fuego. An Anglican missionary would accompany them, and together they would establish, through example and leadership, the seeds of civilization in that land at the ends of the Earth.

Of course Fitzroy's character was critical to Darwin, he reflected. If most aspects of seafaring remained mysterious to him, the first principle seemed obvious—the success of any voyage depended, at bottom, on the captain. While Fitzroy was without question an intriguing fellow, his family's aristocratic lunacy and his own overly serious demeanor remained somewhat worrisome. If he broke down under the pressures of command, everyone aboard the *Beagle* would suffer the consequences.

Yet, Darwin reprimanded himself, to quit the voyage now because of vague doubts about Fitzroy's sanity would itself be lunacy. Tomorrow, finally, they would sail for all the exotic places he had read about. The jungles of Brazil, the pampas of Argentina, the deserts of Patagonia all awaited with little-known plants and animals, spectacular geology, and who knew what else. Beyond Tierra del Fuego and the Straits of Magellan, the fronds of palm trees beckoned in the trade winds, crowning the white sand beaches of the atolls that speckled the vast Pacific.

To be sure, he reflected, the voyage's main purpose was more mundane than visiting exotic places. The *Beagle* was to chart the southern coasts of South America. Fitzroy had already undertaken one such survey as first lieutenant aboard the *Beagle* and now was to further that work as her captain. He had refitted her with all the latest instrumentation, including two-dozen chronometers to determine longitude and the new Massey's Patented Sounding Leads. To match that capacity to chart, Fitzroy also intended to collect plant and animal specimens, note geology, and describe whatever other unknown phenomena presented themselves. Darwin and Earle would fulfill that much more exciting, to the young naturalist, secondary goal of the voyage.

All qualms thus buried under visions of exotic landscapes, Darwin was waiting at the quay when the jolly boat arrived. He had even put aside that morning's doubts about the adequacy of the tiny *Beagle*, anchored well out in Barnett Pool but clearly visible now that the rain had stopped. He had become so excited at the prospect of finally getting underway that he stumbled when boarding the jolly boat, enticing the seaman at the tiller into testing the mettle of an obvious lubber.

"Beggin' your pardon, guv'nor. She's a right small sloop, *Beagle* is, don't you say? For a voyage roun' the world, I means, sir."

Darwin, startled at the question, stammered, "A sloop?! A sloop...? Captain Fitzroy told me it was a brig...."

"Well, she's a sloop 'cause she's small, sir, not even two fifty ton and no more'n ninety foot stem to stern. Havin' two masts be what's makes 'er a brig, sir."

"But it's got three masts!"

"Aye, that she do, guv'nor, now. But she were built wi' two. The yard just added the mizzenmast a few weeks ago, turnin' 'er into a barque. 'Er be a ship 'cept on account the mizzen's rigged fore an' aft. That's what's make 'er a barque, sir."

"A barque? Not a ship? A brig? Bloody hell, man!"

"Just as you say, sir. Coffin brig us calls this type on 'count o' the hellish lack o' freeboard, what's puts 'er awash right easy wi' any sort of sea runnin', sir."

Darwin let the sailors have their silent laugh behind their beards, making no comment and turning inward again, where he had often found himself since arriving in Plymouth. He even chuckled at himself. A year ago he never would have imagined that he would now be here, about to embark on a voyage around the world with these rough men. He neither knew much nor wanted to know much about ships—and even less about something called, apparently, barques. He had first experienced sea travel only a few weeks ago, while taking the steam packet from London to Plymouth. He had treated that short trip as a trial of his seamanship, to judge if he would be susceptible to seasickness and if he would be able to endure, if not enjoy, the cramped life aboard. He felt he had passed on both counts. The details of masts and rigging need be no concern of his. Still, the term coffin brig worried him.

They had drawn close to the *Beagle* now, and he was comforted by her businesslike appearance if not her tiny size. Fitzroy had spared no effort in equipping the brig to complete the immense task before them. He had assured Darwin that the *Beagle*, once refitted, would be like her canine namesake: small but quite capable and dogged in pursuit of her mission.

As the jolly boat pulled up to the gangway and the sailors tossed their oars, Darwin recalled that during the refit the dockyard had indeed added the mizzen, purportedly to aid maneuverability in the inshore waters where their mission would take them. They had also added a sheathing of two-inch fir planks over the oak hull to guard against catastrophe while working close in to reefs. An outer skin of new copper would resist the boring of teredo worms in the Pacific. She looked very earnest with her black and white paint, the fresh copper glistening just above the gray chop of the harbor. Running from the copper up to the top of each mast, Harris's Patented Lightning Conductors would guard against the ferocious lightning storms they could expect in the tropics. In addition to the jolly boat, six other boats built to Fitzroy's specifications would allow exploration of shallow estuaries. The victulator had provided ample provisions, much of it in the form of tins of Kilner and Moorsom's Patented Preserves of meats, vegetables, and soups. Stores of antiscorbutics such as lemon juice and pickles would keep them all healthy. And, dearest of all to Darwin's heart, ample supplies of jars, barrels, and preservatives would keep his botanical and zoological specimens from spoiling.

As Darwin looked up at the perilous looking gangway ladder, he saw Augustus Earle watching him over the bulwark. Whatever had occupied him at the Admiralty offices had not taken long. By the time Darwin had scrambled awkwardly up to the deck, though, the artist had disappeared.

The *Beagle* churned with final preparations. A chain of sailors was noisily passing water casks down into the hold. Officers were directing other work gangs to check cordage and sails. Fitzroy would want no accidents while leaving port under the gaze of the Admiral's telescope.

Darwin looked up at the rigging and just shook his head at the seeming tangle of rope. He wished the *Beagle* were a steamer, like the London-Plymouth packet. No weight of intricate rigging and obscuring sails would hang overhead, dependent on capricious winds and justifying the jargon that sailors used to the confusion of passengers. The packet had been elegant in its simplicity, the slim stack sending up its column of smoke while the paddlewheels steadily pushed her along the coast straight into the wind. But the *Beagle* was not a steamer. The Royal Navy was too stodgy to rush into such new technology and too cautious during peacetime to become reliant on coal that was not as ubiquitously available and free as wind.

With barely acknowledged greetings to his preoccupied shipmates, Darwin quickly made his way aft toward his cabin under the poop. Strong smells of paint, tar, and rosin alternated in the crisp air as he picked his way among the gear, ropes and men that filled the deck.

As he opened the door, his teenage servant, Syms Covington, welcomed him to what officially was the chartroom but on this voyage would serve as Darwin's accommodation. "Greetings, Mister Darwin. They were working on charts earlier so the stove has been going a while and your cabin's nice and warm. I'll just fetch your baggage from the gangway."

"Thank you," replied Darwin as he took off his cloak and hung it by the stove. As Syms shut the door, it somewhat broke the waves of noise coming from the deck, and he turned to look around the cramped cabin he had first seen two weeks ago. It seemed even smaller than he remembered, his imagination having enlarged it during the time ashore. It was only ten feet on a side, with bookcases, cabinets, a wardrobe, a washstand, and the stove lining the walls. A large table dominated the center of the space, leaving a strip of open floor no more than two feet wide to walk around, all the while cracking one's skull on the deck beams and tripping over the tiller ropes. Even at that, the mizzenmast angled down through the cabin and obstructed the narrow strip of open floor to the right of the door, thereby making a complete circuit of the table impossible. Under the skylight, a hammock hung above the charts spread on the table.

When Syms returned and was stowing the baggage, Darwin asked, "Who was looking at charts, Syms?"

"Why, it was the captain and Mister Earle, sir. Also, the captain asked that you join him and the senior officers in their mess at eight bells."

Darwin, curious, inspected the charts. Many were rolled and piled on shelves under the table, but a few were spread out as if in use, weighed down with heavy brass dividers and rulers. On top was a chart of the coast of Brazil around Rio de Janeiro. Darwin could not imagine what in particular might have occupied Fitzroy and Earle, and no pencil marks betrayed their purpose.

Little the wiser, he shooed Syms out of the cabin and began a final check of the equipment he had brought aboard upon first arriving in Plymouth. Anything forgotten now would be difficult to acquire en route. Eight bells in the afternoon watch, four o'clock, would leave time to do a thorough inventory. The wardrobe seemed in order, so Darwin turned to the instrument cabinet. He had been able to borrow some of the items from the British Museum. Most of the rest he had purchased in London. The microscope, made by Bancks & Son in their workshop on The Strand, rested snugly in its padded wooden box. An array of square leather cases held various compasses, altimeters, and clinometers. They would be essential for geological work. A larger, cylindrical case held the refracting telescope, also made by Robert Bancks. The thermometers and hygrometer, with its delicate mechanism actuated by the tension of a human hair, would serve to determine atmospheric conditions. The camera obscura would help him to accurately draw specimens. Every single one would be sketched, cataloged as to location and behavior, wrapped or bottled, skinned or dried, and packed away in the hold in crates for shipment to Henslow in Cambridge. Syms had wrapped the instrument cases in tarred sailcloth to keep out the damp, then fitted them tightly into the cabinet, padding with more cloth where necessary to prevent any shifting as the *Beagle* rolled. Darwin took his time reassuring himself that every piece of equipment was in working order before carefully redoing Sym's handiwork. Then he placed the guns and boxes of percussion caps and cartridges he had just brought aboard in the chest beside the washstand.

Everything seemed to be well stowed so he turned to the bookcases that held the brig's library, opening the glass doors that would keep the salt air and the rats from the paper. The five volumes of Cuvier's *Recherches sur les Ossemens Fossiles des Quadrupèdes* rested next to the four of von Humboldt's *Personal Narrative of Travels to the Equinoctial Regions of the New Continent*. Beside them, he slipped in the three Humboldt volumes he had taken ashore and Lyell's *Principles of Geology*. Fitzroy had contributed such volumes of Hakluyt's *Principal Navigations* and Purchas's *Pilgrimes* as were relevant to their itinerary as well as a few fuller accounts such as Father Falconer's book on the Jesuits in Patagonia. Reference volumes on botany, zoology, surveying, phrenology, astronomy, taxidermy, and Spanish and Portuguese grammar, rounded out the small library. Milton's *Paradise Lost* and *Paradise Regained* would provide a bit of an antidote to all the science.

Darwin pulled *Paradise Lost* from its shelf and began to flip through the dozen cantos. He knew the lines so well from long hours of study that he barely saw the words, reflecting instead on Milton. The great poet had also studied for the clergy at Christ's College in Cambridge. But he had ultimately decided not to enter the Church, to instead further and share his spirituality through writing. Could, Darwin wondered, he ever attain that sort of self-discipline? Or did he require the structure of the Church to lead a productive life? He did not want to become like his brother, Erasmus. 'Ras seemed to be adrift, ostensibly pursuing a career but in reality doing little but spending the stipend their disappointed father provided.

Only the striking of eight bells finally distracted Darwin from his musings, and he quickly hurried down to the officers' mess. Crowded around the long table were the people who would lead this expedition and the other two supernumeraries. They, like Darwin, were essentially Fitzroy's guests and had no official standing in the Royal Navy. With some twinges of guilt, Darwin noted that the entire mess was no bigger than his own cabin and that the officer's cabins giving onto the mess, some with doors standing open, were little more than half the size, albeit not burdened by a monstrously huge chart table.

Darwin was slightly late, the last to arrive. When he entered the rest grumbled their greetings and immediately turned toward the head of the table, where Fitzroy stood expectantly. Everyone had already been introduced over the past several weeks, so their captain launched straight into his briefing.

"Gentlemen, we have seventy-two souls aboard, all men but the one Fuegian girl. It is our duty to lead them in our multifarious purpose. I'm afraid that our service to the King will be rather more humble than that of our predecessors against the Frogs and Dagos—but, nonetheless, not unimportant. What we lack in prize money, we will make up for in a multitude of additions to scientific knowledge and our Lord's flock."

As Fitzroy paused, a compliant mixture of agreeable murmur and knowing chuckle spread around the table. On one side of it stood the two lieutenants, John Wickham and Matthew Sullivan, Sergeant Beareley of the Royal Marines, and the sailing master, Edward Chaffers. The master was striking, his face so deeply lined and tanned by a life on deck that it might have been one of the fossils Darwin hoped to collect. The others were all much younger, in their twenties, but like the master looked to be confident, sanguine men who knew that next to the captain they would shoulder the bulk of the responsibility for the voyage. Across the table stood the senior warrant officers—the surgeon and the purser, Robert MacCormick and George Rowlett. They made a matched set, both well into their thirties: the surgeon short, thin, nervous, and Irish; the purser short, fat, lymphatic, and Scottish. The two midshipmen, Arthur Mellersh and Philip King, barely into their teens, skinny and awkward, pressed their narrow backsides as close against the wall as possible. Beside and towering over Darwin stood the enigmatic Earle. Even his age seemed indeterminate, anywhere between thirty and fifty, thought Darwin. Richard Matthews, the Anglican missionary charged with the daunting task of converting Tierra del Fuego, nervously hovered next to Fitzroy. He was about the same age as the captain and Darwin, as tall as Earle, but gangling where the artist was muscular.

"As you will not be unaware," continued Fitzroy, "our main purpose is to survey the coasts of South America, principally those of Patagonia, Tierra del Fuego, and the Chilean archipelago. Those coasts remain largely uncharted in any detail, but we know they are forbidding, lending all the more import to charting their few safe anchorages and supply points. In addition," he continued without an iota of sarcasm, "we are to continue westward across the Pacific in order to circumnavigate the globe. Our highly precise set of chronometers will allow us to fix the longitude of key locations and thereby resolve the disagreements that currently exist over said locations among the leading authorities. All of which will be quite a feather in our cap, so to speak. Now that Britain controls the seas, the Admiralty is highly desirous of promoting safe and rapid shipping to all parts of the globe by providing reliable charts that are accurate and precise in all respects. Our particular part in fulfilling that objective, and a not unimportant part, is to chart potential bases out of which to patrol the South Atlantic sea-lanes and approaches to Cape Horn, it being, as you are all not unaware, a shorter passage to the South Pacific than the Cape of Good Hope. In addition, I have taken on Misters Darwin and Earle here as supernumeraries, at my own expense, to record and collect all manner of exotic phenomena we will most certainly encounter. And, finally, the Admiralty has sanctioned the return of our three Fuegians to their own land and the establishment there of an Anglican mission, again, not in small part at my own expense. Mister Matthews here has been charged with undertaking that brave project. Perhaps one day civilized indigenes will succor sailors who wreck rounding the Horn and we, gentlemen, will have a not insignificant part of the credit for it."

Darwin, easily bored by pontification, allowed his thoughts to drift. While in London, he had heard quite a lot about the Fuegians, whom he had yet to meet. Apparently, while surveying the coast of Tierra del Fuego on the previous voyage of the *Beagle*, a party had taken a whaleboat to spend a few days exploring a narrow inlet. One morning they had woken to find the boat gone. The beach where they had dragged it up was empty except for the thieves' footprints. After roundly cursing themselves for having failed to set a watch, they had built a rough craft from driftwood and the sail they had used as a tent. Blessed by fine weather, unusual enough in those latitudes, they had reached the *Beagle* late the next day. Pringle Stokes, the captain on that voyage, had spent an entire week chasing the stolen boat. Each village had turned up some article, an oarlock or piece of rope, but never the boat itself. The Fuegian inhabitants had invariably fled into the forest, but Stokes did manage to capture three young men and a girl, intending to barter them in return for the boat. That strategy had been futile, however, the boat apparently being much more valuable to its new owners than the freedom of their kin. The hostages had nonetheless proven so valuable as guides and so generally intelligent, quickly grasping the rudiments of English, that Fitzroy had requested leave to take charge of them at his own expense, educate them in England, and return them home at some future opportunity. Little had anyone known then that Stokes would die on that voyage, Fitzroy assume command of the *Beagle*, and his opportunity to return the Fuegians come so soon.

"So!," continued Fitzroy, interrupting Darwin's musings. "You can see that our mission is indeed multifarious, so to speak. The Admiralty has projected that we might accomplish all within two years. I am not unconfident that we shall not disappoint. Are there any questions, gentlemen?"

Chaffers, who had been on the previous voyage and, in fact, had commanded the party that had lost the whaleboat, glanced around to be sure of having the floor before raising his gravelly voice: "Think we'll ever get that blasted boat back, Cap'n?"

"No, Mister Chaffers; it's likely firewood by now. But we carry a headstone made of good Scottish granite for Captain Stokes, who, as you'll remember, sorely resented having to give up on that boat. Four years is long to make do with a wooden cross, but I expect it's still standing at Port Famine and that we'll find his grave so as to make it up to him."

"Amen to that, sir," said the master.

Of those present, the purser and surgeon had also served on the previous voyage. Now they were both looking intently back and forth between Chaffers and Fitzroy. Some among the other eight shuffled uncomfortably with this first articulation of a distinction between those who had shared something unspoken in Tierra del Fuego and those who had not.

"Then, gentlemen," exclaimed Fitzroy, reaching for a glass of port from the table, "I give you the King!"

The others took up their own glasses with a ragged chorus: "The King! God save the King!" The midshipmen showed the most gusto of all, with a high pitched but still rousing "God save King Billy!" After all, when a boy no older than them, King William had also served as a middy in American waters. It made no matter that in those days the whole world had been against Britain and very nearly destroyed the Royal Navy that now ruled the seas.

For the first time during the briefing, Fitzroy smiled. "Very good, gentlemen. Carry on if you will. Apprise your juniors of our activities. We sail on the morning ebb and there'll be no mistakes. There's always a chance for a slip 'twixt the crouch and the leap.' But make no mistake about it; we'll have no slips!"

As those who would not shortly be eating in the mess filed out of its narrow door, Fitzroy motioned to Darwin with his head and said, "Please be so good as to join me for dinner in my cabin, Dahwin."

As they crossed the passageway to Fitzroy's door, they could hear the volume of conversation in the officers' mess mounting. It seemed the same insipid mix of facetious sparring, clichéd puns, and stale jokes current among the whist players at the Devonport Inn. Darwin thought such chatter a bore but supposed it a small price to pay for sustaining spirits while minimizing conflicts. He suspected that by the time this voyage was over, minor habits would have become major irritants.

Fitzroy's cabin was twice the size of Darwin's and without a large chart table occupying most of it. The padded berth looked regal compared to a hammock. Doors led to a spacious storeroom aft and a private water closet. The storeroom held the food that Darwin's father had partially paid for and that the two would share at the small table. The skylight over the table pierced the quarterdeck just forward of the wheel. The discordant ticking of twenty-four chronometers filtered in through one of several other closet doors. Fitzroy's servant, Henry Fuller, and Syms had set a fine table of roast pork, potatoes, and carrots.

"I'll tell you this, Chawes," said Fitzroy as he peered over the rim of his wine glass after a sip, "when Henslow first wrote me about you, I could barely believe my luck. I thought I would have to suffer the voyage without any gentlemanly company at all. Yet here sits a Cambridge man! And you're thinking of joining the clergy as well! No prospect could warm my heart more."

"And the good doctor spoke even more highly of you, Robert. But your officers seem a likely enough bunch."

"Oh, yes. Competent, steadfast, and not unorderly. Wickham and Sullivan have gone through the Portsmouth naval school, of course. They know everything an officer ought to know and nothing more."

To Fuller and Syms, waiting for further orders as discreetly as possible in such a confined space, Fitzroy said "leave us in peace, if you please," and nodded toward the door.

Only after the two servants had gone, did he continue. "Sullivan in particular has a genius for spit and polish. Mellersh and King will also do, but none of the officers have gone to Eton or Shrewsbury or indeed to any school of any repute at all. And Cambridge!? Completely beyond them in the conception, I dare say!"

Darwin did not like such snobbery and tried to shift the conversation toward a more constructive direction. "I sorely miss Cambridge. We were a close bunch at Christ's College."

"Fond memories, indeed. I most miss the chapel at King's College. Say, did you know George Simmons when you were at Shrewsbury School? Birmingham borne and bred. Not enough of a Tory to go to Eton so he stayed closer to home. He would have been an upper boy when you started."

"Actually, yes. I fagged for him."

"Really, Chawes...? Hope he wasn't too hard on you, so to speak?"

"No, not much. Usual stuff. Found him quite a likeable chap."

Fitzroy suddenly raised his glass and voice in a toast: "Here's to your Shrewsbury, then, Chawes! Waterloo wasn't won on its playing fields, but it's one of the great schools nonetheless."

"Indeed, indeed," murmured Darwin into his glass, trying desperately to think of a topic that might elicit more interesting conversation. "Say, tell me, did you attend Doctor Sedgwick's geology lectures at Cambridge?"

"Geology is one of my passions actually, and partially because of Doctor Sedgwick's lectures. He could diagram the strata by waving his hands through the air."

"Well he's still at it. I ask because I've been reading Lyell's new book. His *Principles of Geology*. Disturbing in the extreme. It's as strikingly convincing as it is contrary to Scriptures. I keep at it only on the strength of Sedgwick's recommendation, you see?"

"Lyell does not convince me in the least. I've looked at his book. Mainly a load of unsubstantiated opinion, if you ask me. You must remember that he has not seen much of the world. A bit of England, a bit of the continent. The result is a wealth of philosophizing and a dearth of firsthand experience—typical for Oxford men, I must say. I've always closely observed the strata along the coasts I surveyed, and I invariably see evidence of the Noachian deluge, such as thick layers of fossilized marine shells in cliffs far above where the highest tides now reach."

"Yet," continued Darwin, for the first time feeling some enthusiasm for the conversation, "Lyell claims that such strata are due to the same slow, steady, inexorable, natural workings that we observe today. He abjures falling back on Biblical explanations such as the

Flood. Your marine strata, according to him, derive from the slow emergence of the land from the sea due to the pressures of volcanoes and earthquakes. In other places the land, he argues, has slowly submerged beneath the sea, in a sort of compensatory effect."

"Ah, Dahwin," Fitzroy shook his head in exaggerated exasperation, "I find it surprising that someone as familiar with Scriptures as yourself, more so than myself I would wager, should give credence to such irreligious speculations. The Flood was universal, contemporaneously and contiguously covering the Earth even unto the highest mountains. How else can you explain what I have seen...? There are vast level tracts of land in Patagonia, as you will see for yourself soon enough. As Lyell should see. Those tracts are strewn with the crushed remnants of shells, of the type that live in shallow waters just offshore but broken into sharp fragments as if from being suddenly and violently submerged under a great weight of water. They are not at all rounded as shells are when tossed repeatedly onto a beach by the natural action of surf as the tide slowly goes in and out. So, the sea must at one time have risen up quickly, crushing the shells under its weight as it rushed in upon the land, carrying the shells with it in one catastrophic flood. And when the waters receded, extensive tracts covered by sharply broken shells were exposed to the air. Do you follow? I have seen them with my own eyes—unlike Lyell."

"Quite, quite, Robert." Darwin did not appreciate being lectured at when he wanted to discuss. It wasn't quite condescension, but neither was it conversation. Yet at least his musings were finally finding voice. And Fitzroy, he had to allow, had a much broader experience of the world than himself.

"And if that catastrophic Flood," continued Fitzroy, "sent by the Almighty to cleanse the Earth, happened in those places I've seen, in the manner I've described, the tendency of fluids such as water being to equilibrium, so to speak, it must have happened everywhere the same. The many stories of floods among the tribes of the world, such as those of Tierra del Fuego, merely confirm my observations and Scripture."

"Well, you are right in that Lyell has not seen much beyond England. He perhaps relies overmuch on the descriptions of others. I'm greatly looking forward to seeing these Patagonian districts you mention...," Darwin trailed off.

"But anyone should see that the rocks of England Herself suffice to disprove Lyell's ideas. Are we to believe, as he claims, that the Earth is old enough that mighty mountains have been eroded down to hills by the slow action of the tides against the shore? You told me that you have traveled between Cambridge and Brighton. So you crossed the sand hills of the Weald between the chalk of the North and South Downs. Only the sea rushing in upon the land in a great and rapid and tumultuous deluge could have eroded out the chalk to expose the underlying strata of the Weald. If, instead, we posit the slow action of the tides we see today against chalk cliffs, as we can observe at Dover, the maximum rate of denudation we can possibly imagine is an inch per century. And at that rate the Earth would need to be a preposterous hundred million years or more old! Just to form the Weald! All perfectly impossible, my dear Chawes."

In the face of Fitzroy's conviction, Darwin could barely muster a rebuttal. "I'm sure you're right, Robert, but Lyell does point out that the Earth might indeed have such antiquity. He shows that types of plants and animals, now known only as fossils, occur in distinct rock strata. It's as if those species went extinct during different periods, when each of those strata was forming through the slow accumulation and consolidation of sediments. And, if we can accept that interpretation, then the Creator did not author all species at the same time but, rather, created new ones to replace those that went extinct during each period. Surely that process would have taken eons to transpire, Robert, perhaps even more than your hundred million years."

"Again, logic and observation give the lie to Lyell. That's a good one, eh?," chuckled Fitzroy, "the lie to Lyell.... But think on this. And I'll put it to you very clearly. God created all species when he created the Earth, as revealed in Genesis. Some went extinct during the Flood. The differentiation of their fossils into distinct strata is easily explained by the fact that objects of different densities sink to different depths in water. So it is no surprise that one finds large dinosaurs such as we do not find today in different strata than those in which we find small mollusks. Each sank to the depth corresponding to its density and became encased in the debris that swept down as the sea violently flooded in upon the land. When the waters receded, the strata became exposed to the air and hardened into rock. Ipso facto, Lyell is rubbish."

Darwin could only concede: "Robert, you're convincing. I can only look forward to seeing your Patagonian tracts of shattered shells for myself in the coming months."

After dinner, Fitzroy asked Darwin if he would like to see his chronometers while Fuller cleared the table and set up the chess set. When Fitzroy opened the closet, the dissonant ticking flooded into the cabin. Each wooden chronometer box nestled in a bed of sawdust within a compartment on one of two shelves. Each ticked at its own pitch and volume to contribute to the cacophony. Fitzroy pulled out and opened one box. Within, set in gimbals that ensured the mechanism remained perfectly level, rested a chronometer, about six inches in diameter, ticking loudly as its hands measured out Greenwich time.

"Fuller winds them once per day, beginning at exactly two bells in the forenoon watch," noted Fitzroy like a proud father. "As you can see, these are the best scientific chronometers, made by Molyneux, French, Morrice…, some of the finest instrument makers around. If I can't clear up the various confusions about longitude, no one can."

Darwin did his best to express enthusiasm but was too upset that he had not been able to muster enough of Lyell's arguments to mount a more credible discussion. He himself was far from being convinced of the veracity of the *Principles of Geology*. But he did feel the issues involved were far from black-and-white, and he would have appreciated a more sympathetic appraisal from Fitzroy, a balanced discussion rather than a categorical rejection. Conversations with Fitzroy, despite the captain being only four years older than Darwin, were starting out to be more like those he had suffered through with his father than those he had enjoyed with Henslow.

So after dutifully complimenting Fitzroy on the chronometers, he was grateful to turn to the distraction of chess.

Fitzroy opened with his king's pawn. "Henslow mentioned you are a demon at chess, even beat him sometimes."

"Maybe once or twice, no more I'm sure."

"Well, I never could beat him. What do you think of M'Cohmick?"

"Our surgeon?

"Yes. An Irishman who did a year at medical school and now fancies himself a naturalist. You've shadowed my first two moves, but this will stop you," he said while moving his white bishop to threaten Darwin's queen's knight.

"Yes. He mentioned that he went to Edinburgh. I did too, for two years before moving to Cambridge."

"Only five moves and we've got the middle chockablock. What made you switch to Cambridge? Think I'll castle."

"I did not have enough interest in medicine to do well at Edinburgh. Spent most of my time wandering the countryside and the shore of the Firth of Forth, collecting insects and starfish."

"Well, M'Cohmick is not my choice of surgeon, but since he was already assigned to the *Beagle*, it would have caused too much of a fuss, so to speak, to get rid of him. I see I gave you the chance to finally bring that knight to bear on your king's pawn. But that allows me to do this!" Fitzroy moved his own knight forward to the fifth rank.

"That's easily solved," responded Darwin as he moved his rook's pawn up to threaten Fitzroy's knight.

"Can you believe he thinks he should be the First Lieutenant on this voyage?! He's one of those Irishmen that my grandfather the Marquis of Londonderry so abhorred. Bad enough they hate us, worse when they want so desperately to ape us, like his affected speech. I had my fill of him last voyage. It's a bit late for that pawn because my purpose is to take this here pawn."

Darwin in turn took the knight with his king. "Thank you for the knight, then. I understand that the tradition in the Royal Navy is that the surgeon acts as ship's naturalist?"

Fitzroy moved his white bishop back a rank. "Check!"

"Ah. Well, I won't retreat back into my hole. There."

Fitzroy walked his queen up the diagonal to the edge of the board. "Did M'Cohmick tell you that? It's not uncommon but hardly applies to this voyage. This is a scientific expedition, and M'Cohmick must learn to stifle his pretensions and concentrate on his medical duties. He let us down last time, you know, in Tierra del Fuego."

"How now with my knight?" I will bring my own queen into play, directly behind her king."

"Ah, but mine is a deceitful bitch and checks you with a single sideways step."

"And my lowly pawn takes your regina horribilis, putting me a knight and queen ahead of you!"

"As I warned..., *deceitful*." Fitzroy took the pawn with his black bishop. "Check. And mate! And in only twelve moves! Either I am much improved since Cambridge or I need to apologize for distracting you with all this talk about our Irish surgeon. Shall we play another? I promise to keep mum."

They played the second game in silence while smoking Havana cigars and sipping Marsala wine. The second game took three times as long as the first. Darwin opened with his king's pawn, and Fitzroy pursued the Sicilian Defense but failed to develop his pieces well enough to counter an attack by Darwin's queen and bishops in the end game.

They would depart very early in the morning, given a fair wind, so they left off chess at a game apiece and turned in. The long voyage ahead left many opportunities for a rematch.

2

AT DAWN THE *BEAGLE* warped out of the harbor on the ebb tide. The weather had indeed turned. Smoke from a steam packet leaving port rose high into the sky before dispersing westward. Only a few scattered cat's-paws rippled the water. High clouds like mare's tails spread across the blue sky.

Once outside the breakwater, Chaffers ordered full sail to catch the east wind that would soon freshen and carry them down the Channel and out into the Atlantic. "Hands aloft," screamed the mates. "All hands! All hands! Stand by to make sail!" The crew swarmed up the shrouds and spread out along the yards to unfurl the canvas. From Darwin's position at the taffrail, the spread of sail marched up the mainmast to fill the view ahead. The spanker cracked full directly above him. As the *Beagle* gathered way, the houses of Plymouth became less distinct minute after minute. With all sails trimmed and a wind freshening from abaft the beam, she sped out into the Channel. If any admiral had his telescope trained on her, he would witness an auspicious beginning to the voyage.

With the favorable wind, leaving port suddenly seemed so easy. The three supernumeraries had gathered at the taffrail, where they could stay out of the way. They had already heard the crew refer to Fitzroy as Old Hot Coffee, apparently because he had a tendency to boil over in the morning, and none of them had any wish to antagonize him this early in the voyage. At the taffrail they could keep a low profile and watch England sinking out of sight below the horizon. The weeks of waiting were behind. Ahead lay months of uncertainty.

Darwin, rubbing his hands together to warm them, left off looking down the trough of the wake and turned to where Earle leaned comfortably on the rail beside Matthews and asked them, "Have either of you ever been on a sea voyage before?"

"Why yes, Charles," replied the artist after a slight pause. "I returned from Cape Town just a few months ago."

"The Cape! How exciting. What were you doing there?"

"Some landscapes. A few portrait contracts.... One on Saint Helena as well."

"Did you see anything of the Boer agitators? I read in the papers that they grow more restless with our rule by the month."

"I didn't see any of that, Mister Darwin. I keep to my painting," answered Earle, turning away again to focus on the horizon at the point where Plymouth had disappeared.

Darwin desperately wanted to say something that would make Earle less terse and draw Matthews into conversation, but he could think of nothing. So the three gazed astern in silence.

Then, minutes later, Earle quipped, "Do you know the sailor's lament, Mister Darwin? Do you Mister Matthews? No? It goes something like, 'Banish forever all thoughts of ever seeing old England again....' But that's just something they used to say during the war. We're not going to war, are we?"

Two mornings later the wind backed to the northwest. By nightfall a full nor'wester had forced Fitzroy to order Chaffers to come around and lay to under a close-reefed maintopsail. Every wave that smashed into the larboard bow forced the *Beagle* a point or two to the east. Every wave filled her waist with white water. Every wave relentlessly drove her to leeward and closer to the reefs that rimmed the Bay of Biscay. But the *Beagle* always righted herself, her lee scuppers gushing and her head coming back around to the north. Watch after watch set the pumps clanking. A leaden sky hid the sun by day and the stars by night. The *Beagle* had become a bobbing cork in a tempest, location unknown. All her occupants could do was hang on and hope that the gale abated before they heard the crash of breakers under their lee.

On the second night the wind in the rigging began to ease its shrieking. By noon, the nor'wester had slackened considerably and the clouds thinned enough for Fitzroy to sight on the pale disk of the sun. "The storm has not driven us as far into the Bay as we feared, gentleman," he announced. "We still have some sea room. Wear ship until she's west-by-so'west, Mister Chaffers," he addressed the master. As the wind slackened through the day, the *Beagle* added more and more sail. She corkscrewed across the waves at a shallow angle, rolling to starboard as she dropped into each trough and to larboard as she climbed toward the next crest, the spray bursting over her forecastle.

When she was running well under courses and treble-reefed topsails, Fitzroy finally went below for some sleep. Before lying down, he sprinkled some powdered chalk on the glass faces of a few of the chronometers. Despite the hull shuddering with every plunge and the wind vibrating the rigging, the fine powder lay perfectly still. He used a hand lens for magnification, holding his breath so as not to disturb the chalk, but even so could not detect the slightest movement. The Sawdust and gimbals perfectly isolated the chronometers from the shocks and vibrations of the hull. After standing hunched over with the lens to his eye for a full minute, bracing his shoulders against the doorway to avoid losing his footing, he smiled in satisfaction and finally allowed himself to go to his berth.

As he lay on his back, he reflected positively on the *Beagle* and her crew. They had done well, even if he had seen worse seas in the Bay. Yes, they had done well. He had not seen Darwin since clearing port, and it seemed that he must be a bit weak in the stomach. But hopefully his seasickness would pass because he made for interesting conversation and, although a bit confused at times, seemed essentially a right thinker. The voyage had begun in excellent fashion, starting with the flawless departure from Plymouth. They should still, even allowing for the best part of a week in the Cape Verdes to rate the chronometers, be able to reach Brazil in time for Earle to make contact with Palmerston's agent in Rio de Janeiro.

Fitzroy's last, only half wakeful thought, was of the admiral's florid face reiterating just how important timing was in this business. Lord Palmerston did not want any slipups to embarrass the new government. The Prime Minister would sack him as Foreign Secretary. But before the PM forced Old Pam out, he would undoubtedly punish a few people himself, including the admiral. And the admiral, in turn, would be sure to end Fitzroy's naval career.

Meanwhile, a deck above, Darwin was suffering what seemed like one continual puke. He had not emerged from his cabin since going below the night after sailing, having discovered that a trip on a coastal steamer bore no resemblance to crossing the Atlantic on a brig. Vomiting—gut wrenching, nauseating, quivering regurgitation—so debilitated him that he confined himself to his hammock. His cabin provided few alternatives except to stand, which his quaking knees precluded, or to sit on the chest next to the washstand. Syms attended him faithfully, bucket ever at the ready. He had even thought to cover the charts on the table with a square of tarred sailcloth so as to avoid Fitzroy's wrath in case of mishap.

Darwin lay there day in and out, listening to the bell striking its couplets on the half hour around the clock. Through the skylight, he heard the officer of the watch barking orders: "'Nother pull on the weather main brace! Mind your heading!" From just beyond the door, he heard the affirmations of the quartermasters: "Aye aye, sir! Course so'west by south! Full an' by!" Feet pounded the decks as the crew ran to trim the sails. Every noon he heard the officers reporting their sextant readings and the clicks of chalk on slate recording the latitude. As the sun climbed higher by the day, the numbers fell—first down through the forties, then into the thirties. Once they had put Cape Finisterre astern, they settled onto a south-by-southwest course. The sounds of the crew going about its business only added to his sense of alienation. He could hear them, but they were oblivious to him. He relied on them to see the *Beagle* across the Atlantic, but they cared nothing for his thoughts on geology and Creation.

And he was thinking a lot about Creation and reading Lyell, especially now that the worst of his sickness seemed to have passed with the storm. Or perhaps he felt somewhat better because of Syms's ministrations, consisting of encouragement, dry biscuit, thin soup, and weak tea. Fitzroy's reasoning on geology had been convincing to a degree but so was Lyell's, thought Darwin, as he considered and reconsidered passages on Vulcanist versus Neptunist arguments and, especially, on Mount Etna. Lyell had spent considerable time in Sicily and provided clear diagrams to buttress his inferences. The essential problem, concluded Darwin, was that he had neither Fitzroy's nor Lyell's direct experience of the world. When either described strata to support their views, Darwin could do little but nod in agreement. He became convinced of only one thing: he needed to make his own observations to test the competing theories. If only the blasted sailing would end so that he could get ashore and see something.

By the time they were well into the thirties, the *Beagle* had picked up the northeast trades and was moving much more smoothly, running very nearly before the wind. A long swell textured by choppy whitecaps had replaced the ranks of humpbacked rollers further north. Darwin nonetheless remained in his hammock most of the time. Even so, the view through the skylight took in the spiraling head of the mizenmast beyond the spanker, keeping his stomach queasy.

The easier pace also allowed punishment to be meted out. At first Darwin did not realize what was happening just outside his cabin door. Only later, when he had actually witnessed a flogging, did he fully understand the sounds of a grating being rigged up against the break of the poop followed by the sound of the pipe summoning all hands. He began to understand what was happening when Fitzroy read out the charge of drunkenness and desertion of sentry duty on Christmas Eve, followed by the plea for anyone to speak up on the culprit's behalf. But no one did, and Fitzroy read out the relevant article and ordered the punishment, "Half a dozen strokes. Seize him up and proceed with your duty, Bo'sun." Then, to the macabre quick roll of the marine drum, Darwin heard the swish of the cat-o'-nine-tails, the thud as it cut into the man's back, the scream, and the boatswain's count before he hauled back for the next. By the second lash, Darwin had covered his ears.

They had come south thirty degrees in three weeks. The *Beagle* moved easier, the Bay of Biscay forgotten. The air was warm and felt softer and smelled of the verdure of Africa. That dark continent was hidden well below the eastern horizon, but the trades carried its essence far out into the Atlantic. White, fluffy clouds marched by against a blue sky. The little brig worked its way further south through the archipelago of the Cape Verde Islands to the island of Saint Jago, sailing into Porto Praia under topsails.

The calmer inshore waters and the tropical airs revived Darwin enough to get him up, and he was on deck as Chaffers took the *Beagle* in. The old master had been to Porto Praia many times and now carefully gauged the approach to the anchorage, bellowing orders from the quarter deck: "Tops'l sheets there! Shorten sail! Anchor party muster to the fo'c's'le! Helm alee! Shorten sail!" As the *Beagle* turned into the wind and lost way, he gave one final yell forward to let go the anchor. And it splashed into the clear green water followed by its roaring chain.

The gritty little town of Porto Praia wasn't much, thought Darwin. The desolate plain around the anchorage supported hardly a blade of grass. The more verdant uplands that rose inland were barely visible through the dusty haze. Beyond the white buildings of the town, only the groves of coconut palms on its outskirts relieved the grayish brown landscape.

Yet those palms were a marvel to Darwin. He knew *Cocos nucifera* from botany texts and herbarium sheets, of course, but had never actually touched a live one, felt its rough bark, or stood in its shade. The trunks all leaned to the southwest under the steady pressure of the trade winds. The feathery fronds rustled continuously. A flock of some type of Psittaciformes squawked overhead. Sometimes they seemed to scold him with a high-pitched screeat, screeat, screea, screee. Other times they soothed him with a rhythmic peweeo, peweeo, peweeo. They had dark slate-gray heads and bills, bright yellow bellies, and green backs. The wings, gray below and green above, were no more than six inches from tip to tip.

He spent hours under the palms, reveling in his first tropical experience as if he had just received a passport stamp to a magical kingdom he had long read about but only ever dreamed of entering. Or maybe he simply reveled at being on dry land again. It amazed him how his stomach had settled the moment the *Beagle* was swinging downwind of her anchor.

Once satiated with palms and parrots, Darwin turned to the coconut grove's surroundings. There too were wonders, but of a different sort. Even the craggy shores of the Firth of Forth had more life than these rocky plains. By all reports, verdure had once cloaked the environs of Porto Praia, but the goats introduced by the Portuguese had stripped every blade and leaf. Here geology was laid bare, waiting to be read as if the pages in a book on natural history.

Since the *Beagle* would remain at Porto Praia several days, Darwin would have some time to geologize. Fitzroy had taken some of his telescopes, almanacs, and chronometers ashore and set up shop in a courtyard loaned by the governor. Apparently they had arrived the day before a predicted planetary occultation, and Fitzroy was ecstatic because that lunar would fix Greenwich time to within seconds. In the meantime, Rowlett took a party inland to see if he could scare up some fresh fruit in the more humid valleys of the interior mountains. Other officers went hunting for the reportedly abundant guineafowl. Unless detailed to a shore party, the seamen were ordered to remain aboard. Porto Praia had both women and liquor, and Fitzroy wanted neither Venus's curse nor drunkenness aboard his command. So the men were kept busy with the interminable maintenance of cordage, canvas, caulk, and paint. Darwin took a room in Porto Praia's only, and very modest, inn.

The geology was the most striking he had ever seen, or perhaps only seemed so because he had just studied Lyell to death and seemed to see rocks as he never had before. A strikingly horizontal white band in the face of the otherwise black sea cliff ran for miles along the coast. That this stratum, perfectly parallel to the sea, was everywhere synchronous in its genesis and recorded some event in Saint Jago's geological history thus seemed certain. So Darwin followed the shore while looking for a place to clamber up and observe the layer more closely. From the rocky beach, black lava rose some forty feet to the narrow white stratum. Above it, more basalt rose to the desolate plateau that stretched inland. A dry streambed finally afforded a path up the cliff and, with some scrambling along narrow ledges, close access to the white stratum. It consisted of numerous seashells embedded in a calcareous matrix that, without doubt, itself derived from decomposed shells. The shells that he could distinguish were by all appearance of the same types as those he had observed washed up on the beach. Living beds of them probably occurred just offshore. The heat of the lava had altered the topmost part of the shelly stratum into a crystalline, limestone-like material. In other places the shells had been scoured up by the scoriaceous bottom of the lava flow and altered into wondrously radiated fibers that resembled aragonite.

One would expect just such a thin bed of shells to mark the Flood, thought Darwin, accumulating there before the waters receded in the manner Fitzroy had conjectured and then being capped and preserved by a lava flow. But something did not fit that story. Why did the calcareous layer lay so close above the present sea? Had not the waters risen to cover even the highest mountains until all people and creatures that lived on dry land died, only those in the Ark being preserved? Had the land since subsided? Given a week or two, he thought, he could explore inland to see if similar strata occurred higher above the sea. If Lyell were correct, he should find the same pattern of a shelly, calcareous stratum trapped between two basalt strata exposed in cliffs further inland, repeated several times over. Each such cycle of strata would mark, from bottom to top, an eruption during which the island was lifted higher above the sea, a quiescent period during which offshore beds of mollusks accumulated just below the new shoreline, and another eruption during which the island emerged still further from the sea and, in some places at least, lava flows covered the shells of the newly stranded mollusks. During each interval between eruptions, tides at the new shoreline would have eroded another cliff face that exposed the strata before another upwelling of lava lifted that sequence above the reach of the sea.

While returning along the beach, musing on how this island's geology compared to Lyell's description of Sicily, Darwin encountered Mac-Cormick peering into some tidal pools among the rocks. He was behaving oddly, edging close to first one side of a pool and then jumping up to run around to the other side, then back again.

"Good day to you, Charles," shouted out the surgeon when he noticed Darwin approaching. "I may call you Charles, may I not?"

"Why certainly, Robert. We are both of the same inclination after all, it seems, today and generally," responded Darwin amiably. It was a glorious day on the beach, intensely bright but with a cooling breeze, and he had just had an intellectual breakthrough. It had been as if the Biblical scales had fallen from his eyes. He was seeing this landscape for the first time. Lyell had never seen it at all, yet he felt as if he were seeing it through Lyell's eyes, that he understood it as a particular instance of the general principles he had absorbed while laying sick in his hammock.

"Why yes, laddie, it seems there are two naturalists aboard the *Beagle* on this voyage. Most peculiar, but there you have it. I'm still not quite sure why you need have stirred yourself from your comfort on shore when I've been in this navy since before the day you were born, but there you have it. I suppose Fitzroy thought that two sets of eyes would be better than one and all that, eh?"

Despite MacCormick's somewhat resentful tone, understandable enough at having his position as ship's naturalist usurped by someone half his age, Darwin enthusiastically blurted out his still as yet half formed thoughts on the geology that towered above them. MacCormick turned to look up at the cliff and listened without a word. But when Darwin began to speculate on what he might find inland, Mac-Cormick interrupted him.

"See with your own eyes how trifling these waves are, laddie," he intoned as if from the pulpit, a finger stretched out seaward. "They could not have carved this cliff above us from the hard rock even in thousands of years. Know you not that James Ussher, no less than the archbishop of Armagh and chancellor of Trinity College, calculated that Creation began at nine in the morning on the twenty-third day of October in the year 710 of the Julian calendar, no more than some six thousand years ago? And the archbishop was a most careful scholar. Such cliffs can only have derived from the Flood, whilst forty days and forty nights of rain such as never seen before nor never since caused enormous Diluvial waves to crash in upon the land and carve into it the cliffs and valleys we see today. Now, for God's sake and your own, laddie, leave off wild speculations and direct your attention to these Cephalopods."

Darwin looked into the pool at their feet and for the first time saw the object of MacCormick's attentions laying at the bottom: some sort of small octopus. Normally it would have excited him to be so close to an animal he had never seen before, but he was too busy boiling internally at MacCormick's arrogance. It was even worse than Fitzroy's because the surgeon clearly lacked even an iota of intellectual creativity. He spouted dogma and relied on the authority of his age to intimidate. "Laddie, my ass," fumed Darwin under his breath. Few things upset him much, but one was people who gave precedence to age and power over logic and facts. He was about to point out that Archbishop Ussher had died nearly two centuries ago, before scientific geology had even begun to develop, and that his method had consisted of simply summing up all of the begats in the Bible. But, just then MacCormick reached for the octopus and it jetted away.

The two spent the remaining low tide going from pool to pool trying to catch octopi. They had a chameleon-like ability to alter color according to the nature of the bottom and depth of the water. When in deep water, they were a brownish purple. When in shallow water, they took on a yellowish green. After much exertion, for their quarry could jet from one side of its pool to the other in a flash, they finally caught one and were able to examine it. Its true color was a French gray with numerous minute spots of bright yellow. Darwin conjectured that altering the size of the spots yielded the color changes but said nothing to MacCormick.

"See, laddie," exulted MacCormick, "how such creatures, whilst ugly to some eyes, manifest God's everlasting grandeur. He created every beast according to its own kind, even this cuttlefish to occupy this small pool on this rocky shore of this tiny island. The Almighty created such living variety for us to appreciate—and, through it, Him. The same goes for those geological strata that so interest you. Nature is a celebration, laddie. A celebration of the Almighty! You might exercise your mind about these cliffs all you like, but there you have it."

Rowlett's return from the interior with several mule loads of bananas was the signal to return to the *Beagle*. Darwin, cradling the jar containing the octopus, went back in one of the whaleboats with Fitzroy and his instruments. Darwin enquired as to the astronomical observations but quickly realized that Old Hot Coffee was boiling over at something. Apparently some of those left aboard had gotten up to mischief. Fitzroy wouldn't give details within earshot of the seamen manning the whaleboat, but it had something to do with the Fuegians.

The Fuegian man and boy—York, about twenty-five years old, and Jeremy, about fifteen—were bunking in the seamen's mess. The girl, Fuegia, also about fifteen, had a cabin that the carpenter had built in part of his forecastle storeroom. It was not much, but it was private, or so Fitzroy had thought.

The seamen's cook, a round, jolly little Welshman named Ley, had bored a hole in the deck between his galley and Fuegia's cabin. Whenever the girl took in hot water to bathe, Ley would watch her sponging her lissome body and satisfy his lusts. But not content to satiate his own perversities, he then sold peeps to the other seamen.

That the men had been sucking the monkey, as it was called, had not helped. Some of the locals had rowed out with fresh coconuts to trade. Lieutenant Sullivan had not seen the harm until he noticed the ensuing drunkenness. Fitzroy chewed him out for having fallen for such an old trick, in which the coconut milk was replaced with liquor.

Fitzroy would have put the cook ashore then and there, but he was good at his job and could neither be spared nor replaced. A good flogging of all concerned, the cook and all the peepers, was the only solution. Unfortunately, York and Jeremy had been just as ready to trade their tobacco for a peep as ten others.

The minute they had stood out of the anchorage and settled on their course for Brazil, Fitzroy ordered the boatswain to rig the grating and had the men piped to witness punishment. "Bring forth the licentious miscreants," he roared from the poop where, dressed in his gold-laced uniform and wearing his sword, he stood with hands clasped behind his back. The marines marched the accused to just abaft the mainmast.

"Jonathan Ley, cook," said Fitzroy very deliberately and loudly, "you are charged with scandalous conduct unbecoming the Royal Navy. Do you deny the charge?"

"No, cap'n sir. I done 'er."

"And do you or anyone else have anything to offer by way of excuse?"

Fitzroy waited a full half-minute, intending that the silence itself emphasize the heinousness of the crime. And the grins among the seamen did slowly disappear. Then Fitzroy took off his hat and read from the Articles of War: "The second article states that all persons in or belonging to His Majesty's ships or vessels of war, being guilty of profane oaths, cursings, execrations, drunkenness, uncleanness," a pause, "or other scandalous actions in derogation of God's honor, and corruption of good manners," another pause, "shall incur such punishment as a court martial shall think fit to impose according to the nature and degree of their offence. Seize him up, Bo'sun." Fitzroy coolly replaced his hat while everyone else waited to hear the punishment he would met out. Despite his temper, Old Hot Coffee was known as a fair captain, but also one who knew full well that flogging was essential to discipline. "A dozen strokes, if you please, Mister Sorrell."

This time Darwin could not cover his ears. The first stroke elicited no more than a grunt, but soon the knots on the nine cords had cut Ley's back to shreds. The drum beat and the blood flowed freely and it splattered against the door of Darwin's cabin, the boatswain untangling the gory cords by running his fingers through them after every stroke. With the last stroke of the cat, the drum stopped. Ley, hanging his full weight from the lashings, punctuated his punishment with a final, gasping, breathless scream.

The other ten seamen followed in turn with a half dozen lashes apiece. The boatswain and his mates spelled each other with the cat so that the force would not slacken with fatigue. A total of seventy-two strokes fell that day. None denied their guilt, none seemed to regret their actions, none offered excuses, and all seemed to accept that flogging was an inevitable and necessary part of their little society afloat.

Fitzroy had the three Fuegians watch together with everyone else but would not flog York or Jeremy, considering them too puerile to have known better. The Church Missionary Society at Walthamstow had taught them some English, the plainer truths of Christianity, and something of husbandry and gardening, but they remained far from civilized, too primitive to be able to rule their passions. Fuegia, of course, in Fitzroy's view, shared in the sin of Eve and was no more to blame for men's lustful actions than any other woman.

After the flogging, the boatswain cleaned and put the cat-o'-nine-tails back into its red baize bag and had the blood scrubbed from the woodwork. Meanwhile the carpenter and his crew nailed sheets of copper to the ceiling, floor, and walls of Fuegia's cabin to prevent further peepholes. A marine sentry would henceforth guard her door.

Ten days out of the Cape Verdes, just north of the equator, in mid Atlantic, the northeast trades petered out and the *Beagle* lay becalmed. The sun drummed down on the Doldrums though a thin, high haze. Sharks gathered to sample the accumulating apron of kitchen slop. Floating weed appeared and disappeared and reappeared. Random cat's-paws occasionally ruffled the placid swell. Sometimes those breezes intersected with the limp topsails hanging from the yards and blew the bow around to a new heading. Clouds formed during each long, hot, interminable afternoon until they released their rain. Sometimes it reached the *Beagle* and pelted her deck so hard that the scuppers gushed. At night, lightning flashed all around the horizon and Darwin was glad that Harris's Patented Lightning Conductors connected the tops of the masts to the waterline.

Everyone knew that they could only wait for the slow current to carry them across the equator and into the southeast trades. In the meantime they followed the shadows around the deck while scanning the smooth swell for the next cat's-paw that promised the possibility of a cooling breeze. By the third day, when their sextants demonstrated that they were south of the equator, the heat had crushed any thought of the usual celebration at crossing the Line.

At dawn the next day, the masthead lookout cried out, "Sail ho! Deck there! Sail fine on the starboard quarter, four points abaft the beam! Looks to be a schooner!"

Sullivan was the officer of the watch and climbed halfway up the mizzen shrouds with a glass. "She's a schooner all right!," he shouted down to the group that had quickly assembled on the poop deck. "Still hull down but a Baltimore clipper by the look of her rig!"

By noon the other vessel was less than two miles off, hull up and broad on. Everyone with a glass could make out the low hull with sharply raked stem and overhanging counter. By the end of the watch, the two vessels had drifted close enough together to see clearly the stars and stripes that hung limp from the staff above the letters painted across the transom—Claire McKay, Baltimore. The Yankee had lost any wind she had had at dawn and, like the *Beagle*, was wallowing aimlessly on the swell as the two vessels drifted on their convergent courses. No one needed to see the human cargo to recognize a blackbirder. Built light and sleek to elude the anti-slavery cruisers, the clipper would be able to out sail the *Beagle* the moment any wind came up.

As the two drifted ever closer together, the dark shroud of a moonless night descended over them. Except for the gleam of the slaver's stern lanterns, those gathered along the starboard rail could almost convince themselves that the nearby slaves, brutally crammed into the hold and bound for a life of misery on some sugar or cotton plantation, did not exist. A slight breeze interrupted that illusion. First it carried the clanking of chains as the Africans were allowed on deck for exercise. Then, like the thunderclap that follows the lightening flash, the smell came rolling over the *Beagle*.

"You see, gentlemen," said Fitzroy, with heartfelt disgust, "how they try to hide their heinous trade from us. They know we cannot legally board and search them. Nor do they fear us reporting them to their own navy, which dares not interfere despite their own laws. But we shame them, gentlemen. We shame them so much that they hide behind darkness. Qui male agit odit lucem!"

A series of splashes interrupted the clanking. Flashes of phosphorescence showed near the slaver's lanterns.

Darwin ventured, sounding half hopeful and half horrified, "Fish jumping?"

Fitzroy stared straight out into the night and waited what seemed a long time before answering, "Likely, Mister Dahwin. But sharks, not fish. Sharks gorging on human bodies. I didn't hear enough splashes for it to have been their entire cargo. And why should they? They know I'll not flaunt the treaty by sending our boats across to inspect them. And once the wind gets up they can easily outrun us. They'll be in home waters before we raise land and can report them. Likely they are just dumping those who have died from disease and despair. They must have left the Bight of Benin with four hundred and will already have lost a score or so. I've heard it said that some blackbirders throw the nearly dead overboard with the already dead. Only those that are healthy enough to fetch a good price survive the Middle Passage. The rest are claimed against the cargo insurance."

"The Americans are beastly for perpetuating slavery!," burst out Matthews, his horror overcoming his introversion.

Earl, too, felt strongly enough to interrupt the ensuing general murmur of assent and disgust. "Tell that to our Jamaican planters, Matthew. Sugar brings a better return on capital than anything else. No slaves, no sugar, no profits."

"Aristotle himself, I believe," chimed in MacCormick, emboldened by Earle's comment, "recognized slavery as the natural state of the inferior races. One need only observe the differences between the crania of the Negro, the indigene of America, and the European to recognize the latter's much superior capacity for intellect. Don't you agree, Charles? I believe you mentioned that you too had studied medicine whilst at Edinburgh. Surely you must have heard Doctor Combe lecture on phrenology?"

Before Darwin could answer, though, Fitzroy calmly interrupted to stifle all further discussion: "Indeed Mister M'Cohmick, but it does not follow that we should enslave Negroes any more than that we should enslave children. They are our long lost brethren, negatively affected by their tropical clime but not irredeemably so given adequate tutelage. But we have a more immediate problem than philosophizing, gentlemen. The Claire McKay also has boats, not to mention a well armed, vicious crew." He turned to Wickham, who had the last dogwatch: "Double the lookouts, rig boarding nets, and load the guns with canister, if you please, Lieutenant. And pass the word for Sergeant Beareley."

Foregoing the stifling heat of their berths, many idled about the decks to watch the gun crews prepare a deadly reception for the Yankees should they try anything. So by the time a lookout shouted down from the mast about the musket fire on the starboard beam, a crowd had already rushed to the bulwark. Flashes followed by pops marked the deck of the Claire McKay. Inhuman screams punctuated the clash of cutlasses. Every eye and ear strained to make out what was happening aboard the slaver while the marine drummer stuttered out the tattoo calling all hands to stations.

Hours passed. The slaver's stern lanterns went out. Dozens of splashes measured out the remainder of the night. Dry lightning did little to dispel the darkness but much to further fray nerves.

Dawn revealed a mass of Africans packing the deck of the Claire McKay. Most wore nothing from the waist up, women the same as men. They and the crew of the *Beagle* stared at one another across the hundred yards that still separated them. Not a white face appeared among the black. They had removed their chains and taken up the firearms and cutlasses of the dead crew. Some of the muskets pointed toward the *Beagle*.

Fitzroy firmly quashed all talk of aiding the Africans to return home. He would not, as several officers solicitous for the Africans' welfare suggested, risk putting a crew aboard the Claire McKay to sail her to Freetown or anywhere else. Nor would he put the clipper in tow and thereby delay their mission. Besides which, he argued, the Africans outnumbered his crew four to one and were well armed. They could easily use the clipper's boats or six pounders to attack the *Beagle*. The most he would promise was to report their last known position to the Commander in Chief of the South American Station when, wind allowing, they reached Rio de Janeiro. In the meantime, the crew would standby to defend the *Beagle* as necessary. Several, including Matthews and Sullivan, appeared ready to continue to press the Africans' case, but Fitzroy bombastically quoted Seneca's dictum on slavery: "Qui mori didicit servire dedidicit! They are on their own, gentlemen, and that will be quite enough." He knew that no one but Darwin was likely to understand Seneca, that being his purpose; a little Latin usually made the less educated recall their place.

Noon brought the long awaited southeasterly wind and the call to make sail. When last seen, the new crew of the Claire McKay was struggling to teach itself how to trim her sails and set an eastward course. Most were no doubt farmers, and they would have to sail close hauled against the trades to reach West Africa. The best they could hope for was to hail a British antislavery cruiser that would tow them into Freetown. But they were more likely to fall prey to slavers, either at sea or upon reaching the coast. Among those gathered at the taffrail, many felt some guilt for not intervening.

As the wind freshened across the beam, the sea came up a bit and the *Beagle* once again settled into her familiar corkscrew roll. Brazil was more than a week away, and Darwin retreated to his hammock under the poop skylight. There he would endure until reaching Rio de Janeiro.

Fitzroy came to visit on Darwin's birthday, enquiring after his health but unable to suggest any remedy other than a stiff upper lip. "Think of England, Chawes!," suggested Fitzroy. Apparently he had never felt seasickness grip his own guts so could offer only faint empathy. Instead, he put most of his effort, futilely, into stirring Darwin to a game of chess.

MacCormick came to ply his medicinals but had little to suggest beyond Syms's lay ministrations. The surgeon took advantage of Darwin's weak state to pontificate on phrenology, however. "I know you would have supported me on the slavery issue if Fitzroy had not interrupted, Charles. He is not a scientific man like ourselves and has not heard Doctor Combe's remarkable lectures on phrenology. You have, have you not?"

"Indeed, I heard him speak on several occasions. Very interesting ideas, particularly on the regularity of variation in cranial morphology among the races. In fact, you will find his book on the shelf over there."

"Exactly!" exclaimed MacCormick, sensing an ally. "And there was that article on just that topic in the *Phrenological Journal* of last year. The mesocephalic European has a high brow, and his generally pronounced anterior and coronal regions balance the intellectual and vital temperaments with the motive ones. In contrast, the Negro's dolichocephalic cranium has a low brow and crown. The overbalanced posterior yields a preponderance of motive temperament. Great stamina, strength, fecundity, etcetera; but little originality, eloquence, reasoning ability, or propensity for benevolence or sublimity. The Negro's role as slave on the European's plantation seems natural enough when seen in those scientific terms, and there you have it."

"I'm sure that I'm not up to debating such a contentious matter in my present state, Robert, but I tend to agree with the captain's beliefs. You might be correct as far as you go, but surely you must admit that by exercising various faculties, they may be improved upon and such improvement passed on to the next generation? In fact, one's external appearance varies for better or worse to the degree that one exercises the mind one's Maker allowed one. With tutelage, generation-by-generation, the lower races might thereby improve. In fact it is our duty to help them improve, not to enslave them."

"Don't you, as a religious man as well as a novice naturalist, think that such improvement, even were it possible, goes against God's design?"

Darwin had already begun to weary of MacCormick's condescending manner on the beach at Porto Praia. Such conversations neither enlightened nor gave pleasure. Henslow, for all his years and intellect, had always been willing to genuinely debate with even the youngest students. So enough!, thought Darwin, his eyes narrowing, his words carefully chosen, "Please, Robert, might we discuss this when we reach Rio de Janeiro?"

"Of course, of course, laddie. But allow me to leave you to mull the following point whilst you rest. You'll agree that all races are the progeny of Adam and Eve? They became differentiated when Shem, Ham, and Japheth populated Europe, Africa, and Asia. The American indigenes are surely descendent of Asiatics who migrated to the New World long ago. Each race is thus fixed according to its progenitor, in God's image to be sure but to different degrees of perfection. They do not change, son. They cannot change, and there you have it. They are immutable, their variety a living witnesses to the glory that is God's purpose."

"Quite, Robert, now please...."

"And you also know full well that Noah cursed Ham's son, Canaan. 'Noah awoke and knew what Ham had done unto him!,' Scripture tells us. And so he cursed Canaan for his father's incestuous trespasses. And he cursed the children of Canaan and their children to be slaves unto the children of Ham's brothers, Shem and Japheth, and then unto their children, generation after generation. Ham means scorched, and he was Noah's dark-skinned son, as was Canaan himself dark skinned, as are all the Canaanites or southern tribes. And there, in Scripture, you have it."

Later, through the skylight, Darwin overheard MacCormick pontificating on the same topic to Matthews. "I tell you, Richard, I am right on this point and your Mission will therefore come to little. I have examined our Fuegians and they are classical brachycephalics, as is typical for the indigenes of the New World. They are elevated in the crown and broad about the ears. Thus they are vastly exaggerated in the vital temperaments, especially secretiveness, acquisitiveness, and fatalism."

"Yet they have learned much in England, Mister MacCormick. Fuegia in particular speaks English very well. York...."

"Please, laddie," interrupted the surgeon, "do not be so easily deceived. Their brows are certainly higher than Negroes but they are not capable of original or analytic thought. They best the Negro at imitativeness but no more than that. They will mimic you well enough whilst under your care, but the moment you leave them to their own devices the poor buggers will revert to their base natures. Mark my words."

As Darwin lay in his hammock listening, he resolved that he would never discuss slavery, geology, natural science, religion, or any other topic, with Robert MacCormick ever again.

3

THE BRAZILIAN LANDSCAPE bedazzled Darwin. The vegetation was riotous. Tree trunks towered like Grecian columns. Some had enormous flat buttresses that, suitably roofed and doors cut between, could serve as a house. Parasitical plants grew on other plants. Elegant grasses waved their inflorescences overhead. Colorful, fragrant flowers everywhere shouted the tropical luxuriance that the palm grove at Porto Praia had only whispered of. The noise from the insects had been loud enough to hear from the *Beagle*, but silence pervaded the shady interior of the forest that backed the town of Rio de Janeiro. He felt he was in an immense cathedral, a temple of and to God. The arboreal foliage was so thick that an ordinary English rain would never have penetrated to the ground, but a shower that overtook him on the way back to town soon sent miniature cataracts down the trunks and elicited fresh aromas where the water soaked into the mold of the forest floor. Droplets collected along the numerous spider webs that crisscrossed the trail, some of them thick enough that Darwin speculated they might catch small birds. The authors of the books he had so passionately perused, learned naturalists all, with their lists of species, each with its distinguishing characteristics, had not been able to prepare him to experience the immense, lush, untidy hothouse he had stepped into.

Darwin had escaped the *Beagle* almost immediately upon arrival. Fitzroy had announced that they would be in port the best part of a week and then had hurried off to the flagship to report to Rear Admiral Sir Thomas Baker. No doubt the uprising aboard the Yankee blackbirder and fate of the Africans still weighed on Fitzroy and he hoped to send an official, even if futile, complaint about the owners of the Claire McKay to Washington. Earle headed for the town with his easel and paints, claiming he wanted to search out a vantage point from which to capture the sweep of the scene. Matthews, having well learned in Porto Praia that seamen idling about are a playground for the Devil, took his Fuegian charges ashore to stay with some fellow missionaries. Before heading into the forest, Darwin had found a room in an inn that Rowlett recommended. The affable purser knew Rio and even gave directions to some likely spots for botanizing and geologizing. But he warned that once away from the breezes that blew inland off the bay, Brazil was "'ootter than the 'eenges of 'ell."

The rain ended as Darwin emerged from the forest trail, and the sun blazed down on the vista that stretched out before him. The bright sunlight enlivened every tint of green in the forest that framed the scene and reached verdant fingers down among Rio's white buildings, which clung to the slopes around the bay. All manner of small boats sprinkled the blue water with white sails. The most impressive vessels were those of the British, American, and French squadrons, each having three ships in port at the moment. With his glass, he could see watering parties plying back and forth between the *Beagle* and the shore.

Sugar Loaf Mountain towered from the harbor's southern headland—alien, monstrous, seemingly freshly thrust up from out of the depths of the Earth. The strangely domed peak appeared to be exfoliating like some gigantic onion, with thick sheets of rock imperceptibly peeling off and sliding down its smooth surface. It really did look like a loaf of sugar or, as the locals called it, Pão de Açúcar. It must have cooled and solidified while under great pressure. The subsequent release of that pressure resulted in the layers splitting off. Either the Noachian Flood had created that pressure at the bottom of a profound, universal ocean or the Earth was so much older than generally allowed that the slow work of rain and waves had conspired with gravity to erode away a thick overlying stratum of rock. The latter, mused Darwin, is what Lyell would conclude.

As Darwin wound his way through the town back towards his inn, the picturesque scene from the hillside gave way to the reality of Rio. In the aftermath of the rain, a drenching humidity had settled into the narrow streets between the whitewashed walls of the houses. Mules and other stock freely defecated and urinated in every plaza and courtyard. Smells, including his own drenching sweat, assailed his nostrils.

Nearly naked Africans—men or women, no matter—crowded the narrow streets. Some of the girls, not yet used up by hard labor and childbirth, had gorgeously firm breasts and supple torsos. But he felt so beaten down by the humidity that he hurried on to his inn without taking time to more fully enjoy their beauty.

A note inviting him to a soirée at the British embassy awaited him. Wonderful!, he thought: botanizing during the day and a party in the evening; what could be better? All the misgivings of Plymouth and frustrations of seasickness were behind. A glorious voyage lay ahead. And, fortunately, he had brought a decent suit of clothes ashore and come back early enough to bathe away the aromas of his exertions.

The group that gathered at the white stone mansion, the Embassy of His Britannic Majesty to the Court of Dom Pedro II, that evening was small. Admiral Baker, the Commander in Chief of the South American Station, attended together with some officers of the other Royal Navy ships in port. Fitzroy had invited lieutenants Wickham and Sullivan together with Earle and Darwin.

Ambassador Ian Douglas was the mulatto son of a Scottish planter and a freed Negress from Barbados. He had spent his early boyhood on the family sugar plantation in British Guyana before going to school in Lanark, his father's hometown. Except for black eyebrows, he had tightly curled white hair, the muttonchops that adorned his cheeks making his dark skin appear even darker. He thus seemed the perfect ambassador to Brazil, where the majority of the free population was an assortment of zambos, mulattos, quarterons, and quinterons.

His daughter, Lucinda, or as she preferred to be called, Lucy, was charming. Her mother was dead, like Darwin's own, but he deduced that she must have been white because Lucy's lovely olive skin was light enough for her to be a quarteron. She listened attentively and held up her end of any conversation with a seemingly eclectic knowledge and Cartesian logic. She conversed as engagingly with Fitzroy on naval history as with Darwin on natural history.

The Ambassador meanwhile regaled his guests with stories of his diplomatic adventures, both in Jamaica and Brazil. "It's really quite stable here compared to when I came during the Cisplatine War a few years ago," he reflected. "I can tell you that I had to work hard to convince these Brazilian buggers that Uruguay would best serve as a buffer between them and Buenos Aires. In the end I think they only agreed because the war was bankrupting them."

"Barings Bank took a beating on it, too, of course," Sir Thomas ruminated. "Deuced difficult situation…," he trailed off, giving the impression he was regretting having lost a few pounds himself.

"I'll say," interjected Douglas, "damned tricky negotiations. It's better now, but with Dom Pedro abdicating in favor of his son we are left with a child emperor. A child, don't you know?! If some province or another isn't in rebellion, the parliament is fighting with the regent! And the bloody French are up to their old tricks again. Keeps me busy, gentlemen, it does. Keeps me busy, but it's nothing that can't be handled."

On learning of Darwin's time in Edinburgh, Douglas changed the topic to reminisce about walks along the banks of the Clyde and around the shore of the Firth of Forth. Darwin conversed agreeably enough even while thinking to himself that the riotous life of the tropics made Scottish flora and fauna pale into insignificance.

As the evening drew to a close, Darwin excused himself and stepped out onto the veranda for a breath of the wonderful tropical air, so full of the earthy smells that he felt like he was breathing in the force of life itself.

But as he stepped though the French doors, hushed voices distracted him. Earle and Lucy were apparently arranging to meet in the morning to leave on some outing. Startled at Darwin's appearance, Lucy explained that she had invited Earle to the Douglas fazenda, the coffee plantation her father kept as an investment and diversion. Carved out of the forest about two day's ride toward Cabo Frio, the fazenda apparently had a sensational setting and Earle hoped to spend a day or two painting the rustic Brazilian landscape.

Eager to get out into the forest again, Darwin enthusiastically asked to go along. "I would love to see more of the country than Rio! Fitzroy will be busy here a week yet, and I didn't join the voyage to idle about the *Beagle* or her ports of call."

At first Lucy resisted, suggesting that the environs of Rio had as much potential for botanizing as the fazenda. Earle said nothing, though, and Darwin persisted so much that she eventually relented with a gracious smile. "Very well, Charles. We'll be delighted to have you along. The more the better, actually." So the three of them agreed to meet in the embassy's courtyard at dawn. Two of the fazenda hands were in town and would arrange the extra horses for Darwin and Syms.

"Bring a gun, Charles," said Lucy at the door as she bid the guests goodnight. "The further one gets away from this town, the more game there is."

The two mulatto farmhands, Alvaro and Floriano, led the little column. Well behind, Lucy and Earle rode together. And Darwin and Syms brought up the rear because the two of them were always stopping to collect specimens. Flowers and other plant parts went into bags for later pressing. Insects went into small envelopes or pillboxes with a few camphor crystals. To carry the mounting collection, Syms led a packhorse. The party kept up a steady pace in order to reach the only inn on the road to the fazenda, forcing the two laggards to gallop after every collection stop.

The path wound through forested hills swathed in a cornucopia of exotic life. Large, brilliantly colored butterflies fluttered around their faces. Over the path, bright green tree ferns arched their fronds. Woody vines, some of them a foot or more in circumference, hung from the trees. Smaller lianas twisted about the larger ones. Fungi grew upon epiphytes that grew upon trees that grew upon the mold of the forest floor. Insects hummed around the many blossoms, like the bright red Malvaceae with their erect staminal columns that thrust out into the path. In the occasional grassy openings, enormous conical anthills towered over the riders, even over Earl, the tallest among them.

In form, reflected Darwin, the anthills looked like the mud volcanoes at Jorullo, in Mexico. The Baron von Humboldt had depicted them in one of his many beautiful plates. Curious how animal and mineral phenomena could so closely mimic one another in their gross form. He could imagine conducting a detailed study comparing mud volcanoes and anthills. He was sure the editor of the *Annales de Sciences Naturelles* would be receptive to publishing such a piece. Without time now to sketch more than a rough diagram of the anthills, he hoped that on the way back he and Syms could stop here a while before returning to Rio. Earle should be willing to do a painting. Perhaps von Humboldt would even be receptive to sharing some of his unpublished observations. Darwin was sure the famed German had more important things to do than collaborate with a novice naturalist, but one never knew until one tried. Or maybe he was being too ambitious? Well, he concluded, he could always simply become a parson as his father wished, perhaps for some country parish where he could enjoy the pleasure of being an amateur naturalist without all the pressures of a university post.

By bringing up the rear, Darwin had a good view of Lucy, and his musings turned from alternating between self-doubts and fantasies about a career as a renowned naturalist to the ambassador's intriguing daughter. Fanny and Lucy were opposites; that much was clear. Even when the riders passed through breaks in the canopy and the bright sunlight nearly blinded him, her skin appeared a light brown, like the skin of a common mushroom. Fanny's was as white as a mushroom's meat. And Lucy rode better than Fanny, assertively guiding her sorrel along the rough track while she talked with Earle, the words lost among the sounds of insects and the bubbling of the small streams they frequently forded.

While following the high bank of one such stream, they came suddenly on a group of women washing themselves in a pool under the further bank. Except for turbans to keep the heat from their heads, they were naked and as black as those who had crowded the deck of the Claire McKay. Their bright cottons lay spread out to dry on the boulders that bounded the pool. Alvaro and Floriano waved and shouted boisterously, and the women laughed and squatted down to immerse themselves up to their necks and waved back. The road was so much higher than the bathers, though, and the water so clear, that immersion did little to hide their bodies.

When Darwin finally tore his eyes away, he saw Lucy looking back at him. She smiled broadly before turning her horse and riding on. Embarrassed for having stared at the black breasts shimmering just below the surface, his face flushed bright red. He had seen breasts before, of course. The image of the packed deck of the Claire McKay came back to him, the half naked bodies and the staring faces. He had even dissected the breasts of cadavers at medical school, carefully using a scalpel to trace out mammary ducts in the stiff, cold, bloodless white flesh. He suddenly remembered the overwhelming aroma of formaldehyde that had permeated the dissection room, but the memory evaporated in the rich smell of earth from where the moving water was undercutting the bank and its overhanging vegetation. Letting Syms get ahead of him, he lingered a moment to look back for a last glimpse of the bathers.

They stopped for lunch in a meadow at the base of a granite tor, a miniature version of Sugar Loaf Mountain, that provided welcome shade. No one spoke about the bathers. They had been too familiar a sight to Alvaro and Floriano to provide them more than momentary distraction. If Lucy had not been there, the others might well have compared notes. But none wanted to offend the ambassador's daughter, a charming enough distraction in herself.

Over the sausage, cheese, and cassava bread, Lucy related the notorious story of their picnic spot. Runaway slaves had once lived on the tor's rocky summit. They had subsisted by cultivating a little manioc in soil that they carried up in baskets. Rain that collected in potholes in the rock provided sufficient water, and the exfoliating slabs created overhangs to shelter from sun and storm. The runaways managed to remain hidden from passersby for many years, but eventually they were discovered and a troop of soldiers came to seize them. The soldiers routed them out of the rockshelters and cornered them against the edge of a steep cliff at the summit. All surrendered except a young woman. Clasping her baby to her breast, she threw herself from the cliff to the meadow below, dashing herself and infant to pieces.

As Lucy had reached the climax, they had all looked up from their lunch as if they might see bones glinting in the rank grass. Darwin commented that the woman had displayed a noble love of freedom.

Lucy thought awhile before responding: "Perhaps, Charles. I suppose that would be the motive ascribed to an Englishwoman, or to some Roman matron of old. I'm afraid Brazilians merely regard it as the sort of brutal obstinacy typical of slaves. But I do like your explanation better."

That evening they stopped for the night at an inn so decrepit that Darwin wondered whether he should sleep in his so-called bed or in the paddock with the horses. He had been assigned one of several wooden platforms with, as a concession to the concept of a mattress, a thin straw pallet. And when he saw the filthy latrine, he decided to do his business in the forest behind the inn. On the way back he came up behind a squatting figure fully engaged in a similar mission. Her dress—Lucy's riding dress, he realized—was pulled up around her waist. He quickly averted his eyes and hurried off but not before catching a glimpse of her round arse and more.

By the time he had returned to the inn by a roundabout route, Lucy was having a heated discussion with Pereira, the innkeeper. Like Darwin, Earle spoke some Spanish but no Portuguese and could only report that the argument generally concerned their dinner. The grubby little Pereira seemed a jolly enough fellow, but his was the only inn for miles, he knew it, and he accordingly seemed to feel obliged to be as usurious as possible. All Darwin and Earle understood was a liberal sprinkling of "Senhor Pereira" and "Senhorinha Docklas." A final "Obrigado!," by Lucy, ended the negotiations.

They dined on rice and capybara, using their hunting knives, fingers, and crude wooden spoons because the inn lacked proper cutlery. The two water-hogs—*Hydrochaerus capybara*, according to Darwin—they ate looked something like guinea pigs but were about two feet long. They had square snouts and partial webs between their toes. "Small ones," Lucy had observed as Pereira tied them up by the hind feet to skin and gut them. Darwin could not help but recall the fossils of huge saber-toothed tigers, dire-wolves, cave-bears, and other now extinct animals he had seen at the British Museum. The capybara, enormous compared to its guinea pig cousins, seemed to be one of the few species to have survived from that age of gigantic mammals. The meal was greasy but the coffee was the best that he had ever tasted. Later everyone sat on the verandah together, smoking the local cigars and watching the fireflies before saying their boa noites and turning in.

It was not the snoring of his roommates that kept Darwin awake, nor the sweltering heat, nor the insect and rodent noises moving around the room. It was the memory of Lucy's lovely buttocks. In the hope of distracting himself, he went out onto the veranda. The tall trees pressing in close about the inn made the night blacker than Tobijah's ass, and he could hardly see his hand in front of his face. Only the interminable shrill cry of the cicadae and crickets and the periodic nickering of the horses indicated that anything existed beyond the verandah.

Then he saw a reddish glow out by the horses. Thinking that Earle was smoking a cigar, Darwin went over, slowly feeling his way across the uneven ground. As he approached, the smoker drew and the cigar glowed more brightly. The reddish light illuminated Lucy's face, not Earle's. She was leaning against the flank of one of the mares. Darwin stood mute with his gaze fixed on the smoke curling out of the corners of her beautiful mouth until the glow subsided. She drew again and this time held the glowing ash under his face.

"Ah, Charles. Would you like it?"

The question hung between them without response, so she moved the cigar closer to his face until it almost burned him and he took it and put it in his mouth and drew it. He made to pass the cigar back to her, but the glow fell on the flank of the mare. She was gone.

Then he felt her hands moving up his leg and taking his penis out and cupping it. As he grew erect she pulled him closer to where she knelt and took him in her mouth. She ran her tongue around the glans while fondling the shaft and scrotum. When he moaned, the cigar fell from his teeth. Lucy stopped, picked up the cigar, and stood up. She stroked his erection with one hand while drawing on the cigar until it glowed again. Then she moved her hand to his shoulder and pushed down until his trembling legs gave out and he was kneeling in front of her. She hiked up her skirt and put her right leg over his left shoulder and forced his face toward her crotch. Images flashed through his mind of the genitals of the cadavers at medical school and of the cloacae of the pigeons he had kept as a boy. And then his nose was brushing Lucy's soft mons pubis while he inhaled the fragrance that was intermingled with the tight curly hair his lips had found. She had a hand in his hair now and was pulling his face into her vulva. His tongue found her labia minora and hymen, slippery and sweet with mucal secretions. He licked up and down between vagina and clitoris. His penis was rock hard, and he cupped her buttocks with his hands and pulled her even closer as she rocked her hips against him. Then she rested her full weight onto his face and forced him to the ground while a low groan spilled from her throat. She moved backward and lowered herself onto his erection. The cigar remained clenched between her teeth and never made a sound, the smoke curling orange out of the corners of her mouth. When Darwin's eyes rolled upward and he began to cry out, she clamped her hand over his mouth until he had finished ejaculating. Then she placed what was left of the cigar in his mouth and left him lying beside the mare. Later—seconds, a minute, he did not know—he heard her urinating in the darkness.

They reached the fazenda in the afternoon of the next day. Its buildings, arranged around a plaza in a rough quadrangle, occupied the flat crest of a low hillock. Darwin thought the main house curious. It was plain, with whitewashed walls, unglazed windows, and a thatched roof. But the gilded chairs and sofas would have been at home in a townhouse. Enclosing the other sides of the quadrangle were a granary, a stable, houses for the majordomo, the farmhands and their families, and various workshops such as a smithy. In the center of the quadrangle lay a large pile of coffee beans drying in the sun. Slaves occasionally raked the beans back and forth across the stamped earthen patio to ensure even drying. Arranged in a line along the north foot of the hillock were the slave shanties, each with a fire pit in front and an extensive garden stretching behind. On the opposite side of the hillock stood a small chapel. All around the miniature village were the fields, mainly full of coffee bushes but also with patches of manioc and maize. Cattle and horses pastured here and there, enclosed in corrals with living fences of agave and other spiny succulents. The high green wall of the forest loomed all around.

The Douglas's majordomo greeted them cheerfully. He seemed especially glad to see Alvaro and Floriano back, and so did their wives and children. By evening, the slaves had set up long planks on trestles in the plaza. Coals glowed in the fire pit. And the makeshift tables groaned under the weight of food. The slaves kept the platters full of grilled beefsteaks, pork, turkey, venison and hot cassava bread. Various liquors made the rounds. One old man had the job of chasing away the hounds and dozens of little children who scurried about under the tables. To Darwin, all Brazilians seemed given to music, but Floriano and his family, numbering a wife and some half dozen children, seemed particularly adept. Once everyone was well stuffed, they brought out various percussion instruments, and before long the whole party was dancing and singing, each to the best of their uneven ability. Thousands of insects swarmed around the suspended lanterns that lit the scene. And, at the bottom of the hill, the slaves threw their own, parallel party.

What, wondered Darwin to himself, would MacCormick think of it? He could see every shade of skin color, from his own very white, though by now burnt ruddy, to the blackest African. He could see every type of skull known to phrenological science, from hyperbrachycephalic to hyperdolichocephalic. And they combined with skin color in many combinations. The variety of the celebrants, in fact, denied the very concept of race. In a way he wished the arrogant surgeon were here to appreciate that insight—but not really. MacCormick was the type who had enslaved his sight to his model of how the world was, not the type who was willing to make systematic observations and modify that model accordingly.

When all the guests had bid the majordomo boa noite, they gathered on the verandah of the main house to smoke cigars. But Lucy, Earle, Darwin, and Syms were not the only guests. A tall, lean gentleman whom Lucy introduced as Señor Fulano was also sojourning at the fazenda. He had held himself aloof from the revelry, preferring

51

to observe from the verandah. He volunteered little about himself, and Darwin was too stuffed, tipsy, and worn out with riding and his awkward dancing, not to mention his lack of sleep the night before, to wonder about much more than where to find his bed.

The next day, Darwin took Syms out to hunt birds in the surrounding forest. His rifle was a Brown Bess musket manufactured on the short-barreled India pattern but subsequently rifled and modified to take percussion caps. It was accurate enough, but its three-quarter inch slug tended to destroy the parrots and toucans Darwin was after. Finally, after a wonderful day exploring the environs of the fazenda but nothing in his bag except the mangled remains of several birds, he bought an assortment of live parrots and toucans from the slave children who kept them as pets. After he had made diagrams and notes, Syms simply broke their necks and skinned them. The hunt thus produced a wealth of observations on bird behavior while the purchases produced perfect specimens. This system proved so effective that Darwin resolved to employ it whenever possible throughout the rest of the voyage.

Writing in his journal on the verandah in the late afternoon, Darwin noted how carefully Syms was working at his side, rubbing the bird skins with arsenic soap and stretching them on frames of twigs. "Although usually so closed mouthed that many at first take him for a mute," he wrote, "my young servant is working out admirably." Besides having a talent for preparing specimens, Syms had become more like an apprentice than a servant. Darwin enjoyed sharing his store of knowledge of plants and animals. Syms equally delighted in learning about them. Both found that in the course of concentrating on some feature of a specimen during the lessons, additional details often became apparent. They had rapidly become an efficient and enthusiastic collecting team.

Darwin wrote nothing about Lucy. He had glanced at her many times since their encounter in the paddock of the inn, but she had returned none. He hardly understood what had happened, and she did not seem inclined to discuss it. She had not been avoiding him, but neither had they interacted much the last two days.

On returning from the outing with Syms, Darwin had found her with Earle and Señor Fulano on the verandah, deep in a discussion that they terminated as he approached. He had hoped that Earle would have been working; only a landscape painting could do justice to the riotous life that surrounded the fazenda. His own collections merely sampled a fraction of the diversity and besides that took the specimens out of their context, out of their web of relationships with other species. But the only sketches that Earle had made all day were a portrait of Fulano and another of Lucy. Darwin thought them excellent art but wished Earle would concentrate on the task he had been hired for. Fitzroy hoped that he and Darwin would publish an account of the voyage of the *Beagle*, and they would need plates showing landscapes, not portraits of beautiful women and mysterious men.

The next morning Darwin awoke before dawn, half dreaming about Lucy, and rose to walk out to see the early birds. The slaves had already gathered at the chapel and were singing a morning hymn, mainly in Portuguese but interweaving what sounded like African chants. They would work the day in the coffee fields before spending an hour or two in their own gardens. The fazenda life made slavery seem so idyllic, a paternalistic little society in pastoral retirement from the cares of the wider world. If only one could squint and forget that most of the people living here had come against their wills on blackbirders like the Claire McKay. If only one could forget that any of them might be sold tomorrow, possibly forever separating parents from children and husbands from wives.

In the growing light, Darwin sat down beside the chapel to observe a wasp flying back and forth to the nest it had built under the eaves. The wasp was harvesting caterpillars from manioc plants in the nearest slave garden. It flew to a caterpillar, hovered, and stung. When the caterpillar had slowed its wiggling, the wasp picked up its partially paralyzed victim and flew to the nest. Darwin could imagine the wasp larvae just inside the nest opening, hungrily awaiting the still living caterpillars.

His name, shouted down from above, calling him back up to the main house, interrupted his musings on God's creation of such an efficiently cruel species. Earle informed him that Alvaro and Floriano were already saddling the horses and that no time was to be lost in leaving the fazenda. They would rendezvous with the *Beagle* along the coast. Darwin's astonished questions fell on deaf ears. He could either tell Syms to get their baggage loaded onto the horses or stay at the fazenda, as he chose.

The level road wound among marshes and lagoons, with egrets and cranes fishing on either hand. Orchids and various epiphytic mosses overgrew the gnarled trees that clustered here and there along the sloughs. Darwin thought the moss to be a species of *Tillandsia* but could not stop to observe anything as closely as he wished. The wind blew the smell of the sea straight into their faces. The siliceous sand of the road was so fine that the hooves made a curious chirping sound at every step.

In the late afternoon, Darwin heard a pistol shot from the front of the column and dug his heals in to gallop up, thinking someone might have bagged a crane. Instead he caught a glimpse of an evil looking fellow with enormous moustaches, spurs, a slouch hat, and a poncho that might have been brightly patterned if it had not been so filthy. The unknown rider was galloping off clutching at a red patch spreading on his thigh while zigzagging his big bay and looking back over its hindquarters. Earle was already ramming a new patch and ball down the barrel of his pistol while spitting the end of the cartridge out on the ground. Darwin saw all of these details in a few seconds, as if time had slowed to a crawl.

Lucy broke the spell by shouting, "Quickly, off the road!" And they followed Alvaro through some trees and in among the sloughs. They rode carefully but quickly, losing themselves in the labyrinth of narrow ribbons of land that separated the sloughs. A scruffy growth of mimosa, in places forming a carpet only a few inches high, in other places scratching at their boots as they forced their way through, covered the ground. Soon the road was hidden behind the copses of trees. They followed game trails beaten down over many years by the deer, pigs, capybaras, and feral cattle that occupied the marshlands. Occasionally Alvaro led them down a bank and across a sandbar. And, eventually, they emerged out of the watery labyrinth onto a path that twisted between sand dunes.

The concentration required to keep up with the leaders on the narrow trails dissipated Darwin's shock at seeing Earle shoot someone. He had not even had time to be scared. He only wanted to stop and find out what had happened.

After alternately trotting and walking the horses for the rest of the afternoon, Alvaro and Floriano pulled up and waited for the party to assemble into a little knot of lathered horses and riders. Amazingly, Syms still lead the packhorse loaded with specimens, among them the skins of several quadrupeds, including a capybara and three types of monkey, a dozen types of birds, many snakes and insects, and four presses full of drying plant parts. Normally Darwin would have been most concerned about his specimens, but instead he began to demand to know what was going on. Lucy just held up her hand for silence while listening for the sound of hooves beating on the trail behind them.

After a minute she lowered her hand and said, "That was a gaucho, Mister Darwin, to answer your question. And he must have been only one of several waiting along the roads from the fazenda. We are lucky to have gotten away. At least so far. Only Alvaro's knowledge of the marsh has saved us. And Augustus's telling shot, of course."

"Gauchos," repeated Darwin. "You mean the herdsmen I've read about, the ones that ride the pampas?"

"Indeed, Señor Darwin," interrupted Fulano in precise Spanish. "His poncho marked that one as being from Uruguay, what the Brazilians call the Cisplatine Province and the Argentines call the Banda Oriental, by which they mean the eastern shore of the river."

Floriano spat on the ground. "Argentinos!" Then he looked at Fulano and apologized. "Perdão, senhor. Não Sua Excelência. Aqueles filos da puta…. Perdão, Senhorinha."

The column of seven rode on through the uninhabited dune country with no further sign of the gauchos or anyone else. The sun set, but they rode by moonlight until they reached a small crescent beach that looked out on the Atlantic.

Earle lit a shuttered lantern and began to periodically open it toward the sea. The light winked four times in succession, two long followed by two short.

Darwin found himself next to Fulano and, in his rudimentary Spanish and horrendous accent, asked, "So you're Argentinean, then?"

"I am one of the Thirty-three. The only one who still lives."

"The Thirty-three?"

"Yes, but the less you know the better, Señor Darwin—for both you and for me."

Darwin looked away, towards where Earle continued to work the signal lantern, and beyond him to Lucy. She lay with her head against a pillow of sand, eyes closed, sleeping peacefully in the moonlight.

Fitzroy was scanning the shore with his glass, looking for a light, any light. The moon was up and showed the surf breaking against the beach, but no lantern glimmered against the loom of the land. "Damned skullduggery," he muttered under his breath. He did not appreciate having to lay off a lee shore, no matter how moderate the wind. Lord Palmerston and his Whig machinations, he groused to himself, would be the death of them. Chaffers had nicely brought the *Beagle* to within three-quarters of a mile of the surf, but if the wind came up they would immediately have to beat out to sea. The more wind, the farther they would have to stand off and the longer and harder the boat crews would have to pull.

Then he saw a light, just beyond the surf. He stared at the place he had seen it, right at the head of the bay. Within a minute the proper signal flashed: two long, two short. Turning to the midshipman, he ordered the answering signal. "Two long, four short, Mister King. They should acknowledge with two long and three short."

When the signal came back, he called down to where the first lieutenant and the boatswain had two of the whaleboats standing by in the brig's lee, "Off you go, gentlemen, and God speed. They will keep their light going to guide you in."

Fitzroy continued to grumble to himself about what he saw as a Machiavellian distraction from his honest scientific work. Instead of

Wellington, you now had Prime Minister bloody Earl Grey and Secretary bloody Palmerston playing covert games with Louis-Philippe, who apparently was both the French King and a French citizen. What nonsense. It had all been much more straightforward in his father's day, when the French had had a real emperor in Napoleon and the Royal Navy had known who the enemy was.

He had even more to grumble about when the whaleboats returned and he saw Lucinda Douglas coming through the gangway. According to the plan, she was supposed to have gone back to Rio by land. Yet here she was, another female to cause disruption aboard. He relented somewhat when Earle related the incident with the gauchos. The farmhands were probably safe enough taking the horses back to the fazenda, but Lucy would be a dead giveaway if the gauchos still lurked along the road. With nothing for it but to grit his teeth at having his command turned into a circus, Fitzroy relented and ordered the midshipmen to give up their cabin to Lucy.

Fitzroy did rejoice at something later that same night, when the *Beagle* cut the Tropic of Capricorn. He was glad to put the tropics astern. The pestilential tropical air had laid out two of his crew, Sloane and Childs, both good maintop men. The seamen had spent a day filling water casks near the mouth of one of the creeks flowing into Rio's harbor. Now they lay in sickbay with the shivers. MacCormick was plying them with Schweppes' Indian Tonic Water, but they suffered greatly and might well not pull through. Nor did Fitzroy like his chronometers to suffer the tropical heat and humidity. He had observed a culminating star in Rio that confirmed their admirable precision and all the rigors of the voyage so far had necessitated no more than minor adjustments, but the more quickly they returned to temperate latitudes the better for the health of both chronometers and crew.

For Darwin's part, he had fully intended to get Fitzroy alone and quiz him as to the mysterious goings on he had become caught up in. But his antipathy for the sea had, if anything, only gotten worse after the short break ashore. So the minute Fitzroy ordered the *Beagle* to come about into the wind and head out to sea, Darwin had retreated to his hammock. Three tiresome weeks spent battling southerly winds followed, the *Beagle* corkscrewing through rollers the entire way to the River Plate.

When Lucy came to ask after his stomach, he bluntly asked her about Fulano and Earle, but she evaded with the same answer as Fulano. "The less you know the better, Charley. Remember that you invited yourself to the fazenda." She just as bluntly brought up their encounter at the inn, asking whether he had enjoyed her attentions, but he was feeling too betrayed and reticent to want to talk about that.

Finally they found some common ground for conversation when she mentioned the porpoises that had been pacing the *Beagle*, cutting back and forth across the bows and then racing ahead. He had her describe them in great detail. His appetite for such information was insatiable, and she seemed to enjoy the daily contact. So another day she told him about a cormorant, and another about how the entire sea became phosphorescent at night. "You must see it, Charley. Every part of the surface that during the day was merely foam, is now aglow with a pale light. The ship drives before its bows two billows of liquid phosphorous, a wonderful and most beautiful spectacle. And in our wake follows a milky train. As far as you can see, Charley, the crest of every wave is bright, and the sky along the horizon glimmers with the reflected light."

Fitzroy came to visit as well. Again Darwin asked about Earle and Fulano but Fitzroy would say little. "Damned skullduggery, Chawes," responded Fitzroy in a hushed tone after glancing upward at the open skylight. "Best no more said about it than need be, and no more asked neither. Percunctatorem fugito nam garrulus idem est!"

"But I saw Earle shoot a man, Robert! If he's just an artist, I'm a bloody porpoise. My distinct impression was that we might all have been killed!"

"So I hear, but keep your voice down. I'm not unsympathetic to your curiosity, Chawes, so I'll tell you what. When, and I hope it'll be soon, we are rid of Señor Fulano and Miss Douglas, and perhaps even rid of Mister Earle, I'll tell you what I know."

Childs and Sloane died just after the lookout sighted Punta del Este, where the coastline turns westward and the mouth of the River Plate yawns to the south. The entire crew assembled at sunset to hear the Last Rights as the two maintop men, sewn into pieces of canvas with a few nine-pounder balls, went over the side to Davy Jones as Fitzroy read from the prayer book. "Forasmuch as it hath pleased Almighty God of His great mercy to take unto Himself the souls of our dear brothers here departed. We therefore commit their bodies to the deep. To be turned into corruption. Looking for the Resurrection of the body. When the Sea shall give up her dead. And the life of the world to come, through our Lord Jesus Christ. Who at His coming shall change our vile body, that it may be like His glorious body, according to the mighty working, whereby He is able to subdue all things to Himself."

Later, alone in his cabin, beside Child's and Sloane's names in the muster book, Fitzroy wrote "d.d.," signifying discharged dead. Then he opened the logbook and wrote, "March 18. Off Pta. del Este, Uruguay, Lat. 34° 58' S., Long. 54° 57' W. Chronometers continue highly accurate. By d.r., Lat. 37° 26' S., Long. 53° 12' W."

After beating somewhat further southward during the night to get off the lee shore, at dawn the next day the *Beagle* turned up the River Plate with the wind on her larboard beam. The river, known to the Spaniards as the Rio de la Plata, stretched a hundred and fifty miles between Punta del Este and Punta Norte, like the mouth of a gigantic funnel. Nearly two hundred miles upstream, at the neck of the funnel, the Parana and Uruguay rivers spread their load of mud into an extensive delta. Water draining from a quarter of the continent flowed past Buenos Aires, just downstream from the delta, and spread out toward the Atlantic.

As the *Beagle* steadied onto a broad reach against the press of that mighty stream, Darwin felt the corkscrewing motion cease and left his hammock to take in his first view of the fabled pampas. He climbed the poop ladder and stumbled across the deck like a drunken spider toward the group gathered at the taffrail: Fitzroy, Lucy, and Mac-Cormick. As he came up beside them he vomited over the side with what had become a practiced nonchalance. The others pretended not to notice.

"Ah, Mister Dahwin," said Fitzroy, "I'm glad you've emerged. We were just discussing the nature of the country hereabouts."

Darwin remained focused on the wake for a few seconds. He could see bits of his breakfast biscuit being churned under the surface. More interestingly, the muddy freshwater of the river was floating on the blue saltwater of the sea. The wake was bringing the heavier saltwater to the surface, where the blue and brown mixed in a line of swirling eddies stretching astern.

"Are you all right, laddie?," enquired MacCormick.

"Yes, quite, I suppose," replied Darwin while looking up at the shore. He saw an open, undulating country covered with a uniform green turf. Innumerable cattle, sheep, and horses grazed. Only a few outcrops of granite interrupted the landscape. Scarcely a building or patch of cultivation or fence or hedgerow marred the endless pasturage. Most noticeable of all was the lack of trees in what otherwise appeared to be fertile country.

"Indeed," replied Darwin, "I've not seen the like. What accounts for the lack of trees?"

"Just what we were trying to deduce," said MacCormick. "Miss Douglas is of the opinion that a lack of rain favors the herbaceous over the arboreal. The captain here feels that immense fires like those we saw on our last voyage burn up any seedlings before they can mature. In my own opinion, it is the livestock who eat up the seedlings, as we saw to an even more pernicious degree at Porto Praia. What do you say, Charles, being our *official* naturalist, so to speak? Give us the *official* verdict, eh?"

"Well," pondered Darwin, taking a glass to look at an isolated farmhouse with some trees growing around it, "I doubt it's the climate. That house has trees growing around it, seemingly fruit trees. The settlers might have planted them for the fruit or shade or firewood, or perhaps to break the wind. Or perhaps for all of those reasons. But unless they water them, which would be a laborious undertaking and therefore not likely, there would seem to be enough rain to support arboreal vegetation. And we can, by the same token, rule out some failing of the soil."

"Exactly my point!," jumped in MacCormick.

"Nor would I credit fire in this particular place," continued Darwin. "The sheep have cropped the grass so short there's not enough left to fuel the sort of conflagration that might kill trees, even seedlings. I'll allow that other pastures might carry substantial fires, or perhaps the season's wrong right now, but fire's not the likely cause. As for livestock, that seems a distinct possibility given what we witnessed at Porto Praia, where goats have left barely a blade of grass. Those who took the trouble to plant the fruit trees would have taken the trouble to protect the seedlings from livestock. A simple fence would do."

"Well," exclaimed MacCormick, "it seems the naturalists are in agreement for once! Hallelujah."

"'In Nature's infinite book of secrets, a little we can read,'" quipped Darwin, although he was already regretting getting involved in a discussion with MacCormick too much to chuckle. "But I would hardly say my mind's made up on it or that, therefore, we can be said to be in agreement."

Lucy let go one of her laughs that Darwin found so engaging.

"Shakespeare aside, my larger point," responded an aggravated Fitzroy, "was that, whether fire or livestock inhibit arboreal vegetation, the soil and climate bespeak an arable country in terms of soils and rainfall. And, as I said before you emerged from your repose, one way of alleviating the poverty that has of late beset cities such as Manchester and London is to send the excess population to places like this. Here they might work on enormous wheat farms to feed themselves and their fellows back home. That, gentlemen—and lady—was my principal point."

"But you will never alleviate poverty, captain," responded MacCormick in his sermonizing tone. "The power of population is much greater than the power of agricultural production. As the Reverend Malthus puts it, the former is geometrical and the latter merely arithmetical in its progression. No matter how much food we might produce, the profligate classes will always multiply to outstrip the supply and precipitate their own poverty. Your plan would simply postpone the natural inevitability of their misery. Their only hope is to learn to curb their insatiable reproductive urgings, as have the better classes."

"But, Mister M'Cormick," jumped in Lucy, "surely the way to do so is to allow the poor their own property, to be masters of their own farms here in the New World so they can feed themselves?"

"Now that's not what I meant," objected Fitzroy. "I was thinking of large farms run by men of means and intelligence. They would ensure their workers had enough to eat and export a substantial surplus to England. Am I not correct, Dahwin?"

While the discussion continued on the poop deck, the officer of the watch kept the sounding lead going. The river bottom was never more than eight fathoms below the keel and in places considerably less. In some places the lump of tallow stuck in the end of the lead brought up sand, in others nothing. Because the powerful, irregular currents shifted the mud and sandbanks from place to place, even those having long experience with this river did well to keep a lead going. Also, the lookouts kept a sharp watch for storm clouds to the southwest, the harbinger of a pampero. Such a gale, building up over the pampas in the heat of late summer and blowing unchecked across the inordinately flat plains could put them on the lee shore in a moment. At the first sign of such a blow, the *Beagle* would need to get two anchors into good bottom and strike all canvas and the topmasts.

But no pampero blew up that day, and at sunset the *Beagle* safely reached Montevideo, the nominal capital of Uruguay. The river had narrowed considerably, although still some fifty miles across, and had also become even shallower, leaving less than two fathoms under the keel. About a dozen French and a couple of British and American merchantmen were already at anchor in the road. Cargo lighters passed back and forth to the quays. Two frigates, HMS *Ganges* and the French *Candide*, dominated the shipping. Fitzroy dropped anchor in the long shadow of the *Ganges*, making the *Beagle* look like a child's toy. The frigate was ten times as long with ten times the crew and ten times as many guns, even the smallest of which made any of the brig's eight cannons seem like peashooters. The hard clay of the bottom provided good anchorage, but the vessels all kept well off-shore in case of a blow.

The town itself was home to fewer than fifteen thousand people who lived in a thoroughly unremarkable collection of low buildings arranged in a grid on one of the headlands that enclosed the inner harbor. Surrounding the whole was a partially ruined wall with four gates and a moat. The city's name derived from the so-called mountain on the other headland. It rose like an alp relative to the otherwise low country but would elsewhere have been considered no more than a minor hill. The only notable building was the large fortress that the Spaniards had built during their rule. Its ramparts and bastions rose from the middle of the town, catching the last orange rays of the sun, and its cannons commanded the anchorage. In colonial times those guns had protected the galleons that carried Peruvian silver bound for Seville down the muddy waters of the River Plate, which was why the locals had named it the Rio de la Plata, meaning River of Silver.

An hour after dusk, a boat crew rowed Earle, Lucy, and Señor Fulano over to the *Ganges*. The boat also carried two marine guards. Watching them disappear into the darkness, Darwin and Fitzroy speculated that another boat must be carrying Hood, the British consul at Montevideo, from the shore to the *Ganges*. After ordering the lookouts doubled, Fitzroy led the way below for dinner and chess.

When the dishes had been cleared and the chess set laid out, Syms and Fuller left. Fitzroy offered cigars and some excellent rum that Ambassador Douglas had provided, and which Darwin thought a nice change from the thick, sweet Marsala that Fitzroy usually favored.

After having lit up, Darwin opened with his king's pawn and again broached the issue of Earle, Lucy, and Fulano. "I suppose Douglas presented you with this rum for your help picking us up off that beach?"

First pointing to the open skylight with his cigar while holding a finger up to his lips, Fitzroy answered mutedly. "I don't know much about what's going on, Chawes,…"

"More than I do, I'll wager," interrupted Darwin.

"...but I do know the general lay of the land, Douglas told me a bit more, and one is not unable to infer some of the rest. The Colorado Party of the Republic of Uruguay, led by a rather ruthless chap called Rivera, currently holds power in Montevideo. He has allowed French merchants to become established there and achieve a favorable situation relative to our own merchants, who therefore mainly work out of Buenos Aires despite that being the inferior port. We wanted an independent Uruguay as a buffer between the Brazilians and Argentines, who hate one another but whom we both cultivate as friends. We wanted to achieve some stability after their last war, you see, and encourage safe trade. If all goes well, maybe they will even be able to repay the loans they ran up fighting one another. Remember the Barings default...? Maybe your father lost some money in it...? Anyway, we never foresaw that the French would turn our buffer into their toehold on this coast. Who knows what they've promised Rivera in return for his support?"

The two of them had been following a Vienna opening, but Fitzroy, seemingly distracted, had unaccountably varied it with something like the King's Gambit by moving his king's bishop's pawn to the fourth rank instead of mirroring Darwin's knight advance. Darwin responded by accepting the offering and, more interested in understanding his own brush with violence than Fitzroy's rehash of international politics, pointedly asked who Fulano was.

"That's not his real name, of course, as if you hadn't guessed. It's Oribe, Manuel Oribe. He leads the Blanco Party. They're rural landowners who oppose Rivera's Colorados. They control much of the backcountry, beyond the immediate environs of Montevideo. According to Douglas, Oribe has promised us that if he gains control of Montevideo, he will kick out the Frogs. But, apparently, we can't seem to be involved. So far Brazil and Argentina are being noncommittal toward Oribe. On the one hand, each of them hopes that further unrest in Uruguay will give rise to an opportunity to regain what each sees as its own lost province. So providing arms to the Blancos to weaken the Colorados must appeal to their ambitions. On the other hand, each is so internally unsettled at present that the last thing they want just now is another all-out war. The last one bankrupted them."

"So," asked Darwin, "why was Fulano, I mean Oribe, at a fazenda in the middle of nowhere, being chased by bandits?"

Fitzroy, focusing on his explanation, was playing irregularly and now returned to the Vienna sequence by advancing his king's knight. "Douglas told me that Oribe had been in Rio trying to get support for a major offensive against Montevideo. Then Colorado and French agents began to make things hot for him. You apparently met some of their hirelings on the coast road. So Oribe asked for His Majesty's protection,…"

"But how is Lucy involved?"

"…and Douglas hid him out at that fazenda. Oribe is probably the only one alive who could rally the landowners to move against the Colorados in Montevideo. He was one of the famed, so-called Immortal Thirty-Three, Argentines who crossed the river to liberate Uruguay from the Brazilians, who still call it their Cisplatine Province."

"He mentioned that," Darwin muttered as he threatened Fitzroy's knight with a pawn.

"Well needless to say, then, the Brazilians are not terribly well disposed toward him, but he was trying to convince them that he was the lesser of two evils, so to speak. Apparently he failed, and I think that Palmerston hopes to get him back into Uruguay without alerting the French."

"But damn it, Robert," interrupted Darwin, "tell me plainly how Lucy and Augustus are involved!"

"Keep your voice down," hissed Fitzroy, pointing to the open skylight. "They are secret agents, you fool, working for Secretary Lord Palmerston." As Darwin stared at the chessboard, too shocked by the confirmation of his suspicions to feel insulted, Fitzroy castled.

"I see," said Darwin finally, as he took the knight more by habit than thought. "A dangerous situation. Hence the marines. And your doubling of the watch. But what will they do now?"

"Damned if I know what they're deciding over on the *Ganges* with Hood, Chawes. Palmerston is a cold fish, and I expect our ever so innocuous artist and elegant young lady are just as ruthless. They would probably assassinate Oribe at the drop of a hat…"

"No!"

"…if it suited their purposes. And please keep your voice down. As far as I'm concerned, the Whigs play a dangerous game when they pursue entente cordiale with Louis-Philippe while engaging in this sort of covert chicanery. It lowers us to the level of the Frogs. But I'm not a Secretary of War like my uncle was, just a junior captain in the Royal Navy. All I hope is that those three decide to get the bloody hell off my ship so that we can carry on with our work."

After Fitzroy had lost the knight, both queens had developed rapidly, and Darwin, still stunned to find out Lucy's dangerous occupation but not wanting to seem overly concerned for her personal safety, continued to play mainly by rote. He sacrificed some material to open up Fitzroy's king, now well protected in the back rank, and advanced his forward pawn without backing it up with his knight.

After several minutes silence, while trying to regain some equilibrium, he hesitantly ventured, "But surely they won't assassinate Oribe, Robert? That would simply be doing the work of the French for them, wouldn't it?"

"Quite, Charles. I suppose I simply meant that anything is possible. Oribe is not unexpendable, so to speak. Still, I think that what the PM and Palmerston must really be interested in is Argentina, not Uruguay. They should like to dislodge the Frogs from Montevideo, likely enough, to maintain Uruguay as a buffer between the Argentine provinces and Brazil. But I doubt they will risk their interests in Argentina to do so. Whatever the French have offered Rivera, Palmerston can double. But Oribe's friendship with an Argentine General named Rosas would complicate that gambit. General Rosas is the power in Buenos Aires, and I doubt that Palmerston dares alienate him."

"Why not?"

"When we have a chance to get over to the other side of the river, you will see why anyone would value Argentina over Uruguay. You think this side a level plain? Just wait till you see the other shore. The pampas are even more level, vaster, more fertile. Can you imagine the potential to supply our burgeoning population with meat and grain? The United States remains hostile to our interests, Canada too cold to grow much, Australia too distant. Here, enormous farms and ranches could ship their products down canals to a series of ports along the coast—wheat, beef, mutton, wool. Or the newfangled railroads will become more practicable to even greater effect. Imagine a whole network of railroads spreading out from Buenos Aires to every part of the pampas. And imagine large, iron-hulled steamships carrying grain and livestock across the Atlantic in a matter of weeks. Remember that last year the Great Western made it from Bristol to New York in a mere fifteen days. Think of it! Fifteen days! What was distant has become near—and will become nearer yet. Now our Argentine merchants import Lancashire muslins and calicos or Birmingham hardware and crockery in exchange for hides, tallow, and corned beef. Soon they will be sending England beef on the hoof. Do you see, my dear boy? That's what I was trying to get at the other day on deck, when that fool M'Cohmick began to go on about trees. It's the bloody Irish who are so agitated about landowners enclosing their lands to make productive use of them. Well, there's land aplenty in the Argentine, the best land in the world, and it's going to waste. All that's lacking is capital and labor to make the pampas into England's victulator!"

Fitzroy had become so excited that he had forgotten his own injunction against raised voices, and Darwin had become so concerned about Lucy that he worried in silence, barely listening to Fitzroy or concentrating on the game. By the thirtieth move, after several furious exchanges, both queens and all the knights were gone but Darwin was ahead by a rook and a bishop.

"You might think," continued Fitzroy, again remembering to mute his voice, "that the government favors the agitations of some of our merchants to annex Argentina, as you've no doubt read in that rag, *The Times*. But I really doubt it'll happen with this PM. A Tory government might have the guts, but not these Whigs. What they want is governments that favor trade with Britain and guarantee the security of our investments. In Argentina only a Rosas government can provide such stability. He is a leader of rural landowners, a federalist, and hence a natural ally of Oribe's Blancos. Strange, isn't it, how the Whigs always seem to find that their natural allies abroad are Tories? Haw haw haw!"

67

Fitzroy stopped laughing to study the chessboard for the best part of a minute, especially noting how both of Darwin's rooks and bishops were positioned to close on the black king. But the shout of the lookout hailing the returning boat came through the skylight to interrupt his contemplation.

"It seems I must resign, Chawes," he said. "Thank you for the game, though. Will you join me on deck to welcome back our secret agents? I assume that at least some of them have returned."

In fact all three of them returned from the *Ganges*. Lucy was her usual gracious self, Earle as reticent as ever, and Oribe the same amiable gentleman. None of them volunteered any information. None revealed whether the meeting had resulted in some plan of action. None seemed either upset or hopeful. Earle simply handed Fitzroy a canvas envelope, which Darwin presumed to be from Hood, and the three retired below.

In the morning, once light enough to sound with the lead and navigate among the banks of the ever-shoaling river, the *Beagle* sailed for Buenos Aires and by late in the day came within sight of the Argentine shore. Fitzroy had been accurate in his description. The river and land came together in an ephemeral zone marked by beds of rushes. Beyond the almost indiscernible shore, the surface of the pampas was nearly, other than a few disorganized striations, no more than grassy troughs, as flat and low as the surface of the river itself. The backs of the cattle, enormous herds of them with their heads buried in the grass, were the highest solid elevations on the shore. Above them wove the feathery inflorescences of gigantic cane grass. Much more rarely, the dark green domes of ombu trees rose even higher. Clouds formed through the day and then slashed the plain with sheets of water that spread over vast acreages. The cattle ignored the resulting lakes, standing in them up to their bellies and grazing as if on dry land. Some of the water would eventually find its way down the troughs to the river, and the summer sun would dry up the rest.

Chaffers slowly worked the *Beagle* upstream. As the sun set, he found some hard bottom and ordered double anchors dropped. A little inland, a solitary ombu tree cast its long shadow over a herd of grazing cattle.

The next afternoon, late, the *Beagle* made anchor in the outer roadstead at Buenos Aires. A lug-rigged cutter arrived at dusk with the health inspector, who came aboard through the gangway looking as if he would rather still be taking his siesta. A large man with a small mustache followed. He wore a plain black suit but carried himself with the authority of a military officer and looked like he had never taken a siesta and never would.

While Fitzroy assisted with the inspection, Oribe, Lucy, and Earle met at the taffrail with the mustachioed man. The group conversed so quietly that Darwin, who was standing at the break of the poop and gazing toward Buenos Aires, where the evening sun was glinting from the domes of the churches, could not overhear a single word. By sunset, the inspector had satisfied himself that the crew of the *Beagle* was not carrying cholera, and he and the large man left in the cutter accompanied by Oribe, Lucy, and Earle. They slowly disappeared in the fading light until their bow lantern became lost against the shore lights.

"That," commented Fitzroy to Darwin, "to me, looked like a member of the Mazorca, Rosas's secret police. They transmit all of the intelligence they gather to his wife, the infamous Doña María, who coordinates his political intrigues. It's rumored that the Mazorca have invented engines of torture that surpass those of even the Inquisition. Best to stay clear of Mister Earle and Miss Douglas, I'd say, Chawes. And good riddance to the lot of them!"

4

IN THE MORNING FITZROY and Darwin went ashore and took rooms at a hotel near the Plaza de Mayo, the principal square. Fitzroy intended to secure copies of any charts and reports that the Argentineans had inherited from the Spaniards and that might be pertinent to his work. Any prior knowledge of reefs and shoals, no matter how inaccurate, would be essential to the survey. He also hoped for a passport from General Rosas to ease dealings with local functionaries down the coast. In return, the Argentineans could expect copies of all the charts that the survey produced.

The main public buildings clustered near the Plaza de Mayo. Just to the west, some fortifications separated the plaza from the shore. Across the broad mudflats, numerous quays stretched toward the open river. Dozens of merchantmen, most of them British, occupied the inner road while an endless chain of lighters ferried cargo back and forth. Several Argentinean, British, American, and French warships rode at anchor beyond the merchantmen. Oxcarts with enormous wheels, eight or more feet in diameter, plied back and forth between the lighters, the quays, and the warehouses in the city, sometimes driving out onto the mudflats until their axels nearly disappeared below the water and the oxen were almost swimming. Stacks of cowhide, casks of beef, and bales of wool went out. Crates came in. Darwin guessed they must contain everything from fabrics of cotton and wool to small arms and porcelain.

Thinking of the porcelain, Darwin recalled his mother's brother, uncle Josiah Wedgwood, who was in that business. One of his daughters, Emma, was a good friend of Darwin and Fanny. He must send all of them letters before leaving Buenos Aires. He also needed to ship Henslow the specimens collected in Brazil.

The hotel owner was an Englishman who was, like Darwin, coincidentally enough, a graduate of Shrewsbury. David Lumb had been in Buenos Aires for nearly ten years and offered to show his fellow alumnus around. By the second day, Darwin had tired of the bureaucrats, and apparently Rosas was away in Patagonia on a military campaign against the Indians, so the idea of seeing more of the city became very appealing. Besides, he might spot Lucy somewhere in the streets, and he had been thinking about her a lot lately—and worrying.

So, after breakfast, when Fitzroy once again left for the anterooms of the naval department, Darwin and Lumb rode westward along the main avenue. Compared to Montevideo, the Argentine capital was much more appealing and larger, a real city, with upwards of sixty thousand inhabitants. Compared to Rio de Janeiro, the setting was less spectacular but the plan more regular, with views for many blocks down any avenue. All the streets intersected at right angles and seemed perfectly parallel. Each took its name from some date or personage involved in the recent revolutionary wars. The Plaza de Mayo itself took its name from the month of the declaration of independence. The stone houses of the Porteños, as the citizens of the port preferred to call themselves, abutted one another in a solid front along the sidewalks. All the residences, from the plainest ones lining the streets to those around the Plaza de Mayo, such as the palaces of the old viceroys and their courtiers, had essentially the same plan as Lumb's hotel: a solid square relieved in the center by a courtyard planted with all manner of vegetation, a cool green refuge from the heat and dust of the city. Lumb related how on the flat roofs, rarely more than a single story above the street, the inhabitants would socialize in the evenings, passing around a drink called mate and enjoying the breeze from the river after the sweltering heat of the day. Their roofs had also been the Porteños' refuge when the British army invaded in 1807. The citizenry had pelted the troops with roof tiles and doused them with boiling oil until they retreated to their ships.

In half an hour, Lumb and Darwin had reached the outskirts and were riding along lanes bordered by willows and poplars. Summer was ending, and in some fields, each enclosed by its agave fence, farmers were harvesting the last of their vegetables; in others, tillage revealed the thick, dark topsoil. Occasional olive and peach orchards varied the scene.

71

Lumb and Darwin reminisced as they rode, about Shrewsbury in particular and England in general. Shrewsbury had not much changed in a decade or two, but England had. Lumb was a voracious consumer of newspapers and seemed to know more about current affairs than Darwin but wanted to know what it was really like. "How is it, Charles, to see Stephenson's Rocket steam by? How does it sound, smell, feel when it barrels past on the way to Manchester with a train of cars behind, spewing the steam and cinders they write about in the papers?"

They shared their two very different varieties of homesickness as best they could. The one was a chronic affliction, the product of a decade abroad, the homesickness of the expatriate. The other was the passing malaise of the traveler, having gestated a mere three months and promising to end as suddenly as the voyage. Darwin sensed that even if Lumb returned home, he would forever be homesick for the England he had left a decade ago. Everything was changing so fast. Iron and speed and the invariable tick of the clock conspired to tear up the rural roots of the hundreds of thousands who marshaled in the grimy streets outside the factory gates. He did his best to convey how those changes felt but eventually gave up and focused on the bucolic landscape they rode through, asking his new friend every imaginable question about trees, agriculture, and everything else he noticed.

So when they approached one of the many saltworks that ringed the city, he asked Lumb to explain the details of how the beef was sliced and packed together with corns of salt into the casks. The best salt apparently came from some of the smaller islands of the Cape Verde archipelago, where artificial basins could be periodically flooded with seawater and then left to evaporate under the intense tropical sun. The cost of importing salt from such a distance was so exorbitant, however, that the saltworks mixed in the local salt, mined in Patagonia. It came from natural saltpans and was so pure that it lacked some of the chlorides present in sea salt, which for some reason of chemistry as yet only vaguely understood produced the best quality corned beef. The main reason for founding the town of Patagones, in fact, explained Lumb, had been to mine the Patagonian saltpans. That town near the mouth of the Rio Negro, some five hundred miles south of Buenos Aires, had for the last fifty years marked the southernmost outpost of civilization along the Atlantic coast of South America.

Just beyond the saltworks, a group of gauchos was driving an indiscriminate herd of yearlings, both heifers and bulls, into one of the corrals that supplied the beef market. The gauchos reminded Darwin of the one on the road near the fazenda. They wore big hats with the wide brim turned up in front, billowing fringed leggings, and red ponchos patterned black. Rather amazingly, their feet were nearly bare except for toe-less leather socks and the spurs that they savagely dug into the ribs of their wild looking mounts. The leather sock, fashioned from a single piece of hide slipped from the foreleg of a horse according to Lumb, left the big and second toes free to grasp the knotted ropes that passed for stirrups. The gauchos slashed at the yearlings with their braided leather lassos and crops. Matadors ran from animal to animal, cutting hamstrings. Others followed with heavy hammers, smashing in the skulls of the animals as they wallowed in the gore of those who had gone before. Skinners in leather aprons that reached from neck to ankle peeled the hides from the carcasses as if they were removing their stockings. Butchers carved the carcasses right were they lay and loaded whole carts with sides or briskets or haunches. The legs and bellies of the horses that worked the corral dripped with blood. Piles of entrails lay steaming in the sun. The heavy wheels of the carts crushed the bones that littered the corral and made up its fence. Gore and flies covered every surface. All around the corral, tanners were staking out hides to dry, stretching them taught and scrapping them clean. The floor of the corral and the ground all about was so layered with fragments of bone from decades of slaughter that it seemed like a terrazzo in the dining hall of some cannibal king.

Darwin and Lumb rode on and left the stench of slaughter behind. They made a circuit through the outskirts of the city before taking the southern avenue back to the Plaza de Mayo. "See how fierce those gaucho herdsmen looked, Charles?," said Lumb at one point. "That's why Rosas rules, old man. The gauchos think him nearly a god, and at bottom they are the real power in Argentina."

"I'd heard something to that effect, David," responded Darwin. "But if Rosas is so much in control, why is he off in Patagonia? Why is he not here dealing with the Uruguay situation or negotiating trade treaties?"

"He's a patient and uncompromising man, it seems. He was elected governor of Buenos Aires province last year, which pretty much amounts to becoming President of Argentina, if you can control the squabbling provinces. And he can, old man. He can. Anyway, no sooner did they elect him than he asked Congress to legislate him the powers of a king. He never actually said the word king, of course. That title still leaves a bad taste in the mouth hereabouts. Supreme Dictator, he called it. Absolute power for life sort of thing. When Congress refused, he resigned and left on what he calls his Desert Campaign, down in Patagonia, fighting the savages. My suspicion is that he's just waiting for the situation to get bad enough that the people demand him back. That way he'll be able to dictate his terms. Meanwhile he keeps his gaucho troops happy and practiced at killing. He maintains his reputation among them. And he clears the country of savages for when he does assume absolute power."

"And are things 'bad enough' now?," asked Darwin, trying to calculate the implications for Lucy. "I heard that his wife remains here to pull the political strings while he's on campaign. Are they planning a coup d'état?"

"Who can tell? Right now Congress is controlled by the liberal, Unitario Party. They want to centralize control of the Argentine Republic in Buenos Aires. Every few weeks they go too far for the Federalists, who want a lose confederation of largely autonomous provinces, each controlled by its local land barons. So when the Unitarios legislate greater federal powers, the Federalists declare themselves in revolt and blockade the city. It's usually over in a few days, with yet another group of Unitarios assassinated by the Mazorca or exiled to Montevideo, where they find solace among Rivera's Colorados. You're right about Rosas's wife, María Encarnación. Hundreds of men walk the streets of this city who lack tongues, or eyes, or testicles. They got on her wrong side. Better they just cut your throat and get it done with, eh? My own suspicion is that once enough of the

Unitarios have been done away with, Rosas will return. And that, Charles, will be very good for business," winked Lumb.

"It sounds like a bloody business, David. Is it worth it?"

"I'd say there are nearly two thousand Britons here now. Every year the number grows. Every year we establish more saltworks. Before we started to make corned beef, the cattle just ran wild. The only profit was in hides and a bit of veal for the city. The gauchos hunted the bulls with the desjarretadera, a pike with a crescent blade mounted on the end. They rode behind a fleeing bull and used the desjarretadera to sever a hamstring. Dropped the animal in its tracks. If they just wanted one for a meal they tangled its legs with a bola or used the lasso on it. But the desjarretadera can make short work of entire herds. They took the hides, roasted a few steaks, and left the carcasses to their dogs and the buzzards. You've just seen how they do it now, old man. The corned beef goes to our plantations in the Caribbean, even as far as Georgia and Alabama. In return we import all manner of manufactures, like the woolens for those colorful gaucho ponchos you saw."

Darwin was eager for this sort of information, and his tone betrayed his fascination. "Can one still see gauchos living the free life on the pampas, hunting wild cattle and the like?"

"Oh, sure, where you're going down south you'll see plenty of that, I expect. They hate Buenos Aires, Porteños, anything and anyone that threatens their freedom. That's why they support Rosas and the provincial chieftains against the Unitarios who want to break up the estates, promote immigration, and increase overseas trade. Too bad for them that the liberals don't have the military power to ensure stability. Rosas does, and for all his conservative rhetoric the general knows that the power of cattle barons like himself will more and more derive from foreign trade. If not for our salt works, he'd still be camping out on the pampas with little to his name that he couldn't carry on a horse. Now his estancias include more than seventy square leagues of prime range, and in any given year he runs three hundred thousand head. He'll be back soon, and then the future will be bright indeed. The gauchos think they're fighting to preserve the status quo. Rosas understands his future is linked to trade with Britain."

"So I take it you plan to stay a few more years?"

"Of course, old man, of course," Lumb answered laughingly. "I own the hotel lock, stock, and barrel and also have shares in some saltworks and ships. I came here on a small remittance and in another decade or two will return to England a rich man. Carpe diem, I say, carpe diem."

Lumb left Darwin at the hotel, and after washing the dust away he headed for the offices of the Argentine naval department to look for Fitzroy. But just as Darwin stepped into the street, he came face to face with Lucy strolling arm in arm under the arcade with a young French naval officer. Before Darwin could say anything, though, she averted her face, the couple passed, and the words froze half-formed on his lips.

Shunned, Darwin stood gaping after her. Glad to see her but hurt. Slowly, as he continued on to the naval offices, he regained his composure. But Fitzroy was not there anyway, so Darwin went to the British consulate to look for him, again unsuccessfully. Instead he found that the consulate had been holding a thick stack of letters that had arrived for him on the mail packet HMS *Duke of York*, and he returned to the hotel to read them.

When he opened the door to his room, Lucy was sitting on a chair by the window. He closed the door. She rose and stepped towards him. They pressed their bodies together. Their mouths locked. Neither said anything until they both lay satiated on the bed and the afternoon light was fading from the window. His head rested in her armpit, and he heard her heart and smelled her drying sweat. He thought about how her lips had felt in his hair as she arched her back over him so that he could lick her hardened nipples. He thought about their grunts of pleasure as they slammed together harder and harder until the explosion of gratification and its aftershocks. When the darkness was total, she rolled against him and while they kissed folded her palms around his penis until it was hard again. Then she pushed him inside and they moved quietly against one another until he ejaculated a second time and fell asleep.

When he awoke, it was growing light and she was already dressed. He asked if she would be back later in the day. She replied that she could not. He asked if she would be aboard the *Beagle* when they left on the survey. She laughed and said that she doubted Fitzroy would appreciate her presence. Besides, she claimed, business would keep her in Buenos Aires for the foreseeable future. He asked about the French officer. She replied that he was business.

"Will you please not mention anything about that to Fitzroy, Charley? In fact," she continued, "would you not mention anything about me to anyone? It's too dangerous for you to tell you why, and it's too dangerous for me if you say anything about me to anyone. Do you promise?"

He did promise. And he was both regretful and glad when he closed the door behind her.

For distraction he turned to the letters from home, several from each of his three sisters and one from Fanny that he opened first. She wrote about her sadness that he would be away so many years. She had married Robert Biddulph. Darwin had met him, a wealthy politician from Birmingham. He did not feel sadness or much else besides a little embarrassment, and he quickly slit open the other letters. His sisters did not mention Fanny Owen and all repeated the same unremarkable news from Shrewsbury. His pigeons were fine.

The *Beagle* sailed two days later, with Earle but without Oribe or Lucy. Darwin had not seen Lucy again. He had looked for her under the arcades. He had even borrowed a telescope from Lumb and occasionally stepped to his window to inspect the ladies who strolled the plaza with officers and merchants. But none of the faces that jumped into focus belonged to Lucy.

So he had busied himself with practicing Spanish with Lumb, writing letters, and having his specimens crated before the packet sailed for England. Separate letters had gone to each of his sisters and his father. He had even written his cousin Emma Wedgwood, reporting on the voyage thus far. The long letter described his ecstasy while walking in the forest near Rio de Janeiro and drew comparisons to their strolls together near Shrewsbury. He wasn't quite sure why he had written Emma. She had not written him. Perhaps he had done so in place of the letter he had expected to write Fanny. Perhaps he was thinking of his mother because when she had died, when Darwin was eight, he had gone to live with the Wedgwoods for a year and he and Emma had often played together. He especially remembered their explorations along the stream that ran through the Wedgwood estate and thought she would appreciate his feelings about botanizing in the tropics.

He had maintained a more reserved tone in the letter to Henslow that accompanied the large crate of quadruped, reptile, and bird skins, insects in pillboxes, and pressed plants. He had checked off the specimens, more than two hundred in all, nearly half of them insects, many of them coleopterous. Syms had carefully preserved each specimen according to its character. Darwin had labeled each one and listed them in a ledger with his best identification as to genus and species, or sometimes merely to family or order, followed by an annotation on habits observed or gleaned from informants. Despite being unable to identify some of the specimens, particularly the plants and birds, any more specifically than order, he doubted that any of the species were new, except to him, because so many naturalists had already worked the environs of Rio. He regretted that Henslow would probably not be impressed.

As he stood at the taffrail watching the receding houses of Buenos Aires blend into the flat pampas, he looked forward to the less charted country ahead and resolved to forget his mysterious paramour, Lucy, and concentrate on science. Fitzroy planned to survey the Patagonian coast during the fall and winter months and then return to Buenos Aires to re-victualate. He had procured only a few ancient charts that the Spaniards had made nearly a hundred years ago. The governor of the day had supplied a passport, but he was a Unitario and opposed by Rosas so the passport would probably be worse than useless beyond the immediate purview of Buenos Aires, perhaps even there. Rosas apparently was encamped with his army near Patagones, along the Rio Negro, and Fitzroy intended to head for there to secure another passport in the general's own name.

Both Fitzroy and Darwin had learned more about Rosas from various expatriate merchants that hung about the hotel and were looking forward to meeting him, albeit with some apprehension. Apparently he had first established himself as a leader by building up a personal army of gauchos to defend his estancias from the Indians, who as recently as a decade ago had raided right up to the outskirts of Buenos Aires. Most of the stories told at the hotel related to the rigid discipline he maintained among his men and to his own prowess as a horseman and fighter.

Lumb had told one tale about Rosas's ordinance against carrying knives on Sundays, that being the principal day for drinking, gambling, and fighting among the gauchos. One day Rosas, forgetful of the day and the knife being so much a part of his habitual dress, accidentally violated the rule. When he realized his error, he ordered himself placed in the stocks for the day, that being the usual punishment. Such egalitarian displays delighted the gauchos, their code of honor and belief in equality being profound.

Other expatriates had told stories of Rosas's feats of horsemanship. Apparently the gauchos elected their generals on the basis of equestrian competitions, to which Rosas periodically submitted himself. That he always won might follow from the fear that anyone who bested him would have his throat cut but nonetheless bespoke his talents with horse, bolas, and lasso.

By such means and by conforming to the dress and habits of the gauchos, Rosas maintained his popularity among the only substantial fighting force in the land. Anyone who spoke disrespectfully of him could expect a knife in the ribs. And the murderer would walk away not only free but acclaimed. On many mornings, apparently, the Porteños found corpses hung from iron hooks in the main market square, their throats slit from ear to ear, bloodied sashes of Unitarist blue draped around their naked torsos. The police dutifully investigated but never made any arrests.

5

THE *BEAGLE* ROUNDED PUNTA Norte and followed the low, sandy coast southward, the wind fair and the sea calm. The country stretching inland appeared as fertile as any Darwin had yet seen. Small streams wound across the barely undulating green prairie, losing themselves in a maze of marsh and sand as they approached the coast. One day, Mellersh and King, with the sporadic enthusiasm typical of midshipmen, made a rough count of the cattle that could be seen grazing from the deck. They took the task in turns and by dusk announced that the *Beagle* had passed within sight of ten thousand head.

The coast south of the Rio de la Plata being uncharted in any detail, even the general outline on the old Spanish charts being of doubtful accuracy, Fitzroy had Chaffers anchor the *Beagle* at regular intervals to triangulate her position and that of the few landmarks that adorned the coastline. The mates kept the lead going watch by watch, converting the unseen topography below them into numbers. Sometimes Fitzroy would send out the boats to sound about the mouths of creeks that seemed to have potential as anchorages. But he intended to carry out the bulk of that detailed work once he had built up a general outline and better knew where to concentrate the effort.

For the first time during the voyage, frequent stops and a calm sea allowed Darwin to spend considerable time out of his hammock while aboard. He and Syms busied themselves by trolling nets and lines for whatever they might catch. The fish proved uninteresting, all of them known species, but Darwin asked Earle to sketch them anyway and Syms to preserve them in jars of alcohol. One never knew, reasoned Darwin, what the ichthyologists at the British Museum might make of them. The other marine organisms reminded him of rambles along the Firth of Forth, and he thought them more interesting. One zoophyte might even be a new species of coelenterate. He was not sure but had never seen nor read of anything like it: a Medusa but gorgeously transparent like a salp.

The most astonishing specimen was the carcass of a dolphin that Syms spotted floating alongside and grappled aboard. It had been dead long enough to begin putrefying, but Darwin was familiar enough with mammalian taxa that, even in its bloated condition, he recognized it as a new species of Delphinus and immediately began telling Syms how he wanted it preserved. The smell in the heat of late afternoon, though, was, as Rowlett so inelegantly put it, "enou' tae knock a boozard o' a sheet wagon," and it quickly attracted a group who did not seem sympathetic to anything less than immediate disposal over the side. Only Darwin's inspired offer to name it *Delphinus fitzroyi* bought enough time for Earle to sketch it and Syms to remove and flense the skull. Thomas Sorrell, the boatswain, hovered over the operation the entire time, ready to deploy a crew with swabs and holystones the moment, as he put it, "Young Philos be dun turnin' 'is Majesty's brig int'a bloody fish boat."

Such incidents did nothing to counter Darwin's reputation as an eccentric young gentleman. Three months into the voyage, having been either ashore or confined to his hammock most of that time, he remained the only unknown quantity aboard. The crew had nicknamed him Young Philos and filled in what they did not know with conjecture, invariably negative. Even allowing his patchy beard to grow out did nothing to secure respect. He resigned himself to being Young Philos and looked forward to spending as much time as possible ashore.

Darwin suspected that MacCormick might well be fostering the crew's dismissive attitude towards him. The surgeon was just the type who knew how to make seemingly casual but poisonous comments about people he disliked and had ample opportunity to do so. He had private contact with everyone from the officers to the boys. Anyone with some ill or pain came to the sickbay, and sooner or later everyone had something, from a cut to Venus's curse, which had come aboard in Rio despite Fitzroy's best efforts to keep the crew out of the claptraps. And the surgeon clearly disliked Darwin. MacCormick wanted him to play the pliable, junior colleague who would defer to the pronouncements of his elder. Instead, Darwin wanted to debate, insisting on logic and evidence. He had asserted himself as the expedition's official naturalist by collecting hundreds more specimens in a few months than MacCormick had on all his voyages to date. And, worst of all from MacCormick's perspective, with only a few lapses, Darwin had assiduously avoided him since crossing the Atlantic. The surgeon so resented being ignored that he no longer sought out Darwin and, when they did interact, was openly hostile.

Fitzroy and Darwin shared dinner and chess daily, but otherwise the captain was too busy with the survey to pay any attention to "Young Philos's" sense of isolation. For his own part, Darwin had largely written off Fitzroy as arrogant and uninteresting. The entire crew had to endure their captain's authoritarian character and, in the mornings, his foul temper. Darwin additionally had to endure Fitzroy's dogmatic opinions delivered over dinner during the pretense of an intellectual discussion. Any dissent elicited condescension. And, as Darwin had increasingly become irritated and asserted his own interpretations of the geology they encountered, Fitzroy's condescension had given way to castigation. The captain was especially irked that Darwin increasingly affirmed Lyell's principles of geology.

The breaking point in the relationship came when Fitzroy tore into Darwin for asking if he might go ashore while the boats were sounding a creek mouth. "No!," shouted Old Hot Coffee in plain hearing of all. "I can't afford to hold up weighing anchor because you've gotten yourself lost looking for robins eggs, like some schoolboy!" Darwin could only excuse himself so that Fitzroy and the other officers on the poop would not see his tightening lips and flushed face. But his anger had passed by the time he knocked at the captain's door for dinner that evening, and Fitzroy acted as if nothing had happened. And to him, Darwin supposed, nothing had. Darwin could not avoid Fitzroy as he did MacCormick, but that day he resolved to say as little as possible over dinner and chess for the remainder of the voyage.

By the time the *Beagle* had coasted southward for two weeks, though, Darwin was desperate for companionship and conversation. Earle kept his own counsel. Syms was a fine technician and enthusiastic about plants and animals but little else, certainly not conversation. He had become friendly with Fuller, Fitzroy's servant, and with some of the seamen like Jonathan May, the carpenter, and Ash, the Gunroom Steward, but for the most part Syms kept to himself.

More by default than design, then, Darwin began to seek out the company of Matthews, another supernumerary and another solitary character. And before long he began genuinely to appreciate the missionary's company and wish they had become better acquainted earlier. They had in common their age and the choice they had both so recently faced: whether to pursue a spiritual or a secular vocation. They had both chosen to sail on the *Beagle*, but for one that decision had led toward the secular and for the other toward the spiritual.

At some point in the past few months, Darwin's observations and logic had begun so thoroughly to contradict received explanations that he could no longer maintain a literal faith in the Bible, at least in Genesis, or see himself professing them from the pulpit. He thought he had probably crossed that threshold somewhere between Rio and Montevideo, while laying sick in his hammock. Now he retained absolutely no desire to follow his father's advice to join the clergy. Instead, he dreamed of emulating his friends at the Plinian Society and Lyell, of helping to bring a conceptual order to the world that religion, he now felt certain, could never achieve. Matthews, in contrast, as he had gotten to know the Fuegians better and as they approached Tierra del Fuego, became increasingly zealous about his mission.

Isolation shadowed them both, though, and they empathized with one another during long discussions in Darwin's cabin. They also talked about MacCormick and Fitzroy. Matthews had run afoul of Fitzroy on suggesting that the Fuegians stay in Buenos Aires until the spring, when the *Beagle* would return there to re-victualate before sailing for Tierra del Fuego. But Fitzroy had harshly dismissed the suggestion even though the Church Missionary Society had agreed to fund the room and board. He cited the need to keep the Fuegians from the corruption of urban life and thereby implied that Matthews would not be able to protect his charges. Darwin could well identify with feeling patronized by Fitzroy, and the two of them shared their resentment.

Darwin also tried to reassure Matthews that MacCormick was an opinionated fool, knew little about phrenology, even less about the ability of people to change, and was wrong to predict the failure of the mission. "You should read *Philosophies Zoologique*," Darwin told Matthews, retrieving the book from the case and holding it out to Matthews. "In it, the Chevalier de Lamarck demonstrates that species modify themselves through the exercise or lack thereof of any organ. The giraffe thereby acquires a longer and longer neck through stretching ever higher to browse the uppermost leaves of trees. You see...? That same principle must apply to the brain, right...? If the races of Man are all descended from Adam, each degenerating differently to assume their current characteristics, then they will continue to change and thereby, under suitable conditions, re-converge. Take your Fuegians, for example. They are much like the noble indigenes of the prairies of North America, but instead of being tall and stately, the tribes of the red-skinned race that penetrated to the barren wastes of Tierra del Fuego have been rendered decrepit in appearance. Clearly, with better food and stimulation of their mental faculties, York, Fuegia, and Jeremy have become civilized. So enough of M'Cormick's bunkum!"

The issue nonetheless continued to worry Matthews, despite all reassurances, because the success of his mission depended on whether MacCormick or Darwin was correct. "What if," pondered Matthews aloud, "the moment I remove my tutelage they revert to their primitive nature, as M'Cormick claims they will...? I pray to God for the strength to civilize them and trust I am doing so, but if their nature is against them, the mission must inevitably fail upon my return to England."

Darwin could only continue to encourage him to read *Philosophies Zoologique*, but Matthews was not a reader of scientific treatises and not really capable of debating such matters.

Matthews did, however, counsel Darwin on his love life. The missionary had not the least personal experience with romantic love, but he knew something about spiritual love and commitment. Darwin's emotional trauma consisted not of pain that Fanny had married Biddulph, but that he felt no pain, merely embarrassment at having been jilted so quickly after leaving England. He had long been convinced that he loved Fanny, but in hindsight he could not reconstruct any such feeling. Worse, he confided in Matthews, with Lucy he felt no love at all—only some affection. But he did feel a great deal of lust for her. Matthews pointed out that if Darwin had loved Fanny, he would never have left her to go on a voyage around the world. "She knew that, Charles, even if you didn't." Then he advised Darwin to never again see Lucy. "But what about Emma Wedgwood, Charles? You seem to have some feelings by the way you speak of her? Did you not write her a long letter…? So forego your lecherous inclinations and instead dream of a life with Emma, back in Shropshire, surrounded by family and children." But most nights and mornings Darwin would fantasize about Lucy, picturing her round buttocks hanging over the mold of the forest floor or her firm breasts brushing against his lips. He respected Matthews's chaste dedication to God's work but now knew for certain that such a life was not for him.

That realization did not stop Darwin from sometimes joining his new acquaintance when he instructed the Fuegians, though. And so he learned that contrary to Fitzroy's claim that all three were of the Yahga people, they were really all Yamana. The Yahga were merely the first tribe of Yamana that the *Beagle* had encountered on its last voyage. Besides that error, Yahga was a corruption of Yahgashagolumoala, meaning People Who Live Along the Mountain-Valley Channel. But neither York, Jeremy, nor Fuegia was Yahgashagolumoala. Darwin also learned their real names. York was Shukukurhtumahgoon, meaning son from the house with the grass-thatched roof. Jeremy, having been born at a place called Laiwain, was Laiwainjiz. And Fuegia's real name was Cushinjizkeepa, meaning a female born at Cushin.

One of the main tools of Matthews's instruction was the catechism, which the three Yamana had memorized until they could answer Matthew's questions in perfect unison. York's deep voice contrasted with the lilting tones of the two teenagers, and Darwin found the rhythm soothing and the familiarity comforting.

"How many Sacraments hath Christ ordained in his Church?," Matthews would intone.

"Two on'y, as generally necessary to salvation, that is to say, Baptism, and the Supper of the Lord," responded York, Jeremy, and Fuegia.

"What meanest thou by this word Sacrament?"

"I mean outward and visib'e sign of inward and spiritual grace given unto us, ordained by Christ himself, as means whereby we receive the same, and p'edge to assure us thereof."

"How many parts are there in a Sacrament?"

"Two: outward visib'e sign, and inward spiritual grace."

"What is the outward visib'e sign or form in Baptism?"

"Water: wherein person is baptized in Name of Father, and of Son, and of Holy Ghost."

"What is the inward and spiritual grace?"

"Death unto sin, and new birth unto righteousness; for being by nature born in sin, and children of wrath, we are hereby made children of grace."

"What is required of persons to be baptized?"

"Repentance, whereby they forsake sin; and Faith, whereby they steadfast'y believe promises of God made to them in that Sacrament."

"Why then are Infants baptized, when by reason of their tender age they cannot perform them?"

"Because they promise them both by their Sureties, which promise, when they come to age, themselves are bound to perform."

"Why was the Sacrament of the Lord's Supper ordained?"

"For continual remembrance of sacrifice of death of Christ and of benefits which we receive thereby."

"What is the outward part or sign of the Lord's Supper?"

"Bread and Wine, which Lord hath commanded to be received."

"What is the inward part, or thing signified?"

"Body and B'ood of Christ, which are verily and indeed taken and received by faithful in Lord's Supper."

"What are the benefits whereof we are partakers thereby?"

"Strengthening and refreshing of our souls by Body and B'ood of Christ, as our bodies are by Bread and Wine."

"What is required of them who come to the Lord's Supper?"

"To examine themselves, whether they repent them truly of their former sins, steadfast'y purposing to lead new life; have live'y faith in God's mercy through Christ, with thankful remembrance of His death; and be in charity with all men."

The slow coastal cruise stretched into a third week, one sweltering late summer day blending into the next with little for Darwin to do except sit in the shade of the hammock nettings. Sometimes he worked on his journal or read, mostly Lyell or Milton, depending on his mood. Sometimes he would talk with York, their backs against the bulwark between two cannons. He did not feel comfortable with the two younger Fuegians, still really children, although Fuegia spoke the best English of the three. York was different, a slower talker but more knowledgeable and more willing to tell Darwin about his land and people.

Darwin thus learned much about Tierra del Fuego and the Fuegians without ever yet having been there. The Yamana were only one of four nations living in Tierra del Fuego. They lived in the south, along the coast of the large island and on the many smaller islands just offshore. The Alacaloof people lived on the archipelago that made up western Tierra del Fuego. Both were people of the canoe and lived mainly from the sea, eating fish, limpets, seaweed, whales, otters, birds, and nearly anything else they could catch or gather. The Ona people lived in the interior of Tierra del Fuego and along the north and east coasts, hunting the guanaco for meat and dressing in its hides. The Alacaloof and Yamana, who rarely ventured further inland than necessary to harvest tree fungus, berries, and beech bark for their canoes, feared the Ona. Even safely on the *Beagle,* a thousand miles to the north, York became agitated when he described the Ona. The fourth people were the Aush, similar to the Ona but living only in the extreme southeast of the large island and as mysterious to York as were Greeks to a Welsh collier.

York did not know about the other peoples, but the Yamana had been all but exterminated by smallpox. His grandparents spoke of many big towns, where the people had grown tubers in gardens. But now only a few small tribes remained, and they moved around according to the seasons. He was anxious that in the four years he had been away, the population had been even further reduced. Maybe, he worried, there would be no one left at all when he returned.

Most of all, Darwin enjoyed York's stories about Yamana history, like the one about the first white men.

"Before *Beag'e* came to my country and took me away," York began the story, "before sealers and whalers started coming, before so many died of smallpox, the first white men came to Yamana country."

"Okoko, who in those days was eldest son of most powerful chief, went off alone one day in small canoe to think. His father was getting old, and Okoko spent lot of time worrying about how things would go when he became chief. Okoko was fine young man. He was strong, and no one could best him in wrest'ing. He was smart, and no one could best him in ridd'es. But being chief requires wisdom as well as strength and intelligence, and Okoko was smart enough to know that he was still too young to have much wisdom."

"As Okoko padd'ed around point of land worrying about future, he saw something that sudden'y made him concentrate on present. At mouth of bay he had entered, where yesterday had been on'y open water, there was new island. It was small, but Okoko knew that he could not have forgotten it because it looked different than any island he had ever seen. For one thing, it seemed to move up and down with swell."

"After observing island for few minutes to make sure he was not imagining it, he returned to town as fast as he could padd'e. When he arrived he went straight to tell his father, and when he had recounted all he had seen, his father told him not to tell anyone else. He loved Okoko, and he did not think he was lying, but sun was strong that day and maybe he had imagined something in ref'ections from waves and panicked. Chief did not want anyone to think Okoko was easily panicked."

"So chief asked his son to take him in canoe to see this supposed new island. When they rounded point of land, son was relieved that new island was still there, right in midd'e of mouth of bay, where before had been on'y open water. Chief quick'y forgot all his doubts and urged Okoko to padd'e closer so that he could better see new island with his tired old eyes."

"As they approached, they could see that new island indeed was not like any other. It did move up and down with swell. Also, all trees on it seemed to be dead because they had no leaves even though it was midd'e of summer. More strange'y, their roots seemed to grow from treetop to ground around the shore. But small c'ouds were tang'ed in roots, which made it difficult to see details."

"As they came even closer, chief and son saw human forms that had skins without color, like ghosts. Okoko was afraid, but his father calmed him by pointing out that ghosts on'y visited during night. Then one of new island peop'e, for that is what they seemed to be, no matter how strange they were, came to edge of island and beckoned toward chief."

"Both chief and Okoko were worried, but they had faced batt'e and giant whales and other terrors. So being brave they padd'ed right up to man—for such he was, first white man my peop'e ever saw— where he stood at water's edge. When they saw that island was made of wood, they knew it was not island at all but giant canoe made from strips split from many trees. White chief beckoned again. He seemed to be welcoming them and inviting them to come into his canoe."

"Okoko c'imbed up first and asked, 'Undagarata Yamana?' 'Is there a person aboard?' But white chief did not understand question. He said something—in Eng'ish, of course—and then held his arm straight out toward Okoko, who by then had turned around to help his father aboard. When he turned back to white chief, he still held his hand stretched out toward Okoko, as if to play game of tatoop, which is played by grasping another man's hand and attempting to pull so hard that he goes spraw'ing. So Okoko, who was undefeated tatoop champion among all Yamana, thought white men had come to challenge his tit'e. Okoko quick'y spat into his hand, rubbed it on his leg, grabbed white chief's hand, pulled, and sent him f'ying along deck. Several other white men ran to grab chief and son, but when white chief looked up and saw Okoko holding his sides with laughter, face streaming with tears, he waved his men off. Okoko thought it funny that such a poor tatoop player should have come a long distance to challenge him. He had sometimes strained for an hour before pulling his challenger off balance. This had been his easiest win ever. He laughed and laughed."

"Okoko needed to choose his prize for winning at tatoop, and white chief and his council showed chief and son many wondrous things in their ship. At that time, my peop'e had never seen things made of metal, or mirrors, or many other things we now know, so Okoko and his father had eyes on'y for those wonders and became care'ess and separated from one another."

"Of all things Okoko saw, most fantastic was when one white man made a f'ame with a litt'e s'iver of wood by rubbing it on'y once against seat of his pants. He did not rub it many times, as Okoko had to when starting a fire by rubbing two pieces of wood together. This man rubbed his s'iver on'y one time, on his pants, and then a f'ame shot from its end, and he held it to his pipe to light tobacco."

"Okoko, of course, asked for those magical pants as his prize. Imagine being ab'e to make fire so easily, just by rubbing a s'iver on your own seat, he thought?! When white man with magical pants did not understand, Okoko proceeded to try to remove his prize by himself. He grabbed pants and began tugging them downwards with all his strength. Then white men understood and held Okoko until they could bring him another pair of pants that looked just like fire pants. He accepted those pants, and they all went back to where his canoe was tied up. His father was waiting there, and they left immediately with many friend'y waves and smiles from white men."

"When they had padd'ed back around point of land, chief showed son his small bag of shiny buttons and colorful beads he had been given. Son wanted to show how his prize worked, so he pulled a s'iver from edge of his paddle and struck it against pants. Nothing happened, so he tried again. Then he thought that perhaps he needed to put pants on, which he did, but still s'iver did not burst into f'ame when rubbed against seat. He tried another s'iver and then another and another."

"By the time they reached home, canoe's inside was littered with s'ivers and his father was laughing at him. Whole town came to see what was so funny."

Darwin had begun chuckling when York recounted the misunderstanding over the tatoop game and was roaring with laughter by the end of the story, attracting stares from the poop deck. "What a misunderstanding, York!" he managed to gasp once he had calmed down a bit.

"Yes, I chuck'e every time I think of that poor cap'n who didn't know tatoop and went f'yin along the deck of his own ship. Can you imagine anything more embarrassing."

"I meant about the matches."

"But I know what matches are. Okoko learned about matches too, and other things. Then he died of smallpox soon after he became chief...."

When Darwin seemed not to know what to respond, York asked, "Do you want to try me at tatoop?"

So Darwin and York squared off for a game of tatoop. A crowd soon gathered as they clasped hands and began pulling. Darwin was a bit heavier, despite being the younger man, but York had technique on his side. None of the audience was exactly sure what the object was or how to determine who won, but ignorance never prevented wagering and each time one or the other seemed to gain an advantage the volume of cheers and groans increased. Eventually York gave way so suddenly that his opponent overbalanced, then, just as suddenly, York pulled hard and toppled Darwin. Young Philos rose from the deck to the applause of the crew and officers. If he had lost at tatoop, at least he had won some measure of acceptance among men who judged the world in terms of action rather than intellect. A growing acquaintance with York had also been cemented.

Unfortunately, the next day Darwin's stomach once again betrayed him and he had to retreat to the isolation of his cabin. The wind had backed and freshened until sailing inshore became too chancy, and Fitzroy had decided to suspend the survey temporarily to make straight for the Rio Negro. There, he hoped to find General Rosas encamped and amenable to providing a passport. Then the survey would recommence heading northward toward Bahia Blanca, hopefully with more favorable weather. So the *Beagle* came around to the southwest and began corkscrewing across the waves, white water bursting over her forecastle, Darwin lying miserable in his hammock.

Besides Syms, only Matthews and York came to visit while Darwin remained horizontal through Easter. Their company was a comfort to him, but he began to feel that he should be more worried about them than they about him. Matthews, in particular, was so ensnared in Fitzroy's plan to civilize Tierra del Fuego that Darwin feared for him. But he also feared for York, who would bear, as the eldest of the three civilized Fuegians, the greatest part of the burden of interpreting between two worlds. He chuckled when he recalled Okoko and the tatoop game, but then grew glum again. He had begun to believe that MacCormick was right, although for the wrong reasons. The mission would fail, and quite likely while Matthews was there, not after he had returned to England. But Darwin did not have enough conviction regarding his concerns to raise them with Matthews, whom Darwin had spent the last month convincing of the mission's potential for success. Besides, he dared not alienate Fitzroy further and risk the wrath of his absolute power to punish dissent aboard the *Beagle*.

In a bay near the mouth of the Rio Negro, the *Beagle* anchored to seaward of a dozen or so schooners, none of them above fifty tons and many of them of indifferent design and maintenance. Their crews were transferring cargoes of salt into their holds from the barges that had brought it down the river, and the blinding white heaps of sodium chloride crystals seemed incongruous against the shades of brown and gray that dominated the rest of the scene. The wind and sea had moderated, but the hulks of several wrecks that littered the beach encouraged Fitzroy to order double anchors.

At Fitzroy's behest, the captain of one of the coasters rowed over to share a mug of rum. Once sufficiently lubricated, he reported that the town of Patagones was eighteen miles upstream but that the main channel of the river was deep enough to accommodate the yawl and cutter that the *Beagle* carried in cradles on the main deck. The most welcome news of all was that according to the salt-barge crews, General Rosas was still encamped near the town.

At dawn the next day, Fitzroy led the party upriver. The crews worked the two boats upstream under sail and oar while Darwin scanned the sloping sandstone cliffs that flanked the valley bottom. The lack of the least bit of greenery above the bottomlands confirmed all he had read in Falconer about the aridity of the plains that stretched south to Tierra del Fuego, north to the pampas, and west to the foothills of the Andes mountains. The Rio Negro carried rumors of a country opposite in all respects to the desert through which it flowed. A few months earlier a swollen, muddy stream would have surged between the banks and prevented anyone from sailing upstream. By April, the Andean snows that fed the river had long since melted and the water level had fallen low enough to expose muddy bars and islands. Only the main channel still contained enough water to float the two boats that slowly advanced against the moderate current. The summer flood had delivered an increment of fertile alluvium together with the seeds of pioneering herbs and trees. Their fresh green growth colonized islands as the retreating water abandoned them, engraving an ephemeral green trace into the arid plains that separated the mountains from the sea.

As the boats approached Patagones, Darwin observed to Fitzroy that the town could not be more unlike Buenos Aires. The street plan was more vertical than horizontal and extremely irregular. The houses began above the highest reach of the flood and continued to the wall of the fort that squatted on the edge of the desert plain above. A church tower with its bell rose above the adobe ramparts, which Lumb had already told Darwin also enclosed cisterns and granaries to withstand any siege by Indians or pirates. Below the lowest houses, farmers had ploughed and planted the fresh alluvium as the recession of the summer flood allowed. They would have to harvest their crops of wheat and vegetables before winter rains in the Andean foothills brought the second annual flood.

Most of the some fifteen hundred inhabitants were, again according to Lumb, there because of the salt, great conical heaps of which were piled near the top of the cliff over the course of the summer. The sun evaporated the nearby shallow brine lakes and left behind a thick layer of salt that the miners dug up and carted to Patagones. From the cliff top, aerial tramways transferred the salt to barges in the river. The dilapidated contraptions of wooden towers, cables, and hoppers swung dangerously overhead as the two boats from the *Beagle* passed the town to reach the islands where the army was encamped. The surreal scene of a verdant river penetrating an otherwise sterile, mineral waste left the party largely silent.

General Rosas commanded an army of some twenty thousand made up entirely of cavalry units, their tents and corrals covering several islands just beyond the town. Some of the islands were entirely given over to the herds of mares, which the gauchos used for food but never rode. Fitzroy headed for the flagstaff that seemed to mark the headquarters. Most of the crew remained with the boats, but Darwin, Earle, and Sergeant Beareley with his squad accompanied Fitzroy through the gauntlet of troops. From the great variety of features and colors, Darwin reflected that no two could possibly share the same permutation of European, African, and Indian parentage. And they were as variously dressed and armed as they were bred. They had shared out their uniforms and equipment so that each wore at least a few items of official issue, sometimes a pair of trousers and a shirt, sometimes just a belt and canteen. They carried an assortment of muskets, sabers, and lances. The only item all shared in common was the red stocking, Phrygian cap of liberty that marked them as followers of Rosas. The Indian allies appeared even less disciplined. All stared at the Englishmen as they passed on the way to the headquarters.

About halfway there, a squad appeared commanded by a young lieutenant who might have just stepped off the parade ground. His own dapper uniform merely emphasized the ragtag appearance of the troops. With barely a word of greeting and no ceremony, he escorted the Englishmen to Rosas's compound. The marines remained near the entrance to the square enclosed by wagons and artillery pieces in which the flagpole stood, while the lieutenant escorted Fitzroy, Darwin, and Earle past guards and into the largest of the tents.

Rosas stood alone in front of a table covered with maps, his tall, erect, muscular figure imposing under the low canvas roof. If he were surprised at being called upon in the middle of nowhere by the British navy he did not show it. He was, thought Darwin, startlingly handsome, with an aquiline nose, piercing eyes, light skin, and thick dark hair that spread in two broad sideburns down the sides of his strong chin. His entire manner was militaristic and communicated omniscient knowledge and total control. He bid them welcome in Spanish in the gravest tone, as if they were ambassadors come to negotiate a peace treaty. Just as gravely he asked how he could be of service.

Fitzroy returned the gravity with a lengthy explanation of his coastal survey work. He had repeated the same phrases so often to the bureaucrats in Buenos Aires that his Spanish appeared smoother than it was. Darwin and Earle bowed humbly as Fitzroy introduced them as naturalist and artist. After yet again propounding on the purely scientific purpose of their work and promising to supply copies of the resulting charts, Fitzroy asked for the favor of a passport to facilitate the coastal survey, especially in the vicinity of Bahia Blanca.

Rosas listened patiently, attentively, without comment, until Fitzroy had clearly finished making his case. While the general was thus focused on Fitzroy, Darwin closely watched his face for any indication of surprise or perturbation. When he detected nothing but confidence, he thought that perhaps the military implications of coastal surveys escaped the general, his experience being with the cavalry rather than the navy.

But Darwin and the others received a lesson about the general's capabilities when he commiserated with Fitzroy for having had to waste so much time at the offices of the Department of the Navy and then was able to tell him exactly how many times he had called at those offices and whom he had seen there. Rosas had, in fact, been expecting the *Beagle* for the past week. He had established posts at regular intervals along his army's line of march from Buenos Aires to Patagones. Each such posta had water, wood, and pasture to supply fresh mounts and food for the dispatch riders that kept him informed and carried his orders back to the capital. He probably knew more about the activities of Lucy in Buenos Aires than did Darwin.

The general gave them a more painful lesson about his capabilities when he pointed at the map and, in quite respectable English, said, "I too am a scientist, gentlemen. Look 'ere, at this map of all of the territory between Buenos Aires and Patagones, from the littoral to the Andes mountains." He then proceeded to explain his own work in much the same manner as Fitzroy had explained the coastal survey, seriously and with attention to accuracy and detail but with consideration for an audience that, while expert in their own professions, might not share in the techniques and jargon pertinent to the current subject.

"My objective, gentlemen," he said without a trace of braggadocio, "is to pacify or esterminate every single savage from the lands that this map shows. Any who refuse to settle down and become civilized will die." As he traced out the line of the Rio Negro with his index finger, he continued, "I 'ave an agreement with the Tehuelches, who control all the country to the south of this river as far as Tierra del Fuego. They will kill any who try to escape me by crossing the river and losing themselves in the wilds to the south. You did not notice the escalps that the Tehuelches just delivered? I am forced to display them out of good manners to my allies."

"You mean," blurted Darwin, unable to contain his disgust, "that you condone such barbaric practices, the actual scalping of human beings!"

Rosas replied without emotion, anger or otherwise: "Come now, Meester Darwin. Eet is a technique of my trade. You kill and eskin birds, drown insects in espirits, etcetera. I escalp savages. The noble ends we work toward justify our techniques, yours and mine."

Fitzroy and Earle stared pointedly at Darwin, who resolved to bite his tongue.

"But techniques are mere details," continued Rosas. "Like you, all of you, I deal in broader patterns than individual soundings, or beetles, or brushstrokes. But those patterns become clear only when one 'as assembled enough such individual details, no? In this case, a crucial detail fell into place when I captured three Indian ambassadors riding from near the 'eadwaters of this river toward Bahia Blanca.

With esuitable techniques, the last of the three told me that the tribes are uniting in an enormous encampment at a lake in the foot'eells of the Andes. Already, nearly a thousand warriors are assembled. They are trying to convince more, from both sides of the Andes, to join them. When they 'ave enough they will overwhelm our settlements and estancias one after another. Well, I do not plan to allow eet!," he suddenly shouted. Then, as if to emphasize his outburst, he continued with the calm explication of his plan. "A few of my divisions are even now esterminating any tribes who do not join the pact, encouraging the rest to join their brethren in the foot'eells or ally with me. By next summer, the only savages in this entire region will either be dead or gathered together at their encampment. Then, when the summer sun dries up most of the waterholes on the pampas, we will attack them en masse: I from the east and a Chilean army through the Andean passes. They will be caught in a trap of their own making. Those that escape to the pampas will be caught when they are forced to concentrate at the few waterholes that persist through the summer. Our Indian allies will, of course, be in my vanguard. That technique, I freely admit, I learned by reading your own Lord Chesterfield. Our rule will be to kill every male, whether man or baby, and every female old enough to breed. The girls will be sold in Buenos Aires. These days they are worth about three of your English pounds apiece."

Again Darwin, despite his resolution to keep quiet, could not help but express his remorse at the calculated genocide this fellow European, a man who aspired to be the leader of a modern republic, seemed capable of. "But, sir, the accounts I have read, those by conquistadors and missionaries, say that there used to be Indian towns of several thousand near Buenos Aires. Those people were peaceful farmers and fishermen. Can you not negotiate a way to share the country with them? You might find in them some of your most productive citizens."

"Yes, there were once many tens of thousands of Indians on the pampas, many living in big towns. Now one can ride for two days inland from Buenos Aires and never once see a single Indian. Those that remain live on horseback, hunting and being hunted day after day. They no longer dare to venture north of the Rio Salado. Within a decade, none will remain north of the Rio Negro. Within a century, no one will even remember them. That, gentlemen, must be the reality if Argentina is to take its place at the table of civilized nations. Does England have Indians? No, of course not."

At this point, Rosas looked up from the map at his audience, and with the first smile that had crossed his face, he finished: "I have eet, gentlemen. The main difference between you and me is that you describe existing patterns. I change them. If you would be so good as to abide outside a moment, I will have my lieutenant draw up your passports. Good day."

Too awed with the brutality of Rosas's plans to reply, the three shook hands with him and left. Outside in the yard, even Earle seemed shaken, and they sat without speaking on a gun carriage while Beareley and his marines stood nervously nearby. They had already noticed the grisly strings of black scalps that stretched between the willows at the edge of the island.

Within ten minutes, the dapper lieutenant reappeared and handed Fitzroy the passports. When the lieutenant left again, Fitzroy muttered, "Quid violentius aure tyranni?" To himself, Darwin complemented the sentiment with another: Tis time to fear when tyrants seem to kiss.

Darwin and Earle spent the night as guests of Rosas while Fitzroy and his crew took the boats back down the river. Darwin wanted to explore the country between Patagones and Buenos Aires, besides which he thought he would die of seasickness if forced to return to the *Beagle*. Syms and Earle would accompany him. Earle claimed a desire to sketch the Patagonian landscape, but Darwin suspected some secret motive. They planned to rendezvous with the *Beagle* at Bahia Blanca and then, everything being equal, leave Fitzroy to continue his survey during the winter while they followed the line of postas overland to Buenos Aires. They would then rejoin the *Beagle* when Fitzroy himself returned to port in order to re-victualate before sailing for Tierra del Fuego in the spring.

In the evening, just before Darwin fell asleep, he saw the young lieutenant came to their tent to escort Earle to a second, private interview with Rosas. He dozed off thinking of Lucy's round bottom.

6

THE THREE ENGLISHMEN, accompanied by two of Rosas's gauchos, rose before dawn and boarded the crude ferry that connected the island to the north bank. Some coins from Earle and threats from the gauchos quelled the complaints of the disgruntled ferryman. He sleepily turned his capstan, and the ferry swung diagonal to the stream so that the current began to push them along the cable that spanned the channel. Even the peaceful, moonlit scene, accompanied by the soft gurgle of water against the side of the ferry and the gentle nickering of the horses, did not distract Darwin from dwelling on the meeting with Rosas. As they clattered down the planks onto the north bank and headed towards Patagones, he looked back towards where he knew garlands of scalps marked the boundary of Tehuelche country but could no longer discern those grisly warning signs.

Just outside the palisade that surrounded the lower town, a group of pacified Indians, so-called mansos, had set up their toldos. The domes of hide stretched over bent bamboo poles looked like the ovens of an encampment of itinerant bakers. They had grouped the toldos together according to clan, and beside the mouth of each had planted a slender bamboo lance. Those chuzos sported fringes of distinctively dyed ostrich feathers just below their razor-sharp points, each combination of colors identifying the family that called the toldo home. According to the gaucho guides, Pablo and Martin, this tribe was under a chief, or cacique, called Lucanee. Rosas gave him the army's old mounts, horses that had been ridden to near death and would barely serve as food. The Indians ate what they could and wove the nags' hair into saddle blankets that they sold to the army. When they had accumulated enough money to buy several casks of rotgut liquor, they would throw a howling, weeklong party.

This early in the day only a few old women were up, fussing over the smoky little fires they made of grass canes, dung, and whatever driftwood the flood had carried down from the Andean foothills. The

Indian dogs growled at the gaucho dogs but otherwise the small party passed among the toldos without any acknowledgment.

The riders wound up through the streets of Patagones. They passed the dark mouths of caves that the poorest inhabitants had excavated into the loosely consolidated sandstone. Higher up, just below the fort, they passed the grander houses of the salt merchants. The sun was just rising as they reached the top of the cliff and emerged onto the plain where the fort and piles of salt cast long shadows westward over the plain. They sat for a while looking back down into the valley at the barges piled high with salt and the tents of the army that would soon rouse itself to another day of genocide. A lone bienteveo perched on the church tower interminably repeating its shrill cry: ven te veo, ven te veo, ven te veo,....

Then the column of five headed their mounts into the simplicity of the plain that stretched for eighty miles to the Rio Colorado. Gravel and sand showed everywhere between the scanty bunches of grass and even scantier shrubs. All was brown and gray and dry, withered and stiff and barely able to rustle in the constant wind. Even as the sun rose fully above the horizon, the light barely added any color to the scene. The shrubs, to protect their hard-won leaves from any guanaco unfortunate enough to stray from more humid ranges, had invested much of their growth in a formidable array of thorns. Nothing, to Darwin's eye, moved in that harshness. Not even a single hopeful vulture circled overhead. The land was patiently awaiting the trace of moisture that would fall during what locals, more optimistically than accurately, called the rainy season.

They passed the white plain of a saltpan, its perfection disfigured by the recent digging of the miners and the wheels of their carts. With the sun still low in the east, even the smallest windblown drift of salt on that surface laid out a shadow as black and straight as a line of India ink from a cartographer's pen. According to Martin, great flocks of flamingos would arrive soon after the rains turned the saltpan into a shallow briny lake. To see the bright pink birds wading around in a lake in the middle of a desert was, the gaucho assured Darwin, the most remarkable sight in the world. When Darwin asked what they could possibly feed on in that salty waste, though, what plants or fish could possibly live in such brine, Martin could not answer.

They followed the shore of baked mud for more than two miles. By keeping his gaze on the dark mud beside the dapple-gray shoulder of his horse, Darwin could avoid being blinded by the glare coming from the salina. He noticed large crystals of gypsum, which the gauchos called padre del sal, embedded in the mud. Smaller crystals, seemingly sulphate of soda but locally called madre de sal, lay scattered on the surface.

The pattern, he reflected, was similar to what Botazzi had reported for Italian saltpans in a paper recently published in the *Annales des Sciences*. During the wet season, the slightest precipitation percolated into the coarse sediments and flowed towards any slight depression, dissolving salts from the soil along the way and forming a shallow lake of brine where the water reemerged at the lowest point. Then, during the dry season, the water began to evaporate, the concentration of salts reached the saturation point, and crystals began to precipitate out of solution. The separation of the different types of salt crystals occurred because they precipitated in inverse relation to their solubility, the least soluble first and the most soluble last. Thus, as the lake receded towards the center of the depression, different types of salt formed sequential crystalline bands along the shore. Common salt, being extremely soluble, remained in solution until a briny soup covered only the very lowest part of the salina. As the last shallow remnant of the lake evaporated, the cubic sodium chloride crystals precipitated and created a level sheet of pure salt that could be easily mined. In the minds of the gauchos, the gypsum and the sulphate of soda, being some of the first salts to precipitate every year, thus became the mother and father of salt.

More interestingly, reflected Darwin, the presence of flamingos demonstrated that organisms could survive under such hostile conditions, alternately baked into mud and salt or swimming in brine. The flamingos, he deduced, must feed on some very simple and hardy life form, perhaps a worm that burrowed through the mud in search of confervae or infusorial animalcules that themselves subsisted on the minerals.

Once they had left the saltpan behind, the only thing that changed through the day was the length of their shadows, and those had begun to lengthen substantially to eastward by the time they reached the first well. Just as they were dismounting in the slightly denser growth of grass that surrounded the muddy puddle, Martin shouted, "Vaca!" He and Pablo leapt back into their saddles, spurred their horses, and disappeared in their own dust followed by the four dogs. Within a few minutes, Pablo had returned to the well dragging a dead cow at the end of his lasso. It was scrawny and inexplicable here in the desert, seemingly lost far from its herd. Pablo did not complain, though, as he quickly cut out some brisket and the racks of ribs. In the meantime, Martin had lassoed and pulled out by the roots several bushes. He dragged them into camp and set them on fire to produce a bed of charcoal over which to roast the meat. Before long the red slabs of stringy beef leaned sizzling over the coals.

The gauchos seemed as happy as if they had just sat down to a feast in the finest Buenos Aires restaurant. The serendipitous cow provided a much better dinner than the jerked beef they had been anticipating. They had fresh beef, pasture for the horses, water, and fire. And unlike in Buenos Aires, Darwin thought to himself, they had the freedom of the still night on the plain, their dogs keeping watch while they slept where they liked, unfettered by the many possessions of townsfolk. He fell asleep with the Milky Way blazing a swath above, his head on the sheepskin padding of his saddle, wrapped in his poncho and saddle blanket, listening to the others breathing, and marveling at a country so desolate that he heard not a single cry of any creature. How different than the Brazilian rainforest; how equally magnificent.

The next day the country became somewhat more humid. The gravel decreased in size, replaced by a more finely textured soil that held enough moisture to cloak itself with a denser cover of grass and shrubs. The occasional vulture circled overhead. Still, the only ground animals they saw were agouti, a cousin to the capybara but somewhat smaller and more slender, with long legs that allowed them to bound at high speed across the plain, something like a giant hare. Every few miles another Indian file of these *Cavia patagonica* would cross the trail ahead of the riders before quickly disappearing into the vegetation, the browns and grays of which they mimicked with their fur.

Despite those signs of life, much more than the first day, Darwin could not imagine making this crossing in the heat of summer. Even now, dust dogs interminably pursued the hooves of the horses, and the sun seemed a cruel pestle grinding him into the mortar of the plain's hardness. The wind wore at the riders, snatching away their words when they tried to relieve the monotony of the landscape with conversation, polishing their faces with a cargo of salt dug from some salina. So they pulled their hats low and turned up their collars and tried not to think about the dryness in their mouths.

The gauchos kept a careful watch on the horizon, but the very flatness of the country was their security against marauding Indians. The topography was so unrelieved that no one could hide this side of the horizon, the best part of three miles away and unbroken by any mountain peak that might hide the silhouette of a rider.

Near noon they came to a tree, remarkable both for its solitude and its appearance. It was low and thick, about three feet across just above its gnarled roots. The many branches were bare except for threads that the wind stretched out nearly horizontal. Other threads, hanging more nearly vertically, held tiny bundles wrapped in patches of brightly colored cloth. All about lay the bleached bones of horses. While Pablo dismounted and began to collect the bundles, Martin explained that Indians had left them. They called the tree the Altar of Walleechu, one of their principal gods, and left the offerings whenever they passed. The richer Indians would even slaughter a horse in sacrifice. Inside the patches of colored cloth, Pablo had found bits of dried meat that he threw to the dogs and tobacco that he put into his pouch.

Martin warned that from here on they would need to be especially vigilant for Indians. Near this very spot a few months ago, he and two others had been chased by a dozen savages. The Indians had had fresher horses and slowly gained on the gauchos until able to throw their bolas around the horses' legs and drop them to the ground. Both his companions had been lanced as they were thrown. He had jumped to the ground before his horse stumbled, dodged behind it, and cut the bolas free. He had saved his rifle shot until then and was able to force the Indians off long enough to leap back into the saddle. Keeping just ahead of the razor tips of their chuzos, he had ridden as never before until the posta at the Rio Colorado came into sight and the soldiers rode out to save him. The savages had retreated that day but might yet, advised Martin, be lurking in the area to try their luck again.

From the Walleechu tree the country fell away toward the dark line that marked the Rio Colorado. As the five rode on, now with loaded rifles held across their saddles, the turf gradually became continuous and the dark line detached itself from the plain to become a wall of trees. The posta was no more than a few huts made of poles plastered with mud set in a meadow by the river. A corral to one side held horses and cows, and a narrow ditch studded with stakes was intended to secure the perimeter. A canon on each side provided the principle defense. The garrison consisted of six soldiers commanded by a lieutenant who, on the strength of Rosas's passport, invited them to spend the night before providing fresh mounts in the morning.

The soldier on watch at dawn raised the alarm when he saw a scrotum-shrinking phalanx of fifty Indians charge out of the trees. The attackers raced straight for the posta and jumped their horses over the ditch as if it were not there. Darwin could barely distinguish the men from their horses. Both were naked except for daubs of red and white paint. The Indians rode low, almost horizontally, pressed tight to the withers, black hair tangled in the manes and streaming out behind like the tattered flags of some barbaric legion.

As the first of them cleared the ditch, the lieutenant fired the canon on that side, which he had explained the previous evening was always kept loaded and ready, the exact ranging determined through careful practice. The grapeshot slew a dozen in their saddles, and even more fell in a tangle of wounded and stumbling horses. Those who kept their saddles rode through the huts with a horrible thunder of unshod hooves and battle cries, the points of their chuzos coming through the thin walls.

Darwin was able to shoot one who had lost his horse and was trying to cross back over the ditch. The rifle ball entered beside the left shoulder blade and spun the man around to expose his exploding chest before he toppled backwards among the sharpened stakes. In the haste of reloading before the next charge, he did not even have time to register that he had just killed his first human being.

The survivors jumped the ditch on the other side of the posta and circled to regroup by the riverbank. Meanwhile the defenders reloaded. On the next charge, the lieutenant again raked the attackers with grape, and another dozen fell from their saddles. "Come again you whoresons!" yelled the lieutenant. "Hell's not but half full!" But the remaining Indians again regrouped and then rode into the trees and disappeared from sight.

Gray powder-smoke and reddish dust wreathed the posta. The wounded horses lay screaming in the yard and in the ditch. The soldier next to Darwin had been the only casualty, lanced through the wall into his chest. His filmed eyes stared out of a loophole. Blood soaked his shirt. One hand gripped Darwin's thigh, and he pulled away with a jerk once he had calmed enough to notice.

Enough horses remained in the corral for the entire troop to clear out immediately for Bahia Blanca. The Indians, calculated the lieutenant, probably did not have the stomach to give chase and sustain more casualties. They probably would burn the post, but his immediate duty was to warn the estancias on the north side of the river, along the road to Bahia Blanca.

When the troop saw from the tracks at the ford that the Indians had themselves come from the north bank, they spurred the horses along the road down the river toward the first estancia. The Englishmen followed and rode into the patio of the estancia late in the afternoon, each slowing to a walk as they came within the circle of blackened stubs of adobe walls.

No circling vultures had warned of the scene because the enormous dark birds had already landed and begun their feast. They sat on the chests of the corpses, cloaking them with their wings, looking like avian undertakers. As the column slowly rode up, the chink and creak of their tack disturbed the bloated birds, and they waddled into the deepening shadows.

Most of the bodies lay under the charred roof beams, their gapping wounds torn ragged by the vultures, their bloody eye sockets staring. The Indians had heaped the dead children into the well, its mouth coked with the jumble of their limbs. One cadaver of a woman lay in the wreck of the chicken coop where she had crawled for refuge while dragging her entrails behind her in the dust. Darwin at first thought that, rather oddly, all the dead had close-cropped black hair but then realized that they wore caps of flies swarming in the blood were their scalps had been cut away.

On the far side of the patio a fire-blackened tree hung with three more corpses. The sharpened stubs of branches skewered their heels, and cerebral matter had bubbled up through their nostrils from the heat of the fires built under their charred heads. Each had his severed penis and testicles hanging from his mouth. The heat had caused their lips to shrink back from their gums and the blackened genitals hung from the resulting macabre grins.

With nightfall, a cavalry troop from Bahia Blanca arrived. Captain Miranda, a wizened veteran, had a hundred men and was already on the trail of the marauders who had been terrorizing estancias all along the river. The Indians had kidnapped two young girls at one estancia, and Miranda had orders to track them across the Andes to Chile if necessary.

While the lieutenant reported on the attack at his posta and Miranda's men buried the bodies laying about the estancia, Darwin noticed a column of four horses with Indian women ride up. They wore skirts but had pulled them up around their thighs and sat astride like men, and their daughters rode behind them, sometimes with a second daughter in front. Their bright, black hair hung to their elegantly curved waists. Silver and turquoise bracelets on their arms and ankles emphasized the darkness of their skin and the nakedness of their long limbs. Darwin could barely believe that the Fuegians aboard the *Beagle* were of the same race as these women, but their beauty only confirmed his belief that the harsh conditions of places such as Tierra del Fuego would render any race bestial.

The news that a couple of dozen of the marauders had died during their attack on the posta caused Miranda to order a celebration. A crowd soon formed around an open liquor cask, and Darwin could not have imagined a wilder scene than the ensuing fiesta, very different than the one he had enjoyed so much at the Douglas fazenda. The soldiers drank themselves blind and then drank the steaming blood of the mares slaughtered for supper. Eventually the revelers threw up and, besmeared with filth and gore, returned to the cask.

The Englishmen had made their beds away from the diabolic celebration. Earle had the first watch while Syms and Darwin tried to ignore the wild yelling enough to fall asleep. But the killing of the day had so disturbed Darwin that even when the liquor supply had run low and the noise subsided somewhat, he lay awake thinking about the violence that seemed to define the land as strongly as the lack of forests.

The image of an upside-down, grinning head with a charred penis hanging from its lips was in his mind when one of the Indian girls came to him. He could just see her by the light coming through the trees from the bonfires. She smiled beautifully and then pulled down her bodice. He pushed her long, lustrous hair aside with one hand and reached up with the other. Underneath the heavy silver necklace that was too big on her, he found her pubescent nipples.

When he had finished, he held her tightly against him, one hand cupping the back of her head, the other her hard, narrow buttocks. But after a few minutes she began to squirm so much that he released her and gave her a few coins. She crawled a few yards to where Syms lay. Darwin listened to them while drifting into sleep. The last thought he remembered was that she smelled just as he had imagined when he watched her ride in with her mother.

Halfway through his watch, Darwin was amazed to hear Miranda's troops beginning to saddle their horses, an early start given the debauchery of the night before. By the time Syms and Earle awoke, the cavalry troop was already setting out upcountry on the track of the marauders and the two captive girls.

"Hopefully they have run out of liquor," said Earle when he sat up in his blanket, spitting his disgust on the ground, "because last night a single Indian could have snuck into their camp and slit all their throats."

Martin and Pablo, as well as the lieutenant and his garrison from the posta, had joined Miranda's force, and the three Englishmen were content to set out for Bahia Blanca by themselves. The way, a ride of about three days, was so well traveled that guides would have been superfluous anyway. The three riders followed the riverbank through two more burned-out estancias and then turned northward. As they climbed away from the river, a continuous sward of grass replaced the trees and shrubs, but the way remained obvious due to the wagon ruts that exposed the reddish clay beneath. All three rejoiced at a country that in many respects resembled the pampas around Buenos Aires. The grass was short and, in this season, withered and brown, but agouti nonetheless swarmed over the plain. And little owls, *Athene cunicularia* thought Darwin, stood like sentinels at the entrances to their burrows. All in all, the country offered a pleasant change from that south of the Rio Colorado, where the thorny shrubs demanded riders wear leather guardamontes to protect their legs.

The ride had become so pleasant, in fact, that when the road climbed a high ridge of sand and the three men sat their horses at the crest looking out at a sea of many more ridges beyond, they let loose a collective curse. The ancient dunes, which was how Darwin interpreted the ridges, stretched from horizon to horizon and left no choice but to follow the road across the wasteland. Ridge followed ridge for nearly ten miles, each separated from the next by clay flats from which the hooves stirred clouds of fine dust to choke horses and riders. Sometimes the sand deepened and they had to lead the plodding horses. By the time they reemerged onto the grassy plain at dusk, men and mounts were exhausted and glad to camp on the spot.

As Darwin was falling asleep, he remembered that he had intended to count the number of dunes in order to approximate the volume of sand they contained. The exertion and dust had caused him to forget to do so, but clearly the volume was immense. Given the clayey plain they were on now, which so resembled and presumably was contiguous with the pampas around Buenos Aires, the best hypothesis he could think of was that all of that sand must have blown northward from the desert between the Rio Negro and Rio Colorado.

When the next day Earle spotted an ostrich running across the road ahead, he suggested they follow to find some eggs for lunch. He had tasted ostrich eggs while in the Cape and swore they would make a tasty meal. So the three rode off at a gallop after the big bird. It ran into the wind and occasionally spread its wings to glide ahead. They had followed for half an hour before beginning to believe, somewhat ignominiously, that it must purposively be leading them away from its nest. After Earle had taken a shot and missed, while returning to the road, Darwin realized that ostriches probably lay in the spring, not the fall, but did not have the heart to remind the others that here the seasons were reversed and they would probably have to wait at least until August, perhaps even September, to enjoy an ostrich egg.

In the meantime, increasingly numerous deer and guanaco sufficed for their dinners. The animals were as easily hunted as they were unused to guns, and the three began to feel as if they had entered a paradise.

They were thus feeling quite contented upon arriving at Bahia Blanca late on a Sunday afternoon. The bulk of the fort, some three hundred yards across, dominated the verdant plain. An Argentinean flag fluttered proudly above the high adobe walls. In their shadow clustered a town of small houses. And a broad ditch surrounded the entire settlement, providing the first defense against attack.

An anachronistic joust seemed to be in progress just outside of that ditch, so the three sat their horses looking over the heads of the spectators. The entire town had turned out in its finery to watch. A military band, themselves for the moment spectators, bristled with trombones, cornets, and tubas. And gauchos, more gaily dressed even than usual, were taking turns riding full tilt with their lances toward a small ring hanging from a pole. The ring was hardly larger in diameter than the lances, but the goal seemed to be to skewer it.

As the Englishmen watched, a Quixote-like figure rode up behind them. He was tall and lean and very dark in the face and rode his equine equivalent, a towering black stallion. His gold braid gleamed in the setting sun, as did that of the equally crisp looking officers who accompanied him.

He addressed them in Spanish, speaking slowly to be sure they would understand. "The game is called the sortija, gentlemen, and the objective is to thrust the lance into the ring. I am Commandant Rodriguez. Welcome to Bahia Blanca."

The *Beagle* had arrived the day before, and Fitzroy had asked Rodriguez to watch for Darwin's party. The commandant provided them with comfortable quarters in the fort after proudly escorting them on a tour. The thick, twenty-foot high wall formed a polygon designed so that the cannons mounted along its top could cover any approach. The vast majority of the garrison's three hundred soldiers were cavalry troops who patrolled the surrounding countryside, but a hundred or so typically remained at the fort to defend against attack by Indians or pirates. From one of the gun emplacements, Rodriguez asked his guests to admire the well-watered plain around the fort, especially the streams of fresh water and, along their banks, the pastures in which grazed herds of cavalry horses and beef cattle. Groups of parallel sand ridges covered in shrubland varied the landscape and provided fuel wood. The streams rose in the range of low mountains, called the Sierra Ventana, just visible on the horizon. Lastly, Rodriguez proudly pointed out the clusters of dried scalps that hung clacking together at the ends of poles set into the top of the wall. Darwin had already noticed the grim trophies with their long, thick hair, now dulled by the sun and dust, hanging from flaps of dried skin. He had also noticed the bay. Beyond a cordon of sand dunes, a maze of mud banks mottled the extensive surface of the bay. If the *Beagle* were anchored somewhere among them, though, the glare from the sun prevented Darwin from spotting her.

The next day Rodriguez interviewed Earle and Darwin individually. It went slowly because the commandant spoke no English, and their Spanish, despite practice over the past month, remained far from fluent. He wanted to know what they had seen on the way from Patagones, what had happened at the posta and, most especially, what Fitzroy was up to out in the bay. Rodriguez understood that Rosas had authorized the survey but had become suspicious as to its motivation. When Fitzroy had come ashore to pay his respects, he had, as far as Rodriguez was concerned, seemed a little too enthusiastic about the qualities of the harbor. Fitzroy, believing everyone to share his enthusiasm for coastal survey in the abstract, had proudly displayed a very preliminary sketch of the major shoals and channels of what he proclaimed was quite probably the only large natural harbor between the Rio de la Plata and the Strait of Magellan. Rodriguez had been politely attentive until Fitzroy pointed out that ships of the line might be able to approach close enough to the shore to get their big cannon within range of the fort. No mater that Rosas had conferred his blessing on the survey, the possibility of cannon balls smashing the commandant's beautiful ramparts had sparked suspicions. Now Darwin's claim to be something called a naturalist fueled them. All attempts to explain this strange vocation as someone who knew everything about plants and animals only made things worse.

"How," persisted Rodriguez, "can you possibly know about agouti or ostriches if you don't even have them in England? And if you don't have them there, why would you want to come her to learn about them? Unless, of course, you intend.... And just what are your intentions, and those of Captain Fitzroy?"

Nothing could persuade Rodriguez that the mission of the *Beagle* was as innocuous as Rosas seemed to believe. But in the end, not convinced but out of respect for his general, or perhaps out of fear of him, Rodriguez seemed to satisfy himself with ferreting out every detail of the fight at the posta.

In return, he detailed how Miranda would catch and punish the marauders as he had already done for many of their heathen fellows. A few weeks ago, the old cavalry captain had distinguished himself by killing many of the tribe of a local cacique named Toriano. Popular myth had held Toriano to be invincible because he had evaded every attempt to kill him and had attained the remarkable age of seventy. This time, however, Miranda had bought a spy inside Toriano's own tolderia, and that traitor had reported when all the young men left on a hunting trip. The cavalry had ridden through the tolderia at sunrise and slaughtered everyone, including Toriano himself. They had torched the toldos and sabered the women and children who ran out of the flames. Those who tried to escape on the pampa were tracked with dogs, ridden down, and lanced. When the young men returned to their tolderia they had not believed their cacique to be dead until the scouts sent to the fort had seen his head stuck on a pole over the main gate. Rodriguez had expected them to attack, relishing the chance to massacre them with grapeshot and push the tribe that much closer to extinction. Unfortunately, though, they had ridden to the Rio Colorado and unleashed their furry on the estancias there. Now the survivors of the attack on the posta were probably heading for the Andes to join the coalition of tribes that Rosas planned to move against next summer. Rodriguez had no doubt that Miranda would catch them before they reached the foothills and return with their scalps as well as the two kidnapped girls. Having witnessed the drunken celebration at the burned-out estancia, Darwin had his doubts but kept them to himself, just smiling and shaking the commandant's hand as he left his office.

After comparing notes with Earle, Darwin was sure that only the passports signed by Rosas himself had saved them from summary execution as spies. "Although that might be appropriate enough for you, Augustus," he could not help but comment.

"Rodriguez is more likely to hang a so-called naturalist than an artist, Charles," replied the unflappable Earle. "Get rid of what you don't understand, as it were. But if it does come to that, I can just see Fitzroy's face as he comes up to the fort here and sees our heads grinning down at him from atop a couple of pikes. It might just be worth it."

They shared their first good laugh together over that image, but later found out that they had never been in too much danger anyway. Rodriguez simply had an inherent suspicion of all things English. His father had fought the British army in the streets of Buenos Aires in 1807 and had subsequently transmitted a negative attitude towards all things English to his son.

The commandant nonetheless consoled himself by assigning three gauchos to accompany the Englishmen whenever they left the fort, their first such excursion being to find the *Beagle*. They rode across the plain and through a belt of dunes, a smaller version of those north of the Rio Colorado, to emerge on a beach from where they could see the broad expanse of the bay. Fitzroy had ordered the *Beagle* anchored far out beyond were the four whaleboats were sounding the channels among the maze of mud banks, turning what was an indefinite transition between water and land into chartable numbers. Everyone, Englishman and gaucho, yelled and waved their hats in the air, but they went unnoticed by anyone in the boats. After ten minutes of shouting, Syms pointed to a high point a mile further along the coast and suggested they ride there to build a signal fire.

As they approached, Darwin could see that the tides had eroded the point into a cliff and decided to survey the stratigraphy. As the others turned inland to reach the top of the cliff, he and his gaucho shadow continued along the beach. The cliff, only about thirty feet high, exposed the sediments of the plain over which they had just ridden from the fort. Layers of gravel and sand interbedded with strata of dense reddish mud. A sandy soil capped the sequence.

Darwin was learning, with the help Lyell offered in the pages of *Principles of Geology*, to read such stratigraphic exposures as if they were books, each stratum being a chapter in a place's biography. His immediate impression of the cliff was of an estuary deposit, with mud that had accumulated in backswamps or tidal flats interlayered with gravel and sand bars as the currents and channels of the river changed. But no river large enough to have disgorged such a volume of sediment now emptied into Bahia Blanca. And the sediments had become greatly elevated above the level of the shore along which they had originally been deposited. Yet the cliff indicated a hiatus, perhaps even a partial reversal of the land's emergence from the sea, during which the tides had been able to erode away some of the deposits.

The resulting detritus had ended up choking the bay with mud banks, yet the original source of those sediments was obscure.

Then Darwin recalled riding up out of the valley of the Rio Colorado across a strikingly similar deposit: a cordon of sand dunes resting on reddish clayey sediments. Only there the elevation above the sea had been much higher than thirty feet, and the parallel sand ridges had been somewhat more stabilized by vegetation and formed a much wider cordon.

That broader pattern suggested that the entire country stretching between the Rio Colorado and Bahia Blanca had formed as the delta of an immense river. He tried to imagine it: a huge area of shifting channels; banks of mud; deposits of gravel and sand; and swamps formed in cutoff meander channels. The whole must have slowly become elevated above sea level, with periods of stability during which cordons of dunes had formed along beaches. The dunes north of the Rio Colorado must date to an earlier such period of stability than the ones he was looking at. Or maybe the parallel ranges of dunes and the clay flats that separated them originated as bars just offshore, a process that Lyell described as common along shoal coasts. Such bars gradually accumulated sand and became larger, affording a base for the formation of dunes until they became barrier islands. Lagoons then formed between the shore and the island, gradually silting up with mud due to the protection from currents. The repetition of that process during slow elevation of the land would produce a pattern, as he pictured it in his mind, of dune ridges resting on a gently inclined surface of clayey soil, exactly resembling the features in front of him and north of the Rio Colorado. The desert country south of the Colorado would have provided an inexhaustible supply of sand, which due to the prevailing south wind would have accumulated along successive shorelines along the coast between Bahia Blanca and the River Plate. Just possibly, he pondered further, that great river itself might have formed this ancient estuary. It certainly was muddy enough. As the land continued to rise, the flow south would have become blocked, the river mouth shifted to its current location, and Bahia Blanca would have been starved of further sediments.

Closer inspection of the gravel lenses only served to confirm that flurry of insights. Mollusks became apparent when Darwin probed and scraped with his knife. He immediately identified two species of *Buccinanops* and a *Venus purpurata*. And his collections during the sail southward, had told him that all three species still lived in shallow water along the coast.

Everything seemed to fit, and he was glowing with satisfaction as he explored further along the cliff. Then he saw the cranium. It was near the top of the cliff, too high to reach, but the yellowish-white, curving surface contrasting with the reddish mud could be nothing else. He immediately thought of the engravings of gigantic mastodons in Cuvier's *Recherches sur les Ossemens Fossiles des Quadrupèdes*. The dream of discovering such a fossil, perhaps even being able to excavate and study it, suddenly seemed to be coming true.

The gaucho saw Darwin's excitement and volunteered that this cliff contained many such old bones. They were of little interest, pronounced the gaucho, merely the remains of giant agouti that had perished in their burrows when the sea had flooded in upon them. But Darwin was already riding further along the cliff looking for more fossils.

Shouting from the top of the cliff soon interrupted the fossil hunt, though. The signal fire was belching smoke and the signalers were yelling for added effect. Within a few minutes one of the whaleboats noticed and began pulling for the point.

A smiling Lieutenant Sullivan welcomed his wayward shipmates aboard. The crew was winded from pulling against the ebb but now they raced back to the *Beagle* while making Darwin the center of attention as he recounted the attack on the posta. By the time he and Earle were repeating the details of the journey to Fitzroy in the privacy of the captain's cabin, Syms had become a celebrity and the entire ship was taking about wild Indians and scanning the shore for any sign of them.

When Darwin suggested that he stay at Bahia Blanca a few months to excavate the fossils, Fitzroy gave his unqualified support. Because Bahia Blanca was as full of shoals as it was an important harbor, he would be occupied with surveying the bay and its approaches for months. Darwin would be able to excavate the fossils and then load them aboard the *Beagle* before she sailed for Buenos Aires to resupply.

Darwin was first taken aback by Fitzroy's surprisingly affable support, but the one reason for it soon became clear. The Sierra Ventana, it was rumored in Buenos Aires, contained coal. Confirmation would make the bay even more significant as a port, and Fitzroy wanted Darwin to have time to make a through study of the local geology.

Earle was less agreeable to that plan, flat out refusing, in fact, and stating his intent to ride for Buenos Aires in the morning. Darwin wanted him to sketch the fossils in situ, before excavation disturbed the relationships of the fossilized bones to each other and the containing strata. Such careful records would be essential to determine whether the fossils represented a jumbled collection of bones that had been eroded from older sediments far upcountry or the complete, articulated skeletons of animals that had died shortly before being interred at Bahia Blanca. Darwin had long before inferred that Earle had gone to Patagones only to negotiate something with Rosas and afterwards wanted to return to Buenos Aires as soon as possible. He nonetheless tried to convince Earle to stay and make an important and lasting contribution to natural history.

Earle, for his part, simply continued to insist that duty demanded otherwise: "I must concern myself with the power of men rather than that of nature, I'm afraid, Charles, and will leave in the morning. I will, however," he added, seemingly feeling some camaraderie after their recent adventures together, "carry a note to Lucy,...if you wish."

Taken aback, Darwin blushed: "No,...but thank you kindly just the same, Augustus. Just give her my regards and the news that we're all well. Thank you, though."

Once Earle had left, Darwin and Syms set up a tent among the sand ridges atop the cliff at Fossil Point, as Fitzroy had named it on his chart, and began to plan out how to excavate the fossils. The gaucho had been right about the many fossils exposed in the cliff so, with the help of Commandant Rodriguez, Darwin hired some mansos who lived near the fort to work as excavators.

His initial impression of them was not hopeful. Their few toldos were no more than ragged skins flapping from splintered bamboo poles. The two-dozen men, women, and children sat around almost naked, gnawing at the bones of a roasted nag. Many of the older faces were scarred by smallpox. The only labor they seemed fit for was making bolas, and the clicking of stones knocking together until round suffused the tolderia.

Nonetheless, despite the seeming lack of employment, the cacique drove a hard bargain, adding conditions until just before Darwin reached his limit. Every morning, in advance, he was to pay the daily wage, a pittance to him but a windfall for Old Bernantio, the cacique. In addition, Darwin would pay to move the tolderia to Fossil Point. Sunday would be a day of rest and prayer to "Jesus-man-on-stick," as Old Bernantio put it. And Darwin was to provide a mare every Sunday to celebrate the day with a roast. The rest of the week, he was to pay the same wage to those assigned to hunt food for the tolderia as to the diggers themselves. The deal was sealed with two grins, one nearly toothless, and a handshake.

As the excavations progressed, the solstice approached and the days became cooler, perfect for the hard labor of digging in the compact red mud and gravel. Some nights even brought frost, but it always disappeared by midmorning. Darwin moved ahead of the diggers on the network of rough scaffolding that now leaned against the cliff. He would mark the fossils he wanted and, still annoyed at Fitzroy for not having contracted a real artist instead of Earle, made his own sketches of their placement.

Syms supervised the actual excavations. The men used picks and shovels to dig the sediments away from each piece until a final tug with ropes could pull it free of the cliff's millennial grip to swing clear, suspended from a primitive crane made of spare spars loaned from the *Beagle*. Once hoisted up to the camp that spread back from the cliff top, women and children cleaned off the adhering mud. Buckets of salt water raised with the crane assisted that task. All the work went slowly and carefully so as to break the fossils as little as possible. All were friable because mineral replacement of the bone had not proceeded far enough to fully petrify them, as Darwin determined by grinding some fragments and burning them in a spirit lamp. The flame sprung forth easily from the organic matter that remained, once the living tissue of giant quadrupeds that now lived only in Darwin's imagination. As the diggers moved from fossil to fossil, they left behind a line of pockmarks in the cliff face and, along its top, among the heaps of mud tailings, stacks of cleaned and oiled crania, spines, ribs, femurs, mandibles, and other bones grouped as they had been excavated. At dusk, the mansos, who worked nearly naked to preserve their few clothes from the mud, washed themselves in the bay before dressing against the evening chill. Before long, the camp had begun to look like some macabre industry out of a painting by Hieronymus Bosch.

Every few days, a fossil more incredible than the last would emerge from the cliff. The cranium that Darwin had first spotted turned out to belong to a sloth the size of an elephant, a *Megatherium* just like, although a little smaller, than the one in the Madrid Museum that Cuvier had illustrated in his *Recherches sur les Ossemens*. A certain Friar Torres had excavated that specimen, a complete skeleton, from the banks of the Rio Lujan near Buenos Aires, little more than 300 miles from Fossil Point. The cliff subsequently gave Darwin three more *Megatherium* skulls, each one more perfect than its predecessor, but never a skeleton to match.

The first nearly complete skeleton, lacking only the left front leg below the humerus and some teeth, that did slowly emerge from the sediments belonged to a *Megalonyx*. Again Darwin identified it on the basis of one of Cuvier's engravings, this time of a specimen from the United States unearthed by Thomas Jefferson, who had named it for its gigantic claws. Another type of giant sloth, *Megalonyx* was nonetheless only a quarter the size of *Megatherium* and thus readily distinguishable. And, to Darwin's delight, unlike its larger cousin, *Megalonyx* was previously unknown from South America and thus an important find sure to elicit the notice of even the greatest naturalists.

Other fossils followed. Two piles contained a pair of previously unknown species of edentates similar to *Megalonyx* but, on the basis of dentition, clearly of a different and previously unknown genus. The variety of giant sloths that had once lived around Bahia Blanca astounded Darwin, especially considering that currently no sloths of any type were known from anywhere south of Brazil. If, like existing sloths, the extinct giants subsisted on the leaves of trees, the vegetation of the region must have changed considerably as the estuary became a grassy plain. He made some poor sketches of how the giant sloths must have lived, standing on massive hind legs, balancing like a tripod with their stout tails. Long claws raked through the branches of trees, pulling leaves and fruits within range of their hard lips and tongues, which then fed the proceeds backwards to the molars. Clearly the smaller ground sloths, like *Megalonyx*, browsed lower branches than *Megatherium*, or perhaps that most gigantic of the giant sloths actually uprooted trees with its claws.

And maybe, it suddenly struck Darwin as he completed the sketch, the trees had disappeared not only because the elevation of the estuary had cut off the river and the soil had became too dry for trees. Maybe the sloths had gone extinct for some other reason and the trees had disappeared because their propagation required herbivores. After all, the sloths would have distributed the seeds in their faeces after eating the fruits and pods. The possibilities and inter-linkages seemed many, and approximately nothing was known about such phenomena of natural history. But, he was convinced, continued study of everything from regional stratigraphy to fossil dentition would eventually eliminate the possibilities one by one and leave a residue of truth about the bones at Fossil Point. Certainly the gaucho theory that they belonged to giant agouti that had been drowned in their burrows by the Flood was nonsense.

The commonest fossil turned out to be an entirely new order of herbivorous pachyderm that combined elements of Rodentia, Proboscidea, and Artiodactyla. The girth of the femur seemed incredible to anyone used to living species of quadrupeds. The dental formula was variable, with thirty-four to thirty-eight great hipsodontic teeth. The incisors reminded Darwin of a rodent, perhaps the capybara, the inferior ones procumbent and the superior ones arced. The canines and first premolars, when present at all, were very rudimentary, creating a diastema between the oversized incisors and first molars. Yet this rodent-like animal had walked on hooves. And, to top that incongruity, the cranium was high, with ears and eyes set far upwards. The mandible took the form of a spoon, the nasal processes were pronounced, and the nares retracted—the whole suggesting an elongated, mobile proboscis, albeit much shorter than that of an elephant, or even a tapir. Darwin could picture this giant walking through an estuarine marsh—nostrils, eyes, and ears just above water, plowing through the mud as it waded about on its thick legs, scooping up mouthfuls of hydrophytes. In his imagination, he saw the great head rising, water flowing from the top of the broad maxilla, the upper incisors chopping off the plants and feeding them back to the molars while water gushed out through the gaps in the dentition.

Another amazing find came on a cold day in early July. While excavating one of the *Megatherium* skulls, the mansos found the lower jawbone of a horse. They did not much remark on their find, since horses were so much a part of their everyday lives, but Darwin could scarcely believe what he saw when they raised the mandible to the cliff top. Naturalists assumed that the first horses to graze the pastures of the New World were those that that Christopher Columbus had brought. No one had ever reported an equine fossil from either North or South America. Darwin tired to convey the importance of the small fossil to Syms, but before he had half explained the significance of evidence that horses had inhabited the New World long before 1492, the mansos let out a great chorus of shouts. They had unearthed the edge of a scapula and immediately recognized it as belonging to the skeleton of a guanaco—but one twice the size of any they had ever seen.

Not every day brought such finds. They punctuated slow weeks of meticulous excavation, cleaning, and cataloging.

And some days brought new living species as well as fossils. The children dragged a steady stream of live mammals, beetles, spiders, snails, birds, lizards, and more to Darwin's tent. A brother and sister team, Namuncura and Rayen-Caven, were particularly productive and grew rich in the bits of copper wire and beads that Darwin paid for specimens. Syms killed each day's catch and then skinned or bottled it, as appropriate to its nature. Then Darwin, using Cuvier's modification of Linnaean taxonomy, labeled each as to species and listed them in his notebooks under the relevant phylum, class, order, and family.

Thus, on August 15 he turned to the place reserved for species in the phylum Chordata, class Mammalia, order Edentata, family Dasypodidae. These armadillos were the only close relatives to the giant sloths that still lived around Bahia Blanca, and Namuncura and Rayen-Caven had provided good specimens of three local species. With great satisfaction, he listed them according to their Latin binomials and appended their local vernacular names and brief, since they were well known species, notes as to their characteristics. "*Dasypus matacus*; here called the apar, or three-banded armadillo; diurnal. *D. minutus*; known as the pichy, or pigmy armadillo; diurnal. *D. villosus*; the peludo; nocturnal; quite tasty."

An even greater satisfaction came when the children brought him a toad he was sure was a new species of the genus *Phryniscus*. They called it a tsika; he listed it under the class Amphibia, order Anura, family Bufonidae. In equal parts proud and anxious, he wrote "*Phryniscus darwinii* (?)," tentative to the expert approval of the anuraists at the British Museum. He was, at first, tempted to name it *P. diabolicus* because its coloring suggested the very creature, "squat like a toad," that Milton made whisper lies in the ear of Eve. But *P. darwinii* won out. "The reader," he wrote in the extensive annotation, "will gain a good idea of the appearance if he imagines that it had been steeped in the blackest India ink and then, when dry, made to crawl over a glass that had been freshly painted with the brightest vermilion, so as to color the soles of its feet and parts of its stomach."

Some days Darwin would leave Syms in charge of the camp while he went looking for new species on his own, or almost on his own, since he never got far without one of the commandant's gauchos showing up. On one such excursion in August, by when the days were growing warmer, his gaucho shadow suddenly jumped from his horse and lay on his belly looking intently at the western horizon, the direction in which they had been riding. Darwin was by now familiar enough with gaucho ways to realize the he must have seen something he was now trying to silhouette against the sky. "Three," pronounced the gaucho, "and they don't ride like Christians." Now Darwin had also picked out the other riders on the horizon, little more than a mile away along the crest of a slight slope in the plain that, in this area, consisted of a series of almost imperceptible swellings. All he could make out was three black dots, but he credited the gaucho with much better eyes. After a minute, one of the three dots disappeared back across the horizon.

"Are they Indians?," asked Darwin, surprising himself when he heard himself whispering.

"What do I know?," the gaucho whispered back. "If there are only three, who cares. We have guns. But what if they are scouts and the one who rode off went to report to his brethren below the horizon?"

"Do you think that likely?"

"What do I know? But we had best make sure our guns are ready and get the hell out of here."

So they remounted and, with their rifles across their saddles, walked the horses directly away from the other riders. The two who remained in sight began to follow, also at a walk. Whenever the crest of a slight rise cut the line of sight that connected the pursued and pursuers, Darwin and the gaucho would gallop their horses a while before resting them by walking. The pursuers would soon come galloping over the horizon and also slow to a walk. Each time they seemed a little closer.

Darwin asked, "Why do we not just gallop as fast and far as we can?"

The gaucho looked at him and firmly said, "Not until they do. We don't know how good their horses are. We are heading for the edge of a large marsh I know of so that if they do catch up to us we can gallop into it as far as the horses can go and then lose ourselves on foot. Once its dark, we will make for the fort."

When they reached the marsh and turned to follow its edge, the pursuers cut the corner to ride an intercept course. The gaucho never took his eyes off the pursuers and, when they had come to within a third of a mile, seemed almost ready to order the charge into the marsh when he pulled up his horse and started laughing.

"Women! They are women, Señor! I recognize the sister-in-law of the commandant, and two others, probably collecting early ostrich eggs!"

And now Darwin could himself discern the truth of that observation. The gaucho laughed with relief while giving all the reasons why they could never have been Indians in the first place.

That evening, back in camp at Fossil Point, Darwin recorded the incident in his journal, blew out the candle, lay back in his blankets, and laughed quietly to himself in satisfaction. Who in Shrewsbury or Cambridge would believe his story of the gaucho and the egg hunters? By the end of the voyage he would have enough such stories for a thousand dinners.

And he was having a great time collecting new species, living and fossil. Some of them, like the horse mandible, were so significant that they would earn him a lasting reputation as a first-class naturalist. Henslow would be well pleased he had arranged Darwin's place on the *Beagle*.

He was glad he was not aboard her right now, though, his nostrils full of the smell of the bilges, maybe puking his guts out while she wallowed on a swell, the butt of jokes for collecting specimens. In contrast, the camp was snug, sheltered from the wind among the dunes. He had a comfortable bed, fresh food and, best of all, solid ground. Or maybe the best part was being his own master.

He could hear the mansos singing quietly around their fires. Despite his initial apprehensions, they had turned out to be good workers, especially considering how little he was paying them. Old Bernantio did not allow drink in the camp, and everyone seemed healthy and happy with their newfound employment.

Sometimes he could not avoid staring at some of the younger women while they squatted at work over the fossils, their naked thighs and swaying breasts smeared with red mud, but all were married or very young. Nor would he go with Syms to the whores at the fort on Sundays. The girl on the Rio Colorado had come to him and he had reacted, but he promised himself that he would not seek that out. He resolved to endure his celibacy by focusing on the demands of his work and resisting the urge to fantasize about Lucy. With any luck at all, he would be back in Buenos Aires by spring and she would still be there.

Old Bernantio spent the days overseeing his tribe and making sure that Darwin lived up to his side of the bargain. Syms directed the actual excavations, but the cacique daily decided which of his people would work on the digging and which would supply the camp. Some days he would send a group of men after agouti or guanaco, other days some women to fetch freshwater or children to gather firewood, all readily available in the sand ridges that surrounded the camp. And he kept the accounts, accumulating Darwin's daily payment into a horde of coins that he kept in a bag at his waist. He had an ancient musket that looked to have belonged to some conquistador, and he wanted to buy lead and powder. What else he planned to spend the money on he would not say.

Most evenings, after he noticed that Darwin had extinguished his candle, Bernantio would call out in passable Spanish: "Come sit with me a while, Don Carlitos. We have the rest of the day free from work, if you can use that word in relation to what we clearly take so much pleasure from. Come sit with me and I will tell some stories. I even promise not to contaminate them with too much truth."

And so Bernantio told Darwin much about the local animals, things that would otherwise have continued to puzzle him, such as the familial relations of the ostrich. By the end of August, the ostriches were laying, and Darwin was surprised that the nests he found contained so many eggs, never less than a dozen and often as many as three dozen, and all apparently of about the same age. Since the cocks sat the nests, he deduced that they must be the clutches of an entire harem of hens because no single hen could possibly lay dozens of such large eggs within the space of a week or two. But he remained puzzled, because if he were correct, he should on his excursions note either an extreme imbalance in the sexes or many frustrated males. Yet he tended to see just as many males as females, the two being readily distinguishable by their size and coloring, and each male seemed to guard a nest with dozens of eggs.

Bernantio quickly cleared up the seeming paradox. Apparently each hen laid an egg every few days but moved from cock to cock, thus always laying in a nest containing other recently laid eggs. This promiscuity allowed each hen to lay dozens of the very large eggs over the course of the spring and have the majority hatch success-fully. If, instead, she were to lay them all in one nest, the earliest chicks would eat their younger siblings as they hatched. Or, the alter-native, if the parents waited to begin sitting until the last egg was laid, the earlier eggs would be addled by the time incubation of the last ones began. So by the ingenious arrangement revealed by Old Ber-nantio the number of nests equaled the number of adults, the number of males equaled the number of females, and the number of hatch-lings could be many times greater than both together.

To Darwin, such explanations were infinitely more desirable than MacCormick's assertion that the complexity of life reflected God's grandeur. The meaning of life, thought Darwin, surely transcended the mechanisms of life, but his fascination lay more and more with the mechanisms. And they, no matter how intricate and beautiful, clearly could be understood as to their functions as well as being ap-preciated for their grandeur. Old Bernantio made that increasingly clear with every story.

He tried to repay the cacique by telling him about England, but Old Bernantio did not seem interested. "Perhaps," he wove aside Darwin's offers to tell him about steamships or Shetland ponies, "you can tell me when I visit you there and have seen these things." Then he would launch into a story about how the world came to be, or how smallpox had reduced his people from farmers to nomads. Darwin's favorite story recounted how the animals came to have their territo-ries, and he asked Bernantio to tell it several times.

"When Walleechu first created all the animals," Old Bernantio would begin, "each animal knew the place where it properly be-longed. The guanaco roamed the pampas. The tucotuco burrowed be-neath them. The condor soared on the winds. The whale dove in the seas. The salmon swam in the rivers and lakes. And so on: for every animal, its territory."

"But Walleechu had neglected to tell the animals to consort only with their own kind, and before long some began to wander beyond their proper territories. Tribes made up partly of those with fur, partly of those with feathers, and partly of those with neither wandered through forest and plain, swam in water fresh and salt, and ascended to the highest mountain before descending to the deepest valley and back again. And new animals appeared, the mixed offspring of those with fur and those with feathers, such as the bat. The penguin had a mother who had feathers and a father who was a fish. Others, even more mixed up, like the giant ordor, a snake with wings and a lion's head, now live only in memory."

"Eventually, many animals became upset at the mixed tribes that wandered in whichever territory they wanted. Especially vexing were the mixed up offspring of those mixed up tribes. Some like the ordor were a terror to all. Those with fur thought that those with feathers were to blame and vice versa. Those with neither fur nor feathers blamed those with either, and vice versa."

"Tensions gathered, incidents of trespass led to other incidents, and then one day, during a ferocious storm, four enormous armies converged on Bahia Blanca. The army of those with feathers swooped down on the armies of those with fur, those with neither, and those who were mixed. All four armies met at the edge of the wide mudflat, where land, water, and air met. They attacked each other amid the crashing surf under a sky dark with cloud and flashing with lightning. The water ran red with their blood. The mud became mixed with their corpses trampled underfoot. The dead piled up as high as the clouds. The destruction became so horrible that the four generals finally agreed to a truce while at least some of their soldiers survived."

"The ambassadors of the survivors met at the Sierra Ventana and made a treaty in which they agreed that each animal must henceforth stick to its own territory and consort only with its own kind so that no more mixed tribes would wander from territory to territory and no more mixed offspring would be borne. To establish the proper territory of each animal, a council made up of representatives from all the animals would vote on the proper place for each, and a majority vote would be binding on all and on their descendants for all time."

"Not all the animals got the territory they felt they should, of course, but most accepted the result of the vote. The dog wanted to run wild with the wolf and the fox, but they, his own brothers, voted that the dog would live with man. 'Your faeces smell like man's,' they argued, 'and so you should live with him.'"

"'But the cat already lives with man!,' objected the dog. 'You cannot seriously expect me to live with my worst enemy!'"

"But they did expect it and voted to make it so. So dogs went to live with cats in the homes of men, but ever since have taken revenge on wolves and foxes. Whenever they come to steal from men, dogs raise the alarm."

"The least happy with the decisions of the council were the mixed offspring. But most of those who left the Sierra Ventana indignant nonetheless chose to live by the council's decisions. The bat, for example, could find no sympathy among either those relations with fur or those with feathers. The council voted that bats would be allowed to use the air only at night, when true birds were asleep, and to use the ground only in the deepest caves, where true animals with fur did not go. Likewise, the penguin could find no sympathy among either the fish or the birds. The fish were inclined against any animal that ate fish, and the birds resented the ease with which the penguin caught fish. They thus voted to banish the penguin to the coldest parts of the sea, far to the south."

"Some, though, left the Sierra Ventana in such a rage that they vowed to choose exile rather than a territory they felt beneath them. The ordor flew off over the eastern sea and never returned. The, tribut, who was offspring of a whale and a guanaco, crossed the mountains and then swam off into the western sea."

"And that is how each animal came again to have its proper place and consort only among its own kind. Guanacos run with guanacos and give birth of guanacos. Whales swim with whales and give birth to whales. Condors fly with condors and give birth to condors."

"And that," Don Carlitos, "is also how the clouds became red. Young clouds, born since that great battle are white, but the older clouds became so stained with blood as the corpses piled up that the rains have still not washed all of it out. When old clouds gather over

Bahia Blanca to commemorate the battle, the entire sky becomes red and serves as a warning to all animals that they must continue to abide by the council's decisions or risk another such battle."

"And that is also how the mud at Bahia Blanca became so red and so full of the bones of dead animals that no longer live in the world. The mud became mixed with corpses as the armies surged back and forth and trampled their fallen comrades. Many of the bones are those of the mixed offspring who died in the battle, crosses between giant agouti and horses, crosses between whales and guanacos and, crosses between crosses."

"And that is also how ostriches came to lay so many eggs that the chicks born every year number many more than their parents. When the animals left the council at the Sierra Ventana, all of them decided to start having many more offspring than had been usual before the battle. They realized that if there ever were another such battle, only those tribes with many soldiers would survive."

"And that is also how, while they await the next great battle, the children of each animal came to war continuously among themselves, for so many are born into each generation that not all of them can survive. Sibling thus pushes sibling away from the teat or out of the nest. Those too small or too weak do not live to see their first birthday. The ostrich and each other animal thereby ensures that its soldiers will be as strong and numerous as possible if those with fur, those with feathers, and those with neither ever again join in battle here at the edge of the eastern sea."

Darwin found such stories wonderful, not just as tales to pass the evening around the fire but for their ambitious attempts to explain so much so elegantly. The stories were reminiscent of the Bible, but they did not focus so much on purpose as on mechanism. Old Bernantio always concluded them with, "And that is how...." Did his stories about animals, in fact, contain a higher quotient of explanation to assertion than did Genesis? Were species as they were because God said, "Let it be so," and it was so, and He saw that it was good? Or did, pondered Darwin, the story about the epochal war among the animals actually offer some clues as to the mechanism through which species had come to be so wondrously organized with each other and their environments?

He thought a lot about such weighty questions while stretched out on his back under the stars just outside his tent, mostly about how different animals had come to be the way they were. That each species fit its environment seemed as ironclad a general principle for the few species that lived in the waste of the saltpans near Patagones as for the thousands that lived in the forest near Rio de Janeiro. If a species did not conform to the demands of its environment, it would inevitably become extinct. The geological evidence for environmental change, as Lyell had so well catalogued, thus explained how so many species had gone extinct, not only large mammals such as he was digging up but even larger dinosaurs and much smaller mollusks. When an environment changed, some species, sometimes many at the same time, went extinct because they no longer conformed to the demands of their environment. That much seemed obvious.

The real challenge, then, he concluded, was to explain the origin of species that conformed so well to their environments until those environments changed. Had God created species in immutable form, as MacCormick and so many others believed, each to fit a particular role in a particular environment? Or had, as his own grandfather Erasums believed, species changed since the Creation to accommodate themselves to environmental changes? Had the current species thus come into being as the much-modified descendants of extinct species, not just as their inheritors but, quite literally, as their biological descendents?

That was the great mystery of mysteries, as Lamarck had named it: how had species originated? That Frenchman had proposed that animals could modify themselves through the exercise or lack thereof of any organ, any such change being passed on to future generations and changing the species as a whole. But how would all the individuals of a species know to exercise the same particular organ or, in fact, any organ at all? In his *Philosophies Zoologique*, Lamarck speculated that something he called besoin, a desire to fill some need, compelled animals to use or disuse an organ. To Darwin, and he had mulled over the problem many times over the past month, that seemed an unlikely mechanism. He was not quite sure why he did not like it except that Lamarck seemed to be proposing a sort of dispersal of the will of God among all the individuals of all the species. Why not just stick with God as the purposeful creator? But maybe Lamarck was right? Or maybe MacCormick was? No, he thought as he passed into sleep, it was just that no one had as yet had hit on the correct explanation. It had thus far eluded all of them, perhaps because they focused on purpose rather than mechanism.

He awoke to the red disk of the sun just above the eastern horizon. Dew was already steaming from the tent canvas. His last thought from the night before was still clear: the mechanism, not the purpose, underlying the origin of species must be his focus. But right now he had fossils to excavate, species to collect. Behind him he heard the Indian women building up their fires to heat water for mate. Toward the bay, nothing moved among the washed out shades of blue, silver, and brown except a few gulls wheeling low over the mud banks.

Whenever the *Beagle* was anchored nearby, some of the officers would come to visit Fossil Point. Darwin enjoyed the chance to show off his camp, the first thing worth showing off that he had ever been in charge of. His shipmates, in turn, enjoyed the chance to get some exercise, eat fresh game, and meet some "real, wild Indians," as they put it. The excavations themselves did not attract much interest beyond confirming Darwin's eccentricity. To the officers, he seemed to have turned his mania for collecting dead animals into an industry that employed naked savages to produce old bones. But Darwin's hospitality and the good food kept them coming. Once Lieutenant Wickham and the two midshipmen spent the day crabbing and the entire camp had a crab boil that lasted until midnight. When Rowlett visited, he summed up what he found with his usual wit: "You seem 'appier'n a pig in sheet, Charles. A bloody great pig in a wallow o' sheet!"

And Darwin was happy. MacCormick and Fitzroy did not seem inclined to visit, and he missed them not at all. He suspected that Fitzroy was glad to be rid of him as well, at least for the time being. With Darwin not using his cabin, Fitzroy could more easily spread out his charts on the big table and assemble the details of this coast. And MacCormick, Darwin knew, would be enjoying being the only naturalist aboard for as long as possible.

The only thing Darwin craved, besides Lucy, was intellectual interaction. Syms was no help in that regard. Darwin could expound for an hour while his servant merely nodded his head in agreement while oiling a fossil or building a packing crate. Syms, like most, lived life in a welter of immediate details without ever pondering its broader contours.

So Darwin would wander among the sand hills and debate himself. He would propose an idea and offer argument in its support. Then he would offer arguments against. Then he would revise his idea and begin again. He tried, so as not to cause anyone alarm, to keep his soliloquy to a mutter, although not always successfully and not without frequent gesticulation. He began to conduct such itinerant monologs in July and for a month thought he might be going crazy. But by August he believed he was making progress. He believed he had refined his ideas to the point that he could explain them clearly and defend them from major criticisms.

"The problem of the origin of species, which Lamarck so well named the 'mystery of mysteries,' boils down to three issues," he addressed a gull hovering above his head. Punctuating his points with an upraised finger, he continued, "The issue of mechanism. The issue of time. And the issue of continuity."

"Regarding mechanism, there are two possibilities. The first possibility is the supernatural one set forth in the Bible and for which the main proof is the Bible. It holds that God created all species. Those species have not since changed in form and behavior. Some have become extinct and are known only in fossil form. The remainder persist. The second possibility is the natural one that must be inferred through observing nature herself. It holds that as the extinct species died out, others came into being through a mechanism that must, in general, be the same one through which one generation gives rise to the next. Living species are thus the lineal descendants of fossil species."

"But, sir," he challenged himself, "surely you do not propose that a species can somehow change its form, the old form incrementally disappearing into the fossil record and the new one comprising what we currently observe? And surely you do not propose that the mechanism involved in such preposterous transmutations comprises no more than the ordinary one of procreation, etcetera?"

"That is exactly what I propose. We see, in such examples as the breeding of pigeons and horses, the potential for great diversity of form emerging within a given species. If advanced far enough, breeds will so far diverge from the common stock as to constitute new and distinct species. But allow me to return to this issue of mechanism after having addressed those of time and continuity."

"Indeed, sir, you must. Because even if I accept, for the sake of continuing this debate, that you are onto something regarding mechanism, time must be its enemy. Look, we have been breeding horses since at least the days of Homer, say a thousand generations, and have succeeded in producing breeds as diverse as the Clydesdale and the Shetland. Yet, you must admit, Clydesdales and Shetlands are not different enough to be classed as distinct species. Both remain *Equus caballus*, the proof of that being that, given enough generations, each might be bred back to a common nag. So, given that the world is only six thousand years old, by the diligent calculations of the good Bishop Ussher, how can you maintain that your proposed natural mechanism could possibly be responsible for the origin of distinct species from a common ancestor? That, because of the issue of time alone, cannot be true for species as little diverse as *Equus caballus* and *Equus zebra*. And that certainly cannot be true for the many much more diverse species."

"How? Quite simply put, Ussher is wrong. Lyell convincingly demonstrates that the world has existed for many many millions of years. The natural mechanism I propose has operated for just as long and thereby given rise to the great diversity of species we observe, both fossil and living. Lyell shows how the geological mechanisms we observe today are sufficient to explain all of the geological formations we see around us. The slow elevation of the land due to volcanism. Its equally slow erosion by ice, tides, etcetera."

"Preposterous! The Bible relates the age of the world, and it is some six thousand years."

"'Preposterous' is not an argument, nor is privileging words written in the Bible about the world over direct observation of that world. It is not up to Lyell to prove that sufficient time has passed for natural mechanisms like the tides and glaciers, which you can observe with your own eyes, to have produced the geological formations you can also observe with your own eyes. Those observations are themselves the proof that sufficient time has passed for natural mechanisms to have slowly formed the highest mountains and deepest valleys. In fact, I here propose that any geological feature you point to can be explained without recourse to supernatural catastrophes. That, sir, is the way to prove something: through logic and observation, not through dogma."

"Are you saying that I can point to any geological feature and you will be able to explain its formation through the action of mechanisms we can now observe? That there was no great and sudden Deluge as told in Genesis?"

"I say there is no need, when geologizing, to have recourse to supernatural explanations. The natural mechanisms we see operating all around us are sufficient to explain any feature. And, more than that, I say that the same principle applies to the organic world, both botanical and zoological. Sufficient time has passed for the present mechanism through which each generation descends from the prior one to have given origin to the great diversity of living and fossil species. If you can ever show me a geological feature that I cannot explain through the action of slow, natural mechanisms, I will retract all that I have argued, both with regard to geology and to biology."

"But, sir, even so, your hypothesis that living species are lineal descendants of fossil species cannot hold because there is no gradual progression evident in the fossil record. If living species actually are descended, generation-by-generation, from extinct species, why is there not a continuous gradation evident in the fossil record. Where, for instance, is the gradation from the *Megatherium* you have found and the tree sloths you saw in Brazil or the armadillos, also edentates, that now live around Bahia Blanca?"

133

"Exactly my point. I said there were three issues. Mechanism. Time. Continuity. Regarding your point about the lack of continuity in the fossil record, I answer that we have as yet merely begun to explore that record. Being blinded by taking the Bible literally for so long, we did not look and therefore found only the fraction of that record we stumbled upon. As we look more—and do so more systematically—we will assemble continuous genealogies linking all species. Taxonomy will become genealogy. Consider my new genus, *Toxodon*, for thus I have named it. It combines features of the pachyderms, the ungulates, and the rodents. It therefore quite likely represents a previously unknown order ancestral to the orders Rodentia, Proboscidea, and Artiodactyla. There is thus a progression manifest in the fossil record, consisting of fossil species becoming progressively more similar to living species."

"Well, sir, even if you are correct about time and continuity, to prove that living species are the lineal descendants of extinct species you still need to explain the mechanism involved. You have vaguely proposed something similar to horse breeding. But who is the breeder and what is the purpose? You reject God as having created species. And without a purposeful breeder there can be no direction to your mechanism. Any variation that arises will therefore soon disappear again, in the same way that the purposeless squire who indiscriminately mixes his stallions and mares will soon see his breeds degrade. Do you follow Lamarck, then, in proposing a distribution of purpose among individual animals? And plants? Come, sir, that is preposterous. Plants can have no such purpose, and certainly not a common purpose!"

"For the first time we are in agreement. There can be no purpose to the mechanism, no besoin, as Lamarck calls it, distributed among individual organisms. That sort of fragmentation of purpose seems a recipe for confusion. Yet variation does arise through breeding; that we do know. Perhaps it also arises through use and disuse. What directs deviation from the ancestral stock with sufficient consistency to breed new species from the old? That I do not know. And I simply do not know why a given species should have such wondrous internal homogeneity and perfection. Think of the woodpecker, with its claws, tail, beak, and tongue all working together so admirably to achieve its livelihood. How could Lamarck's besoin result in such perfection of complex, interlocked relationships, more so than the workings of the most intricate chronometer? And I simply don't know why species have an overall, wondrous organization relative to one another. Think of the mistletoe drawing its nourishment from a few select tree species, relying on a few particular bird species to propagate its seeds and on one or two insect species for pollination. I do not know what has given direction to the mechanism through which the fossil species I am excavating came into being only to latter go extinct, but I am convinced that that mechanism is as natural as the one that formed the sediments in which they became interred."

Darwin never shared these soliloquies with anyone else.

MacCormick never did visit Fossil Point, but Fitzroy eventually came to have a look in late August. Darwin was not in the mood for condescension, though, so did not test his ideas on him. Instead, he bit his tongue while giving a tour of the excavations and camp, even when Fitzroy referred to the sediments as diluvium and asserted that the Mylodon had perished in the Flood. When Darwin did not rise to the bait, Fitzroy looked at him as if he read his thoughts but after a few seconds turned to look out over the bay and comment on the weather.

More upsetting, Fitzroy claimed that the *Beagle* could not possibly carry all the fossils to Buenos Aires. So as Fitzroy returned to the *Beagle*, Darwin began the painful job of choosing which fossils to ship and which to abandon. He had collected specimens from more than one individual of most of the species represented, and he chose a single, best example of each one, listing them in his notebook.

"The complete skull of a *Megatherium*. Total live weight estimated at four tons. Previously know from near Buenos Aires."

"The nearly complete skeleton, lacking only the left front leg below the humerus and some teeth, of a *Megalonyx*. Previously known only from the United Sates."

"A nearly complete skeleton of an herbivorous, edental genus similar to the sloths but distinguishable from *Megatherium* on the basis of size and from *Megalonyx* on the basis of dentition. I name the genus *Mylodon* for its mill-like teeth. One skeleton represents a robust species, which I name *M. robustus*, and the other a gracile one, which I name *M. darwinii*."

"The mandible of a horse. Subject to expert evaluation, it is very similar if not identical to *Equus caballus*. In any case, the implications of this find are clearly astounding."

"The nearly complete skeleton of a giant camelid similar to the guanaco or llama but with an estimated live weight of around a ton and therefore much larger than any living species of Auchenia. I therefore name it *Macrauchenia patachonica*."

"The complete skeleton of a previously unknown herbivorous pachyderm the size of a rhinoceros, with teeth like a rodent, with hooves, and with nostrils, eyes, and ears positioned high like a hippopotamus. The cranium is high, the mandible in the form of a shovel, and the nasal process pronounced. On the basis of the several skulls unearthed, but which could not all be shipped, the dental formula is variable, with 34 to 38 hipsodontic teeth. The superior incisors are very arced. The inferior incisors are procumbent, and the third one on each side displays greater development. The canines and first premolars, when present, are very rudimentary, creating a diastema between the incisors and first molars. I name the genus *Toxodon* on the basis of the arced superior incisors."

Syms crated the fossils as well as six-months' worth of plant and animal specimens, including *Phryniscus darwinii*, and Fitzroy sent a crew to row them out to the *Beagle*.

The excavations at Fossil Point had been more successful than Darwin dreamed they would be when he first saw the cranium glinting in the cliff face. He had recovered several new species, perhaps even a new order, and found a New World horse. He had worked out some, he felt, important ideas. And none of the mansos had been hurt. In fact, Old Bernantio and his tribe had grown fat and healthy that winter.

In mid September, on the morning of the last day before he and Syms would leave for Buenos Aires, Darwin announced a farewell fiesta. He sent Syms to town to buy some mares. Old Bernantio sent his people out to gather firewood and other supplies. And that night everyone joined in singing and dancing around bonfires. They ate the mares a la carne con cuero, meaning the mares were not skinned before circular slabs of meat were cut from their backs. Roasted hide-side-down on a bed of embers, the resulting saucers of meat retained all their gravy. Darwin judged it the best meat he had ever tasted, not excepting the finest mutton. The midshipmen of the *Beagle* later told him they had noted flames probing skyward from Fossil Point late into that night and had not known whether to worry or be jealous.

7

AT DAWN, DARWIN AND SYMS rode out past the silent toldos in which Old Bernantio's tribe was sleeping off the fiesta. Only the grandmothers were awake, stirring the embers back to life. Stopping at the fort to pay his respects to Commandant Rodriguez, Darwin also asked for a gaucho guide. But, now that he was leaving the vicinity of Bahia Blanca, Rodriguez claimed that none could be spared. Besides, he assured Darwin and Syms, the way to Buenos Aires was well marked and required no guide: "Buen viaje, ingleses!"

The road was some four hundred miles long, took a dozen days to ride, and had as many postas spaced along it. Even before the fort had disappeared from view, though, Darwin had determined to avoid the postas as much as possible. Neither Rodriguez's suspicious attitude nor the memory of the attack on the posta at Rio Colorado inspired confidence in Argentinean hospitality. Instead he planned to stop at the postas only for horses and to ride a short distance off the road at dusk to camp out on the open pampa, trusting safety to solitude. Every time he and Syms traded in their mounts for fresh ones, the wisdom of the decision to camp out was confirmed. The horses were fine, but none of the postas amounted to more than a scruffy garrison living in a hut or two made of poles plastered with mud. The better ones had a ditch studded with sharpened stakes to guard the huts and corral. Rosas's passport ensured a friendly enough reception, but the food and sleeping provisions promised to be no better, and typically worse, than provided by the open pampa. Besides, graciousness demanded that if Darwin sat at a posta's fire he would have to share his store of cigars, and he planned on making them last all the way to Buenos Aires.

Close inspection of the Sierra Ventana on the second day revealed no coal, no fossils, no sign at all of anything organic among the rocky waste. All the previous day, the range had risen up along the northern horizon. The plain, covered in the light brown of withered winter grass, gently bulged up around the gray slopes, like a muddy sea lap-

ping at an archipelago of rocky islands. The jagged facets of the ser-
rated line of peaks, with summits of nearly three thousand feet,
evoked the epoch when the sea had battered them, long before being
smothered by the mud of the estuary that had also interred the giant
quadrupeds. Even in the morning light, sitting up in his blankets at the
foot of the range, Darwin could see enough details of the bare, grayish quartz slopes to dismiss the rumors of coal. But, he thought, what
a fine venue for the council of animals after their primordial battle.
Half a day's reconnaissance was enough to confirm thoroughly the
lack of coal. Hunching his shoulders against the cold wind that followed them back down to the plain, he took perverse delight that Fitzroy would be disappointed at the news. His careful survey of Bahia
Blanca and its approaches would be a little less significant than anticipated.

From the sierra, Darwin had noted the ruins of a tolderia on the
plain to the north. As he and Syms approached and saw the scatter of
human bone, they realized it must have been Toriano's tribe. The
skeletons had long been picked bare by vultures, bleached by the sun,
polished by the wind. Upon reaching the wreckage of the toldos, the
bones became more numerous, virtually carpeting the pampa, mixing
with the broken bamboo poles, smashed pots, and other accoutre-
ments of life. The tiniest skulls, as thin and translucent as mica,
lacked teeth. The bones continued northward along the road, gradually disappearing where Miranda's troops had ridden down and
lanced the last of the tribe. They rode on without talking, sickened,
trotting the horses until the last of the evidence of human monstrous-
ness lay far behind. Darwin did not regret that Miranda and his men
had never returned from their pursuit of the last of Toriano's people.

As they continued northward day after day, the air gradually became more humid, the grass greener, the nights warmer. The hunting
was good too. Partridge, deer, ostrich, and guanaco became even
more numerous than around Bahia Blanca. The shotgun Darwin had
bought from one of Rodriguez's captains ensured a fine dinner every
day. Sometimes lightning flashed in the distance but little rain fell.
Many evenings they watched the horizon glow with the light of grass-
fires and smelled the smoke. In the morning, a thin stratum of whitish

ash would have accumulated on their blankets. The burned swaths through which the road passed appeared black and dead, but Darwin knew that the first rain of the season would conjure fresh green shoots of grass from among the ashes. They saw no Indians or, in fact, any other riders except near the postas. That did not surprise them because they had seen no Indians except Old Bernantio's tribe all winter. Rosas's sweep of the pampas had been as effective as it was heinous.

At the postas, every conversation began with jubilation at the success of the war against the Indians, with no one having seen any but tame mansos for weeks. Rosas was a hero. The war was just. The pampas were safe. Civilization would prevail. The latest rumor was that Rosas had already returned to Buenos Aires, traveling incognito with a small group of gauchos during the winter and slipping into the city unannounced. Another rumor concerned a foreigner who had been murdered by bandits along the road the previous fall, and Darwin thought it might have been Earle. But the details were as contradictory as they were vague. At some postas, the garrison seemed sure that he had been English and tall, at others just as sure that he had been French and short.

No matter how hospitable the garrison, though, Darwin only once accepted an offer to spend the night. They had arrived at the start of an afternoon game of pato, and the spectacle promised to be so extraordinary that he could not resist the invitation to watch as well as to enjoy the fiesta that would follow. A cavalry troop riding to Bahia Blanca had filled the place up and decided to have some fun. They had sown up a partridge in a piece of rawhide to form a lumpy ball with four loops of twisted leather for handles, the whole forming the so-called pato. As a dozen riders milled about, another threw it into their midst. A dusty melee ensued, with several gaining a handhold and trying to make off with the pato. One finally did, racing off across the pampa with the others close behind. Darwin and Syms sat on the corral fence and watched as the pato passed back and forth from player to player in a series of skirmishes veiled in clouds of dust, each one ending as someone wrested the pato away and tried to carry the pato back to the posta and have the partridge for dinner. Eventually one among the players seemed to have gotten an unbreakable grip on it, half a dozen others pulling in all directions, trying to unbalance him so that he would loosen his grip. Suddenly his entire saddle slipped sidewise, and he rolled underneath his horse. The girth strap had broken, and the horse, confused and panicking, was trampling him. By the time the other players were able to extract him, he was badly busted up and had to be carried back to the posta.

Darwin ran to meet them, but soon realized that the injuries were so severe as to be fatal. Blood flowed freely from the man's nose and mouth, his scalp was partially ripped away, and one leg hung at an impossible angle and dripped a trail of blood. Darwin doubted the man would live another hour. Someone slit a big cow open from anus to brisket, being careful not to lose too much blood by cutting any major arteries. Enough of the blue and yellow viscera were pulled out so that the dying man, shivering uncontrollably, could be placed inside the cavity and the entrails heaped back in on top of him. Darwin could barely believe such medieval medicine but, because death seemed certain anyway, made no move to intervene. The man died inside the cow before dusk and received many toasts as the wineskins circulated around the fires that evening.

That night Darwin and Syms slept outside near the corral, but before the moon had set Darwin awoke to a black warmth sitting on his chest. At first he thought he was dreaming about being inside the cow, with the soft, wet, warm entrails being heaped on top of him. But when he raised his head to look at his chest, a miniature bulldog face stared into his, its bared fangs glistening red in the moonlight. He screamed, and the vampire bat hissed and stretched out its wings to balance. But before it could spring into the air, Syms was suddenly there, folding the wings between his hands and snapping the neck, all in one smooth motion. Darwin lurched to his knees with his bloodied fingers pressing at the two parallel groves in his neck. Only after he had finished cursing, did he exult a little at having secured a specimen of *Desmodus d'orbignyi.*

When they noticed that other bats were feeding on the stock in the corral, though, they decided to move into one of the huts for the rest of the night. Darwin found some space among the snoring troop and quickly fell asleep again, but within an hour something squirming in his hair had reawakened him. No moonlight penetrated to the interior of the hut, but he reached up and felt what seemed to be a fat, round insect. He squeezed, and his hand was suddenly sticky and warm. Again he lurched to his knees, feeling in his pockets for a match. The flare of the phosphorous revealed dozens of assassin bugs feeding on the sleepers. Some were still flat, others already fat with their blood meals. Some of the men stirred and grumbled at the light but none awoke, so Darwin quietly prodded Syms awake and the two retreated outside. After checking each other for assassin bugs, crushing the ones they could catch, they saddled their horses and took the road north, resolving never again to sleep at a posta as they slowly followed the track in the dark.

As they continued north over the next two days, black clouds began to fill the sky and the spring rains began to green the country. By the time they reached the Rio Salado, it was in flood. The current flattened the canes of the pampas grass growing along what were the normal banks, trailing the white plumes of last year's flowers in the muddy water. No ombu tree offered shelter on the south bank, so they squatted under their horses, water dripping from their hats, their ponchos soaked, eating dried meat, sharing Darwin's last cigar, wondering how long before the flood would turn so they could cross. All that miserable day, bloated carcasses of livestock, caught in the flood somewhere upstream, swept past. Sometimes they became so numerous that Darwin joked about riding across on them.

He asked Syms, both of them sitting huddled under the bellies of their horses, "What would be the opinion of a geologist viewing an enormous collection of bones, of all kinds of animals and of all ages, embedded in one thick earthy mass, as these floating by will be when they reach the Rio Salado estuary? Would he not attribute it to an immense flood having swept over the surface of the land, videlicet to the Biblical Flood, rather than to the common order of things, such as we see now before us?" Syms declined to answer, just shaking his head at the horror of the number of drowned cattle. But Darwin realized that he was witnessing exactly how the remains of so many large mammals could have been buried together at Fossil Point, many with most of their bones in their proper relative positions and so clearly embedded in a fresh state, soon after death. Fitzroy would argue that the fossils represented species that had been drowned and gone extinct all at once, catastrophically, in the Deluge and been buried by the so-called diluvium that settled as the Biblical waters receded. Yet here, at the Rio Salado, a natural mechanism was apparent that easily explained the bone beds at Fossil Point. Lyell had written of other instances of floods washing large numbers of carcasses into the sea.

During the sleepless night the rain stopped. By morning, the flood had subsided enough that the horses could swim across the stream without mishap. The country north of the river, was more settled and the turf bright green and as closely cropped as a lawn. Amid the green, Darwin noticed a familiar flower, *Bellis perennis*, the wild daisy, an old friend somehow introduced from Europe and no doubt spread by the cows that through their grazing and fertilizing flops had created this green carpet. "Do you know Wordsworth?," he shouted over his shoulder to Syms: "To me the meanest flower that blows can give thoughts that do often lie too deep for tears." But Syms only smiled.

As Buenos Aires grew nearer, so Fitzroy's prospectus for a vast network of canals and railroads feeding beef and grain to English ships seemed to Darwin to grow more plausible. Immense herds sometimes slowed progress along the road, and fortified estancias that looked more like citadels than ranches began to appear. Some no doubt belonged to Rosas, but Darwin did not want to stop to ask. Villages of scattered houses with extensive gardens and orchards also began to occur at increasingly shorter intervals but he wanted to press on to the city and, hopefully, to Lucy.

In the haze of late afternoon they rode up to a roadside ombu tree just a few miles outside Buenos Aires. A man hung upside down from a limb, suspended by a blue sash around his ankles, his head just above the ground. His murderers had skinned his torso and then slashed open his abdomen so that a dark pile of entrails spilled onto the ground beside his face. Only his own gore and a layer of flies covered his nakedness. He had been dead long enough that the stench did not encourage stopping.

Neither Syms nor Darwin said a word. Both leaned sidewise in their saddles to vomit. Then, without dismounting, Syms placed the muzzle of his rifle at the black hole that had been the mouth and fired so that the top of the skull blew off and brain splattered on the hooves of the horse. The man must already have been dead before Syms pulled the trigger, but he and Darwin rode on without discussing the possibilities, the sash of Unitarist blue, or anything else.

As they passed through the outskirts of town, along roads bordered by agave hedges and willow trees with fresh leaves just peeping out, the city gradually emerged from the plain. The setting sun reflected from the domes of the churches, and by dusk they were riding down an empty avenue flanked by houses. The only other traffic was a mortuary cart heading out to the cemetery, the lantern and bell warning that death passed by. Lime dust covered the stack of corpses piled in the bed like cordwood as well as the driver and attendant, even the two horses, so that all appeared in the dim light to be already in the realm of spirits. Compelled, Darwin looked over his shoulder and saw the corpses rolling back and forth as the heavy cart labored through the ruts, the layers of paired feet jerking from side to side as if in time to some unheard music.

The British consulate had a thick stack of newspapers and letters for Darwin, separate ones from each of his three sisters, from various friends and, somewhat surprisingly, from Emma. Fanny, he was relieved, had not written again. Neither had Henslow, for which he was equally grateful given the poverty of the last shipment of specimens. Darwin looked forward to sending off the next one, if Fitzroy had not dumped the fossils overboard, and hoped Henslow would not have time to write until he had received it. The consular clerk was full of questions about what they had seen in the south, but Darwin avoided getting into a conversation by assuring him that Fitzroy would return soon and make a complete report to the consul.

From the consulate, Darwin headed back to Lumb's hotel, where he had taken rooms for himself and Syms. When they had arrived the evening before, Lumb had also been eager to hear what was happening in Patagones and Bahia Blanca, and the two Shrewsbury alums had spent several hours catching up over whisky and cigars.

On the walk from the consulate back to the hotel, Darwin mulled over what Lumb had told him about Buenos Aires being, as his friend had put it, "in a state of insidious, internal siege." Rosas, apparently, had been in town much of the winter, although he had recently left again to continue his campaign against the Indians. In the meantime, his wife was continuing the campaign against the Unitarios. Her strategy seemed to be to induce a state of anarchy. People disappeared. The law offered neither defense nor retribution. The neutral either gave in to the terror and became Federalists or resisted by joining the Unitarist camp, after which they also disappeared. Doña María Encarnación allowed no middle ground, no neutrality. When she had finished, every citizen would either be behind her husband, dead, or in exile in Montevideo. Rosas's allies, the federalist governors of the other Argentine provinces, ensured that no Unitarios fled upcountry to rouse opposition there. The governor of Buenos Aires province changed from week to week. Balcarce had been the last one brave enough to accept the mandate from congress, but soon no one would dare fill that post.

By the time Rosas returned next year, the citizenry would be so desperate to restore the rule of law that congress would have no choice but to anoint him supreme dictator. Then, thought Lumb, and Darwin respected his Machiavellian insights, the other provincial governors would disappear just as the Unitarios had, and Rosas would become the absolute ruler of a confederated Argentina, a republic only in name. Regaining Uruguay for Argentina would be next on his agenda. If the English balked at Uruguay becoming an Argentinean province, he would probably defer to their power but nonetheless install his friend Oribe as a puppet president.

The Mazorca was the main instrument with which Doña Maria terrorized the Porteños. Mazorca agents had destroyed the liberal newspapers one by one, smashing presses and assassinating writers. The *Comercio* and the *Nacional* had ceased publication months ago. Sarmiento's *El Progreso* survived by being published in Chile and

smuggled over the Andes. The agents of the Mazorca satisfied themselves with intercepting the shipments and killing anyone caught dis-
tributing that last liberal paper. The citizens felt besieged in their own
homes, terrorized by every knock at the door, unable to trust anyone
beyond their immediate families. Every bar, restaurant, and club had
its informant, a paid ear of the Mazorca. Anyone denounced as having
spoken against Rosas, Doña María, or the Federalist party soon disappeared. Most probably ended up in the river, although a few were
hung in the squares or from trees, as Darwin had seen for himself.
Any place known to harbor backroom liberal meetings burned down,
like the Teatro Coliseo did one evening, right in the middle of a
Kotzebue tearjerker. The audience streamed out into the plaza to
watch the fire engulf the building. As the flames consumed the words
emblazoned across the façade, "Es La Comedia Espejo de la Vida,"
the only ones laughing were the Mazorca agents standing in the shadows.

Lumb had also told him once again that, as despicable as the Mazorca undoubtedly were, the end result would greatly enrich English
merchants. As it stood, they already imported as much into Argentina
as did the rest of the world combined, about four million pesos worth
every year. The French would love to get a bigger share of the Argentine market, but they knew that Rosas hated them because of their
support for the liberals. They had backed the wrong horses by siding
with the Unitarios in Buenos Aires and the Colorados in Uruguay.
Now Paris had little choice but to continue supporting them. The former president of the Argentine republic, Rivadavia, was in exile in
Paris and his leading general, Lavalle, in Montevideo. But the frequent rumors that the two would soon land with an army of French
mercenaries were probably more hopeful than true. When Rosas
gained absolute control, he would ensure that French trade suffered
and English trade expanded. Lumb was ecstatic.

By the time Darwin had reached the hotel, he was so exhausted that
for once he decided to follow the local custom and take an afternoon
siesta. When he awoke, however, he felt more tired than when he had
gone to bed. His limbs were so swollen that he could barely get up.

The left side of his neck was also swollen, and the mirror revealed its deep violet color. Shocked at the sight, he yelled for Syms and then, groaning at the edema, lay down again.

The doctor that Syms found with Lumb's recommendation pronounced that Darwin would need to stay in bed until, hopefully, the condition improved. The best cure, according to the doctor, was rest and cold baths. In a few weeks, perhaps a little longer, the condition would improve. The cause, he pointed out to Darwin with the aid of magnifying mirror, was the bite of an assassin bug, the small wound still visible near the centre of the violet patch on his neck. The result of that small bite was worse than any seasickness: fever, stomach cramps, vomiting, diarrhea, and dropsy that became so bad he could not pull on his pants or his boots. He hardly ate and slept sixteen hours a day. Inexplicably, Syms found several bites on his own body but never developed any symptoms.

Darwin did nothing that first week in bed except read back issues of *The Times*, putting the letters aside until his strength returned. The biggest news was that the Reform Bill seemed to have won the day, which would put Fitzroy in a foul mood. Besides that, Earl Grey and Palmerston seemed to be keeping things under control at home and abroad. Tensions between the Russians and Ottomans in Bessarabia had eased. The Boers continued to agitate for greater independence in the Cape but with little effect. Louis-Philippe seemed to be keeping the French from killing each other. Lord Cochrane had been reinstated in the Royal Navy and even promoted to Admiral, surprisingly given that in 1814 he been expelled from the House of Commons, dismissed from the navy, and sentenced to prison for a plot to profit from spreading false rumors about the death of Napoleon. The Birmingham railway was going ahead. Several new steamship records had been set. And Victor Hugo had a new historical novel set in fifteenth-century Paris in which a hunchback named Quasimodo became obsessed with a beautiful witch named Esmerelda. It had not yet been translated into English, but the critics anticipated that it would be just as controversial in London as some of his previous works.

When not reading the newspapers, forcing down a little broth, or bathing himself with a sponge of cold water, Darwin spent most of his time drifting in and out of sleep. He started awake one evening to find Lucy sitting on the edge of the bed. He had been dreaming about her and, only half awake, thought he was still dreaming until she stroked his cheek. She removed her dress and underclothes, slipped into bed, and stretched her body against his. They kissed and she stroked his penis, but even after several minutes he remained entirely flaccid. "Too sick, he giggled," and rested his head against her left breast. She just kissed his hair as he fell back to sleep.

He opened his eyes in the morning with his cheek still resting on her bust, his nose touching the dark brown areola and nipple. He realized as he awoke, trying to focus on the nipple little more than an inch from his right eye, this was the first time ever that he had woken up in bed with any woman. Yet he still could not manage an erection, so Lucy masturbated herself while they kissed and he fondled her breasts while squeezing the nipples between his fingers. After she orgasmed, she dressed and left before Syms brought a breakfast of toast and weak tea.

Lucy returned that evening with a large bottle of laudanum, claiming that the analgesic would revive him. She poured a glass of the reddish-brown tincture and took a sip before passing it to him. The alcohol masked the bitterness of the opium, and he quickly began to feel its effect, a euphoria washing away the pain of the cramps clawing at his guts and the throbbing of his limbs. He lay back in the bed as he felt his head beginning to buzz and Lucy's mouth enfolding his penis. This time he hardened, and Lucy, by now beautifully naked in the candlelight, straddled him to lower herself onto his erection. Afterwards, they shared another glass of laudanum, talked a little about nothing, and slept deeply until dawn. She left the bottle of laudanum by his bedside, a morning sunbeam illuminating the deep reddish-brown liquid with an inner radiance, and promised to return that evening.

He took a sip whenever the pain of the cramps returned and for the first time was able to sit up enough to write. First he wrote Henslow, twenty pages of species lists and detailed descriptions of specimens, geological observations, and instructions for unpacking the casks. "I'm afraid," he wrote to close, "that you will groan, or rather the floor of the storeroom will, when the casks arrive. Without your help I should be utterly undone. Please remember that the smallest cask contains fish; will you open it straight away, to see how the spirit has stood the evaporation of the Tropics?" He left out entirely any comment on his personal experiences, the political situation in Buenos Aires, and his ideas about the origins of species. The closest he came to revealing that he was engaged in anything more than collecting specimens was a postscript request to send, when they were published, the forthcoming volumes of Lyell's *Principles of Geology*: "Perhaps you might mail them to me in Valparaiso, Chile, care of Richard Corfield, a chum from Shrewsbury now resident there." He wanted to share his ideas with Henslow and would once he had worked them out more fully, if ever.

He was trying, and the laudanum, he was convinced, was helping him to think more clearly. But the questions still far outnumbered the insights. Was the *Toxodon*, he puzzled, really somehow the common ancestor of the orders Rodentia, Proboscidea, and Artiodactyla? By merging the features of several extant orders into one extinct species it reminded him of Old Bernantio's mixed up animals. Maybe the story about the epochal war of the animals contained some insight? But why were some of the fossils from Bahia Blanca, like the horse, so similar to ones found in Europe while the current animals of Argentina, such as the ostrich, guanaco, and armadillo, were so different? How could the mutability of species achieve its direction due to some natural mechanism, to the degree that *Toxodon* could have given rise to all the currently living species of Rodentia and Artiodactyla, each perfectly fitted to its conditions? And why where the fossil species so large relative to the current ones: *Macrauchenia patachonica* versus the guanaco, *Megatherium* and *Megalonyx* versus the armadillos? Had some catastrophe indeed occurred, that extirpated the large and spared the small? But, if so, why then would the horse have died out at Bahia Blanca, and throughout the New World? No, if he were right to transfer Lyell's principle of slow, uniform, natural change from geology to biology, then a fossil species must gradually became rare, perhaps over thousands of years, before the last few individuals disappeared entirely. At the same time, a new species must become progressively more common. Yet what was the overall, organizing principle that directed such extinctions and transmutations? He needed something as elegant and general as Lyell's geological principles. But what?

Just as frustrating, Lucy did not fulfill her promise to return. He missed her and worried horribly but dared not ask Syms or Lumb to make inquiries because he feared exposing her to danger. He had wanted to ask her whether Earle had ever arrived in Buenos Aires, or...? He had wanted to ask her what she hoped for herself, and for them...? Each day he planned to call Syms to help him dress and go out to look for her, but he remained so weak that he always gave up on the idea.

Instead, he spent his time sitting up in bed and writing letters. None of the news from home was surprising, and his replies consisted mainly of descriptions of the people and places of Argentina, downplaying the dangerous in favor of the humorous to preempt worries. The second longest letter, after the one to Henslow, went to Emma. She had written to tell him, subtly, that she thought him very brave and that she liked him. He replied that he missed Shropshire and fondly recalled their walks together by the stream, telling her how much he looked forward to seeing her when he returned, how much he looked forward to settling down somewhere close to home. For his father's sake, he did not mention his decision to forgo a career in the Church. And he certainly said nothing of his growing ambition to become a real naturalist like Henslow, even as great a thinker as Lyell or von Humboldt.

By the beginning of November, all his symptoms but some lingering edema had become almost unnoticeable and he felt well enough to go out. He looked for Lucy but did not see her anywhere, not even, as he had before, on the arm of some French officer. In fact, the French were notable only for their absence in Buenos Aires. He also noticed that despite Doña María's campaign of terror against the Unitarios, the Porteños seemed as gay as they had been half a year ago. He saw them enjoying the spring weather during strolls in the Alameda, riding their beautiful horses along the riverbank, and shopping in the street markets. But he did notice that dusk sent them rushing to regain the security of their homes, such as it might be. Darwin followed their example and spent evenings at the hotel.

Only the Mazorca were out at night, and only they seemed to know where Lucy was. One evening, late, just as Lumb and Darwin were finishing their last game of chess, the same agent who had come to take Oribe off the *Beagle*, delivered a thick letter to Darwin. Attached was a smaller envelope inscribed with his name and containing a note: "My Sweet Charley. Please deliver to British Consul. Not safe for me. Until later. L." The Mazorca agent waited until Darwin had read the note before turning and leaving, all without a word.

Coming out of the consulate after doing Lucy's bidding, Darwin met Fitzroy coming in. Any lingering acrimony between the two dissipated at seeing one another again after two months.

The *Beagle*, Fitzroy announced, had just arrived and would be three weeks re-victualating. In the meantime, he would rate the chronometers and draught finished charts to send to the Admiralty and turn over to the Argentinean navy. If that task did not extend beyond the end of November, the *Beagle* would sail for Tierra del Fuego in time to arrive by the summer solstice. He had accomplished much over the preceding fall and winter, surveying the entire coast between the River Plate and the Rio Negro and, for the principal anchorages such as Bahia Blanca, producing detailed charts. Stokes had already surveyed the mouths of the major rivers and other anchorages between the Rio Negro and the Strait of Magellan. So Fitzroy's next priority was to survey Tierra del Fuego. But first, given the hazards they would face in those stormy latitudes, he wanted to ensure that, at a minimum, his work to date would safely reach the Admiralty.

Darwin had already given up all hope of seeing Lucy before the *Beagle* left, so he once again focused on his own work, supervising the transfer of the second shipment of specimens from the *Beagle* to the mail packet. Fitzroy had been correct to force him to reduce the number of crates because even so the captain of the packet was not much pleased with the size of the load. But Henslow, he knew, would nonetheless be much more impressed with it than with the first.

8

THE *BEAGLE* DROPPED ANCHOR in Good Success Bay on Boxing Day, exactly a year after leaving Plymouth. After clearing the mouth of the Rio de la Plata, Chaffers had taken them southward on several broad reaches, staying out of sight of land except for a glimpse of West Falkland Island. Fitzroy had not wanted to approach the Patagonian coast or enter the Strait of Magellan. The previous voyage, under Stokes, had already surveyed the principal bays of southern Patagonia and much of that famous strait. Fitzroy first wanted to concentrate on the largely unknown archipelago to its south. Good Success Bay lay at the eastern apex of the large triangular island of Tierra del Fuego, affording a starting point from which to explore the channels and small islands that stretched westward toward the labyrinthine Pacific entrances of the Strait of Magellan.

Darwin, sick as usual, had missed the entire voyage south. He had bought several bottles of laudanum before leaving Buenos Aires, and recourse to that analgesic had helped—although not enough to spend time on deck even during the Christmas celebrations. Fitzroy had put up prizes for wrestling and sack racing, which the crew competed at with good spirit considering the pitching deck and frequent showers. From his hammock, Darwin could hear them run across the deck, dance, sing, and joke. Occasionally one of the officers would stop by to share a toast, which Darwin promptly surrendered to the bucket. He again felt isolated but was cheered when the news came that the *Beagle* would soon be riding at anchor in a clam bay.

The moment he heard the roaring of the anchor chain, he came on deck to find that the entire crew had gathered at the starboard bulwark to see the Fuegians gathered along the shore. As the *Beagle* had rounded Cape San Diego, dozens of them had followed along the thickly wooded cliffs. They had screamed and shouted all the way to the bay, apparently desperate to trade.

Darwin stationed himself beside York at the main stays to gauge his reaction to this, for him, homecoming. But instead of being joyful,

York seemed agitated. Darwin had brought his telescope and observed that the Indians on shore looked more like Tehuelches than like York.

"They are tall and wear furs," he said to York while continuing to look through the telescope.

"Of course, just as I told you before. They are Aush. Bad like Ona. Better that Captain shoot them than talk to them."

"Ah.... And they are screaming and waving their mantles."

"Of course. They do not have canoes like Yamana. They want us to come ashore to trade. I want to go further west, to home, to Yamana country."

"There are no women or children. Their faces are painted. One has a fillet of white feathers around his brow and two stripes painted on his face. The upper one is chalk white and crosses the eyelids from temple to temple. The other is crimson and goes from ear to ear across the upper lip. Others have blacked faces and bodies, all daubed with white spots. They have spears and bows..., clubs too. All have long, tangled hair. Lord, they look as fierce as devils."

"Of course. If we're not careful they will kill us to steal our things. Do not trust them."

Just then, with a clatter of davits, two whaleboats hit the water. Darwin took the telescope from his eye to see that a party was going ashore to meet with the twenty or so Aush. In one boat, amid the flashing oars, he could see Fuegia, presumably along as a translator, sitting next to Fitzroy in the sheets. In the other were Beareley and some of his marines.

The backdrop to the scene differed astoundingly from the semiarid steppes of Patagonia or, indeed, from any place Darwin had ever been. Forest cloaked the low, rounded mountains that enclosed the greenish gray water of the placid bay, the trees descending right to a beach that was the only open land in sight. There the Aush had built a smoky fire, more to attract attention than to provide warmth, suspected Darwin, because they had taken off their fur mantles and were waving them and shouting at Fitzroy's boat as it approached. Their big, wolfish dogs added to the cacophony. The white smoke rose to blend into the veils of cloud that drifted among the treetops on the slope above.

At first the meeting seemed a confusion of shouts and gesticulations, but when Fitzroy began to hand out strips of scarlet cloth, the Aush became preoccupied with tying them around their necks. Only Fitzroy and Sullivan had left the boats at first, but once the Aush had been thus calmed, Fuegia approached to interpret. A great patting of body parts ensued. First the Aush patted their own chests and upper arms. Then they patted those of Fitzroy and Sullivan. At that contact, Beareley and the marines came up the beach and the meeting lapsed into trading furs for an assortment of cloth, beads, and copper medallions. Fitzroy had had them struck especially for the voyage and had proudly shown them off to Darwin when still in Plymouth: on one side, the figure of Britannia with "King William" and "Britannic Majesty" around the rim; on the other side, "H.M.S. *Beagle*."

When Darwin described what he was seeing through the glass to York, the Yamana spat over the bulwark and dismissed the Aush as being without a real language. "How can she be expected to talk to them if they do not have real talk? They're more like monsters than men."

"Now they are holding one hand to their mouths and sawing at it with the other."

"They are pretending to eat meat with knives. They want to trade for knives. Or to steal them!"

When Fitzroy returned he announced that they would stay for several days to put the ship in order after the passage and to rate the chronometers. Once further east, in his experience, Yamana with canoes would plague them constantly so he wanted to take advantage of this relative peace. The Aush, lacking canoes, could shout themselves hoarse but could not approach the *Beagle*. Fitzroy nonetheless told Beareley to post extra sentries while the carpenter and boatswain set their crews bustling about their many tasks.

The Aush persisted with their smoky fires and shouts for two days. Then they left, melting into the forest so quietly that Darwin wondered if he had imagined them. He scanned the beach repeatedly but only the smoldering fires remained.

The next morning he again scanned the entire scene carefully and repeatedly. When he had decided the Aush must have decamped the area, he asked for permission to climb one of the mountains to gain a view. Surprisingly, Fitzroy immediately blessed the plan and ordered the jolly boat to take Darwin and Syms ashore.

"You might try that one," he recommended while pointing to the slope that rose from the nearby headland. "It is not uninteresting in being the one Banks himself climbed. That's right, Mister Dahwin, Captain Cook anchored here and sent Joseph Banks up there to collect alpine plants. Banks took his assistant, Dr. Solander, and their servants, two black fellows. Banks and Solander became so preoccupied with collecting that they did not notice that the weather had turned cold. When the snow flurries began, though, they realized they had best return so looked about for the servants. They soon found them passed out in the open. They had been carrying the preserving spirits, you see, and when it became cold, which given their tropical constitutions they felt in proportionately greater degree, they took a few sips to warm themselves. Then a few more sips and a few more, and before long, stupefied, they lay down in the heather right on the mountaintop. No amount of entreatment or threat would budge the two or even, apparently, wake them. With dark not far off, Banks and Solander could not hope to carry the servants down the mountain, so they rolled them under some shrubs and returned to the *Endeavour*. The next morning the Negroes were both found dead, completely stiff and cold. So enjoy yourself, old boy! Take guns. Watch for savages. And watch the weather. It's not unknown for these mountains to get snow even in summer. Cook was here in January, you know, and we wouldn't want a repeat of that tragedy, eh?"

The forest began where the narrow sandy beach ended. Most of the trees were *Fagus betuloides*. A tiny minority of other species of beech and Winter's bark provided little variety, although the latter's wrinkled, green bark, a passable antiscorbutic, gave it a visual presence beyond its numbers. Below the canopy, the forest was so gloomy, dank, and cool that only fungi and moss seemed to flourish. The sole sound came from a woodpecker that they never saw. York had refused to come, claiming that the Aush might still be lurking and would try to kill him. So Darwin and Syms alone climbed up the ravine that seemed the most likely path to the summit. A jumble of tree trunks, so large that they must have lived centuries before falling and partially shattering on the forest floor, choked the ravine. In places they formed barricades, in others bridges up to ten feet wide. Several times when traversing a trunk, Darwin had a leg sink to the knee in moldering wood and, fearful of a fall that would certainly cripple him, and perhaps even kill him, he fell forward to hug the trunk until he could extract himself.

By noon the two of them had emerged from the forest gloom onto a ridge covered in stunted trees and patches of sphagnum moss. Once though that alpine zone, having had to struggle calve-deep through the sphagnum and the wind-gnarled, prostrate beeches, the summit of bare rock yielded a view worthy of the climb.

Below, the *Beagle* floated in the bay like a toy in a bath. Beyond, a swell wrinkled the northern reaches of the polar sea. In either direction, irregular chains of low mountains alternated with steep-sided valleys that descended to the sea and blended into inlets. Nowhere did level ground of any extent occur. The whole gave the impression of a mountain range being submerged by the sea, with isolated peaks becoming islands and valleys becoming inlets. Everywhere trees cloaked the land, except where they gave way to rock and ice at the highest elevations or where, in the valleys, waterlogging forced the forest to yield to bog. The leaves of the beeches, though evergreen, had a yellowish brown tinge that colored the nearer slopes. The more distant ones receded into shades of blue and purple, piebald with patches of persistent snow. Scudding clouds constantly obscured one vista and opened another.

At this latitude, just past the summer solstice, light remained until nearly midnight and began to return again at four in the morning. So, unhurriedly, Darwin began to collect the several species of small alpine plants around the summit, most of them bryophytes. He lay on his stomach on a slab of rock with his face close to a carpet of reddish lantern moss and used a hand lens to observe how the rhizoids penetrated the minutest cracks. He was certain that Banks would have collected this species, its capsules arranged in four segments like tiny Chinese lanterns, but could not resist doing so again while imagining how the great botanist had sprawled out on his stomach in the very same spot.

In the meantime, Syms had spotted a solitary guanaco silhouetted along the crest of a neighboring ridge. He tried to work his way close enough to take a shot, creeping from stunted tree to stunted tree along the saddle that connected the ridges. The guanaco remained absolutely motionless until Syms was within two hundred yards. Then it turned its head away, as if consulting with unseen companions on the other side of the ridge. Soon two other guanacos appeared, and the three stood observing Syms for a full minute before disappearing over the crest. Their neighing, like derisive laugher, floated down to where Syms crouched behind a gnarled beech. Within half an hour he saw a long column of guanaco unhurriedly ascending the flank of a distant ridge.

Darwin and Syms met where they had first emerged from the forest just as a heavy rain began and were glad to once again be underneath the gloomy but sheltering canopy. They slipped and slid down the mossy logs and, although the descent was less strenuous than the ascent, arrived back at the beach aching and bruised.

York's fear that some of the Aush still lingered proved correct. They were waiting right where Darwin and Syms emerged from the forest. None of the three were less than six feet and seemed even bigger because of their bulky capes and hats of guanaco hide. Spears, bows, and quivers full of stone-headed arrows bristled from the group. Fierce looking clubs hung from belts, ready to use in an instant.

Darwin literally stepped out of the forest and came face to face with the three. They immediately began to speak, their hands held out palm upward. Cook, Darwin recalled, had not believed the Aush to posses a real language because it sounded more like throat clearing than anything else. But if that dismissive conclusion were correct, he now thought, that throat clearing included the most amazing string of gutturals and clicks. He responded by holding his own hand out and saying, slowly and with great enunciation, "Good afternoon. We are pleased to meet you."

His words echoed back at him, simultaneously repeated by the three Aush: "Good afternoon. We are p'eased to meet you."

This mimicry continued for several cycles, but while Darwin began to feel more at ease, it did not really result in any effective communication.

Fitzroy had sent a boat with some marines under Sergeant Beareley's command, though. And, after distracting the Aush with some gifts of copper medallions, the marines escorted Darwin and Syms to the boat and back aboard the *Beagle*. The Aush gave neither protest nor thanks, merely remaining at the edge of the forest, inspecting their medallions and pointing at the *Beagle*.

With the *Beagle* once again shipshape, Fitzroy ordered a slow cruise westward. He intended to survey the islands and channels of the archipelago that stretched along the south coast of Tierra del Fuego, separated from it by the channel that Stokes had named after the *Beagle*. The Anglican mission would be established upon reaching Woollya Bay, on the western side of Windhond Island. The Fuegians and Matthews were anxious to do so as soon as possible, as was Fitzroy, but he did not feel comfortable subordinating his official mission to that personal desire.

The Dutch had been the first Europeans to sail these waters, and not much had changed in the two hundred years since they had named Windhond Island. Each bay and cove surveyed had its domed wigwams, many in this season stripped of their coverings, the owners having moved west to the sealing grounds on the outer islands. The many middens, great heaps of mollusk shells, signaled one of the principal sources of sustenance available among the inner islands. In winter those who had gone sealing would return to harvest the renewed shellfish stocks and hunt the guanaco that came down to the shore of the *Beagle* Channel from the snowed-in mountains.

As the *Beagle* had left Aush country behind, Yamana began to light fires on every point to attract attention and spread the news that strangers had come to trade. Canoes began to form a halo around the

Beagle. Each had two or three couples and their children squatting on their hams, all absolutely naked except for the odd sealskin thrown over a shoulder or tied around a waist. Like the Aush, the Yamana painted their faces and bodies with white and red or black. Necklaces of trade beads and shells adorned the necks and wrists of the women. The canoes, made of pieces of beach bark sewn together with gut and held open in the middle with wooden thwarts, all had fires burning in them. A bed of moist sand prevented the fire burning through the bottom and also provided ballast. The dogs were much smaller than those of the Aush, about the size of fox terriers, but just as ill natured and quarrelsome. Each canoe had at least two or three, continuously running from bow to stern and threatening, but never quite achieving, a capsize.

The constant cry of the Yamana was, "Yammarschooner, yammarschooner, yammarschooner," which according to York meant, "Give me." The hands held out, palms upward, while others held up fish for Rowlett's inspection confirmed that translation. Whenever the occupants of a canoe had run out of fish, they would retreat with their haul of glass beads, copper buttons, and strips of brightly colored flannel to catch more fish, either with long spears tipped with bone points or lines of seal gut baited with fishtails.

The crew welcomed the fresh fish, and the distraction in general, especially when one of the women was young. The scant clothing gave full view of firm breasts and buttocks, and even of dark pubic hair between soft, rounded thighs. Fitzroy quelled the lechery as much as possible but with a measure of pragmatism. When a canoe interfered with the man in the bow casting the sounding lead, though, Old Hot Coffee boiled over. Finally, after much screaming and arm waving, he assigned York and Jeremy the task of keeping canoes away from the bow. The two would stand on the forecastle and shout insults down at their brethren, with much obvious glee.

Fitzroy, not in the mood for unnecessary delays, would not allow Darwin to go ashore again, a great regret after having enjoyed the freedom of Fossil Point for so long. But at least placid weather released him from his hammock. He ate dinner daily with Fitzroy again, even though the captain was so preoccupied with the survey that he barely spoke. And when he did, he would only worry that they must get more done while this weather lasted, because he knew it would not, or Beaufort at the Admiralty would be disappointed with him. Darwin, for his part, made the most of his confinement aboard during calm weather by spending considerable time on deck trading with the Yamana for plants and animals.

On one occasion, he had a boy dive to the bottom to release one of the numerous giant kelp. Sailors hailed it as a reliable indicator of a shoaling, hard bottom because the maximum depth it grew in was about twenty fathoms and its holdfast, what passed for the roots, could only attach to rock. He and Syms hauled on the rope the boy had tied around the holdfast until the entire plant stretched along the deck from the break of the forecastle to the wheel, about sixty feet. MacCormick came over and pointed out that *Macrocystis pyrifera* was already well described by several naturalists before turning his back. Boatswain Sorrell hovered as usual whenever something dirtied the deck.

But Darwin, busy marveling at the elegance of the design that allowed the kelp not just to survive but also to thrive in these cold waters, hardly noticed MacCormick or Sorrell. The plant on deck was only one of hundreds that he could see floating near the *Beagle*, the canopy of a virtual underwater forest. Along the central trunk, or stipe, as thick as his arm, small bulbs buoyed the plant, each such bladder with a frond growing from its distal side. The rubbery tissue of the stipe and fronds was a translucent brownish green, although all but the section that had been floating on the surface was so encrusted with corallines as to be white. In fact, a whole community of organisms inhabited the plant. Simple hydra-like polypi and beautiful compound Ascidiae lived in delicate structures along the stipe. He had Syms remove a small adult anemone that had miniatures of itself budding around its base. Various uncovered mollusks, patelliform shells, bivalves, and trochi quickly filled the specimen jars. At the bottom end, near the forecastle, the holdfast was damaged where the boy had cut and torn it to release the grip on a rock. But as Darwin gripped the stipe and shook the holdfast, a large pile of small fish, shells, cuttlefish, crabs, sea-eggs, starfish, Holuthuriae, Planariae, and crawling nereidous animals of a multitude of forms accumulated on the deck.

After he had sketched the general configuration and the details of the kelp, Darwin ordered Syms to dump it overboard. As the last of the fronds slipped over the bulwark, Sorrel bustled over with a crew to swab up the mess, and Darwin reflected that MacCormick only continued to confirm himself to be a fool. Naturalists had not by far fully described the intricacies of *Macrocystis pyrifera* and certainly not its many colonists. The organisms shaken out of the holdfast alone would occupy him for a week. And more than that, natural history had a much broader scope than the description of individual species. Without the kelp, all the organisms that lived upon it would disappear and with them the otters, seals, cormorants, and porpoises that constituted the web of living things along the shores of Tierra del Fuego. And without that marine bounty, the Fuegians would no doubt disappear as well.

And that, thought Darwin, would be assured given that the primitive condition of the Fuegians placed them at nature's whim. Whenever he handed down some trinket in exchange for a specimen, the Yamana in the canoe would so marvel at it that Darwin recalled Bougainville's observation: "Ils traitent les chefs-d'oeuvre de l'industrie humaine comme ils traitent les loix de la nature et ses phénomènes." And that inability to differentiate between the works of humanity and those of nature, thought Darwin, ensured that savages were unable to exert any control over nature except the most basic use of fire or crude mantles to keep off the cold. But, as the differences between York, Fuegia, and Jeremy and their wild cousins demonstrated so vividly, after just a little schooling, the power of improvement among savages was vastly greater than among animals.

Whenever Matthews seemed discouraged about his mission, Darwin would emphasize exactly that potential for the Fuegians to learn how to escape the clutches of unadulterated nature. Once, on a miserably cold day, they stood at the taffrail looking down at a canoe containing a woman suckling a newborn. The sleet melted on her naked breasts and baby. Matthews despaired that, "They all seem stunted in growth,

161

their faces hideous, their naked skin filthy, their hair tangled, their voices discordant, their gestures violent.... I can hardly believe them kin to Fuegia, Jeremy, and York. I can hardly, in fact, believe them kin to any Men anywhere."

Darwin replied quietly but forcefully, having long thought out his logic on this issue. "We despair at their condition, Richard, because we see what is possible relative to what is, and the gulf between those two conditions is so vast. Yet the distance between savage and civilized Man only seems greater than that between a wild and domesticated animal because of Man's much greater power of improvement. Look at York. Look at Fuegia and Jeremy. You have much potential to work with, and God will be there to help you."

MacCormick, of course, did his best to encourage Matthews's self-doubts. To prove that Fuegians had an inherently savage character that no amount of tutelage could overcome, he induced several of them aboard every day to record their phrenology. One day he insisted that Matthews and Darwin look at the observations he had just written in his notebook.

"23 Jan. Nassau Bay, T. del Fuego. Male, some 35 yrs. of age. Clr. is reddish brn., between that of rusty iron and clean copper, rather darker than the latter, yet not so dark as good old mahogany, very similar to the Devonshire breed of cattle."

A listing of the man's phrenological characteristics filled the remainder of the page:

> The Properties
> > *Amativeness—full.*
> > *Philoprogenitiveness—moderately full.*
> > *Concentrativeness—ditto.*
> > *Adhesiveness—full.*
> > *Combativeness—large.*
> > *Destructiveness—very large.*
> > *Constructiveness—small.*
> > *Secretiveness—large.*

The Sentiments
  Self-esteem—moderately small.
  Love of approbation—large.
  Cautiousness—very large.
  Benevolence—small.
  Firmness—moderately full.
  Veneration—small.
  Hope—ditto.
  Ideality—ditto.
  Conscientiousness—ditto.

The Intellectual Organs
  Individuality—small.
  Time—ditto.
  Tune—ditto.
  Comparison—ditto.
  Witt—ditto.
  Form—very small.
  Number—very small.
  Language—full.
  Causality—small.
  Innovation—ditto.

Darwin glanced at the preceding pages and saw that each de-scribed a man, woman, or child in the same systematic, highly organ-ized, manner. He felt his forehead beginning to furrow in irritation, his jaw tensing, but before he could say anything, MacCormick began to browbeat Matthews

"You simply must collect as much of this sort of data as you can. It will increase our understanding of the savage mind and, of great import to your reputation, will help excuse the eventual failure of your mission."

Before Matthews could collect himself, Darwin interjected: "Come now, sir. Just observe how much York has improved, how far above his fellows he is in every intellectual trait."

"Indubitably a very temporary improvement, laddie. I was serving on the *Beagle*, you'll recall, whilst that savage first set foot aboard. And I attest that the shape of his head has not changed a wit since then. And not all the schooling in the world will do so. Any seeming improvement in his intellect reflects simple mimicry and cannot therefore be permanent. In fact, my phrenological observations and impartial considerations over many years force me to the conclusion that, according to their bodily organization, they are incapable of so high a degree of intellectual development as the Caucasian race. And there you have it. Our three Fuegians' seeming improvements are the result merely of the undeniable imitative talents of their race."

Fitzroy, who had approached unobserved, interrupted before Darwin could respond. "M'Cohmick, I'll give you this much," he said as the others fell silent and awaited what they knew from his tone would be a long pontification, "it seems not unlikely that here, at the ends of the earth, one would find Man existing in a lower state of improvement than any other place. And, in fact, I can think of no other race quite so base. The Esquimaux enjoys at least some of the comforts of life while snug in his subterranean hut. In his kayak, when fully equipped, he might be said to manifest much skill in his arctic home. The tribes of southern Africa, prowling about in search of roots, and living concealed on the wild and arid plains, are sufficiently wretched but not so much as the naked Fuegian in his wigwam. Of the two races inhabiting the Pacific, the South Sea Islanders are comparatively civilized, with a measure of religious development. It is the other Pacific race, the Australian aborigine, who in his simplicity regarding the arts of life comes nearest the Fuegian in debasement. The Australian, however, can at least boast of his boomerang, his spear and throwing stick, his method of climbing trees, and that of tracking animals. By comparison, the Fuegian's canoe, his most ingenious work, poor as it is, has remained the same since Drake described it two hundred and fifty years ago. And that is not unremarkable given that the Fuegians have in the interim had the example of our boats to copy from to improve their own—but have not. Their skill in matters of acquirements, then, in some respects, is little different than the instincts of animals, for it improves with experience only through great effort on the part of the teacher, as we have demonstrated with our Fuegians. Only then is the spark of religion lit within them."

"But that, gentlemen," he continued with his lecture, raising his voice and glaring at MacCormick alone, "is exactly why we are founding this mission! And that is why it will be a difficult and lengthy process! And that is why, like all things worth doing, we must put our all into it and behind Matthews here!"

As the group dispersed without a further word, Matthews's morale substantially reinvigorated and MacCormick's dislike for Fitzroy even more indurated, Darwin noticed that York had overheard the entire discussion. He approached the Fuegian where he rested against the mizzenmast and began to apologize on MacCormick's behalf. York forestalled any apology, though, by laughing: "These peop'e are not like mine at all, Char'es." He pointed toward the canoes that circled the *Beagle*. "Go look. They are filthy animals and thieves and murderers. My peop'e are much different. They are like me. You will see when we reach Woollya." Then he returned to the forecastle to help Jeremy shout insults down at any canoe that got too close the bows.

Darwin thought Woollya Bay the prettiest place he had yet seen in Tierra del Fuego. A row of small islands spanned the mouth, breaking the weather coming in off the sound. Inland, beech forest covered the low mountains that enclosed a few tens of acres of relatively level meadowland, a rarity anywhere south of the pampas. The dull, brownish beech foliage only made the green of the grassy meadows seem even brighter and more reminiscent of the fields of Shropshire. Once ashore, he saw that colorful wildflowers sprinkled the banks of the small creeks that meandered down to the shore.

Only twenty or so wigwam frames, the coverings removed to expose the bare poles, indicated that people had ever inhabited Woollya. But York, with whom Darwin came ashore, claimed that it had been the site of the large permanent village that his grandparents remembered from before smallpox. Now a much smaller winter village, the tribe was away for a summer of hunting seals in the western islands.

While Fitzroy and Matthews reconnoitered for a site to build the mission house, York showed Darwin the abandoned fishing weirs. They were in ruins, marked by only a few rows of stones across a creek, but Darwin could immediately see how they would have been used to catch fish like mullet and smelt when they swam up the creek at high tide. When intact, the low walls would have nearly spanned the channel, with no more than narrow openings left at midstream. The tops of the walls would have been a few feet under water at high tide, allowing the fish to pass. As the tide fell and the tops of the walls emerged, a net of gut placed across the opening in the wall furthest downstream would allow water to escape back to the sea but prevent fish from doing so. Other nets, placed successively across openings in the upstream walls, would have prevented retreat in that direction and trapped the fish in shallow water between the walls. York's ancestors would easily have been able to scoop them onto the banks. A clever arrangement, thought Darwin, but one that would have required more work to build and maintain than simply dropping a baited line over the side of a canoe. Cleary, to Darwin, the population of Woollya had once been great enough to make worthwhile such an investment of labor—but no longer was.

York next showed Darwin the potato gardens his grandparents had spoken of, a hummocky area near the creek.

"No one bothers with them anymore," York commented. "Not enough peop'e to bother with all that digging."

Skeptical that the Fuegians were capable of agriculture, or ever had been, Darwin said nothing but poked around with his knife trying to find any evidence of an old garden. Certainly, he thought while digging deeper, the indigenes of the Americas did in places have agriculture. But he had never heard of such developments so far south. According to von Humboldt, even the great Aztec and Incan civilizations, with their well-developed agriculture and large cities, were without doubt indebted to the tutelage of some wandering tribe of Israelites or Nabataens. But it seemed unlikely that those itinerant ancients, carrying with them the agricultural and architectural arts, would have wandered so far south, certainly not to the very southern tip of the New World.

In confirmation, Darwin detected no relict tubers to indicate potatoes had ever grown in the mounds, despite their dark, loamy soil appearing to be extremely fertile. Probably, he thought, York had merely mentally transposed the agriculture he had seen in England to his home at Woollya. But Darwin, seeing no profit in refuting his Yamana friend, said nothing as they wandered back to the shore where a vast pile of gear was accumulating.

Fitzroy planned to spend as little time as possible constructing the mission. By dusk of the first day at Woollya, he had selected a site for the mission about a half-mile from the shore on the banks of a creek of sweet water. He had had a camp of new wigwams established to house the crew that would build Matthews's house. And he had had the pile of goods transferred ashore. The Church Missionary Society had provided Matthews with all necessary tools, hardware, seeds, guns and, of course, bibles. Some of the society's crates also contained donations from the generous but poorly informed, and the seamen laughed at the whalebone corsets and beaver hats, crystal wine goblets and lacquered tea trays, cotton bed sheets and sterling sugar bowls that they carried up to the newly scythed grass of the mission site.

By the next afternoon, dozens of canoes were streaming into Woollya Bay. More than a hundred Yamana men gathered around the mission site to trade while the women and children built wigwams near the shore. Before long, the Yamana had begun to interfere with the construction. The carpenters were trying to cut logs into planks but could barely pull their saws because of the Yamana clustering at their elbows. They asked for everything and when ignored tried to purloin what they could. When Fitzroy posted marines to protect the carpenters, a group of Yamana would so bedevil a sentry that one could sneak a hand into his pocket to filch a knife.

Fitzroy, impatient with the nuisance, ordered the marines to use stakes and a one-inch rope to set up a fence around the worksite. With the aid of that demarcation and much shouting and pushing, the marines managed to keep the crowd at bay. The Yamana nonetheless squatted on their hams just outside the rope. Occasionally, as if to test the marine's stamina, someone bolder than the rest would rise and try to cross the rope. One man, his way firmly blocked by the red coat, white cross belts, and musket of a sentry, spat in his face. The marine, under firm orders from Sergeant Beareley, stood his ground but did not retaliate. The Yamana, frustrated and angry, stalked off toward the wigwams, occasionally turning to shout and gesticulate.

York, Fuegia, and Jeremy had initially disappeared among the Yamana wigwams. They went to search out relatives but found only few and distant. Their immediate families were off sealing and would not return for another month or two, depending on the weather. Barely recognized by their own tribe, the three returned disgruntled to the mission.

The mission house quickly took shape during the first week at Woollya, as did the adjoining garden. The days were dry and warm, and the nights were short. The carpenters raised a frame of poles on a foundation of large trunks and then clad it in rough-cut planks. The missionary society had provided windows and doors, stove and tin sink, furniture, and an iron cross to grace the peak of the roof. A cellar underneath the planked floor provided storage for the less useful donations.

The garden occupied the slope north of the house to take best advantage of the limited sun. Matthews induced two young Yamana men to dig the garden in exchange for some rosaries, and he thereby thought himself well begun on his work at Woollya. Darwin had not seen him so positive in weeks. Pinoi and Lukka, the two young men, still adolescents really, became Pin and Lucas to the carpenter's crew. And around the seamen's fire they laughed uproariously at the nightly signing and dancing.

Under Matthews's direction, Pin and Lucas worked hard at the garden. They dug the stones from the clayey soil and mixed in sand from the beach and tilled until they had a seedbed that Matthews judged acceptable. Then he showed them how to plant the eyes of potatoes and the seeds of carrots, turnips, beans, peas, lettuce, leeks, and cabbages. With Fuegia acting as translator, he explained how the seeds would become plants that could be harvested and stored for use throughout the winter.

The evening after the planting, Pin related his thoughts on the garden around the fire. Partially with Fuegia's help but mainly by way of pantomime, he explained that he had no need to store vegetables to eat in the winter because plenty of food was available all year. When there were no seals, then there were otters; when no fish, then clams; when no berries, then mushrooms. And when none of those foods were available, they could kill and devour the old women. At that point, Fuegia refused to translate anymore, and Pin's miming became even more animated and explicit. The gist seemed to be that the Yamana killed their grandmothers, and perhaps the grandfathers as well, by holding their faces in the smoke of the wigwam fire to suffocate them. Pin first imitated their cries and death struggles, and then he imitated carving, roasting, and eating what seemed to be considered the choicest cuts, namely breasts, bellies, hands and feet.

By the pantomime's end, Fuegia and Jeremy had left the fireside and York was laughing. Everyone else seemed struck dumb at the horror of killing one's own grandparents in their own wigwam and then roasting them over their own hearth. Darwin supposed that Fuegia and Jeremy had left in embarrassment at the bestial state of their still wild cousins. Later he asked York why he had laughed, but the only answer was an inscrutable question: "Remember story about Okoko and matches?"

The next morning, all the women and children were gone from the Yamana wigwams. A few of the men continued to hang around the mission site, squatting just outside the rope. Most of the rest took to the bay in their canoes, spearing fishing and trying to trade with the *Beagle*.

Worried, Fitzroy asked York what had happened, but he did not know. He claimed that none of the Yamana confided in him because they thought him more English than Yamana. The best he could guess was that his people thought the English to be demons in search of women and children to abduct, since they seemed to lack any of their own.

After another two days, though, all the remaining Yamana left, seemingly tired of the lack of trade. Even Pin and Lucas left with their rosaries. Matthews was torn between disappointment and relief.

Relief seemed to prevail, though, because when the *Beagle* left he seemed happy and content to have a manageable flock of two for the time being: Fuegia and Jeremy.

York would accompany Wickham, Darwin, and eight men in the cutter to survey the Beagle Channel, discovered during the previous voyage under Stokes. Fitzroy had seen both ends of the channel on that voyage and believed that York might well be correct in claiming that they were connected by a long, narrow, navigable strait that he called the Mountain-Valley Channel. To risk the *Beagle* by sailing against the prevailing westerly wind in such a confined strait would be foolhardy, though. So Fitzroy intended to take the *Beagle* around the outer coast and rendezvous with the cutter at tiny Delta Island, near the western entrance of the Beagle Channel. York would take Syms's place as Darwin's assistant and act as pilot on the cutter.

Before leaving, Darwin visited a last time with Matthews, who had convinced himself that the Fuegians were no worse than he had expected. Rather than worry so much, he had resolved to trust in the instructions of the Church Missionary Society: "You must never lose sight of the great theological principle laid down in the sixth article of the Church of England: 'The Holy Scripture containeth all things necessary to salvation; so that whatsoever is not read therein, nor may be proved thereby, is not to be required of any man that it should be believed as an article of the faith, or be thought requisite or necessary to salvation.'"

The cutter entered the Beagle Channel and headed westward. Even though the lug rig eased sailing against the wind in the confined channel, little more than a mile wide, contrary tides often necessitated recourse to the oars. The expedition thus proceeded slowly, surveying the main capes and bays by charting a series of connected triangles. The main channel was so deep and the shores so bluff that sounding did not seem worthwhile except for those bays that seemed to offer anchorages large enough for a ship.

The straightness, the constant width, and the precipitous bounding mountains of the channel all reminded Darwin of the Lochness Valley, albeit a submerged version. Most of the peaks rose to more than two thousand feet, with an occasional giant rearing up to twice that height. Perpetual snow and ice cloaked their upper slopes. The many cataracts of melt water descended through the mid slopes of barren rock and the dense beech forests of the lower slopes to cascade into the channel. Separating the ice from the rock and the rock from the forest were perfectly horizontal and parallel snow- and timberlines. In some places, glaciers pushed all the way down to the sea, chunks calved from their faces carpeting the channel with miniature icebergs of beryl blue and white. The ice carried the rock it had ground from the mountains down to the sea, depositing everything from fine clay to large boulders at the coastline. Cliffs that the tides had carved from such glacial deposits now stood well above the reach of the sea, which Darwin took as more evidence confirming gradual terrestrial emergence and Lyell's general principles of geology. Along the forested shore, the Yamana lit fires to spread the news that strangers were in the channel. The smoke would first appear as a thin blue line, but as the cutter approached, the Fuegians would feed green boughs into the flames, and the smoke would billow into a dense white cloud that rose until it fragmented and became lost among the ragged clouds that loitered among the treetops. These Yamana, according to York, were the Yahgashagolumoala, meaning those who lived along the Mountain-Valley Channel. The same scene continued day-by-day, emerging out of the gray distance ahead and disappearing into the gray distance astern.

The Yamana canoes that would follow them during the day, at times at a distance, at other times too close for comfort, would by dusk weary of their fruitless quest for trade goods. Wickham would then order the cutter to pull for the nearest quiet cove to camp for the night. At the bottoms of many coves, the loads of mud, sand, and gravel that glaciers had been dumping into this channel for millennia formed beaches that served as pleasant campsites. Currents and surf had somewhat sorted the sediments on the beaches, and usually a flat stretch of sand provided a soft site to pitch the tents just below the precipitous, forested slope that rose inland. The two trapezoidal sails served to keep off the frequent drizzle. Darwin shared the smaller, mizzen-sail with Wickham and a pile of gear. York and the eight seamen shared the mainsail. They kept a careful, armed watch throughout the night, taking warning from the theft of the boat during the previous voyage.

Darwin enjoyed the expedition up the Beagle Channel more than any other experience since arriving in Tierra del Fuego. His stomach did much better in the cutter than aboard the *Beagle*. The weather was cool and damp but not freezing. And the beaches provided endless interest for a naturalist. In all, he thought the trip the finest present for the twenty-fourth birthday he celebrated two days after departing Woollya.

While the crew set up the camp, Darwin would wander the bands of shell, kelp, and wood fragments cast up by recent tides. Most of the shells were clams and mussels, but he also found the occasional wrinkled oyster or gastropod spiral. Later he would examine his finds by the warmth of the fire, its fragrant smoke curling up into the trees, while York told a Yamana story.

"Long ago," went one such tale that particularly struck Darwin, "moon fell into sea and made waters rise in great foaming wave that covered near'y all land. Water rushed to and fro drowning all animals, ripping up all trees, and carving deep valleys throughout land. At end of one month, only small island was left above water. Peop'e living there could see nothing but water all about for many month. Then moon slow'y rose out of sea and waters began to retreat and uncover land. Peop'e and p'ants and animals spread out from island until they had again occupied all land. To this day moon continues to cause sea to rush back and forth over edges of land twice each day. Perhaps one day it will once again cause another f'ood that covers all land."

The parallels with the Biblical account of the Flood were strikingly clear. Wickham and the rest of the men commented on as much.

Darwin himself kept quiet, thinking about how the cove in which they were camped indicated both submergence and emergence of the land. The promontory that guarded the entrance had two wave-cut notches, both now far above sea level, each indicating where the tides had carved away the rock for many millennia. And the cove must have been carved by a glacier that filled it when sea level was much lower. He knew the cove must have formed before the wave-cut notches, which indicated that, relative to the land, the sea must once have been much lower, then rose, and then fell again to its current level, still far above its level when a glacier filled the cove. How that might have happened he was not sure but looked forward to consulting Lyell once aboard the *Beagle* again. In any case, the evidence before him suggested a more complex geological history than either Genesis or the Yamana tale.

Everyone on the expedition grew so used to their idyllic camps that they grew careless. One morning, most of the men were finishing up breakfast around a fire of driftwood about fifty yards up the beach, where the steep slope of smooth black cobbles gave way to a sandy flat. Two promontories guarded the entrance of the small cove, cliffs of black rock footed by glacial moraines of boulders. At dusk the day before, the beach tucked behind the eastern promontory had seemed the perfect campsite. The cliff and a small patch of stunted beech forest eking out an existence among the boulders of the moraine at its foot provided the backdrop to the breakfast fire. Two of the men—the Welsh cook, Jonathan Ley, who had bored the peephole in Fuegia's cabin, and Williams, one of the boatswain's mates—had already finished eating and were stowing the stove and provisions in the cutter.

Those still washing down their breakfasts with coffees around the fire were looking beyond where the cutter was pulled well up onto the beach. Half a mile away, at the end of the cove, a glacier flowing from the peak above terminated in a cliff of ice over a hundred feet high. It must once have reached the moraine behind the campsite and even yet continued to make it a cold place to sleep. Now the glacier seemed to be in retreat, with blocks of ice that had calved from its perpendicular wall of blue and white ice floating in the cove. A few small blocks had fallen during breakfast, to the cheers of those around the fire, each miniature iceberg sending up a spout of water before bobbing to the surface and floating like an insignificant scion at the foot of its giant parent.

Just as the latest cheer went up, nearly the entire leading edge of the ice cliff broke away with a crack like thunder, plunging into the sea, sending a sheet of foaming water aloft and an enormous smooth wave surging across the cove. As the wave reached Ley and Williams, it curled up into an enormous breaker, picking up the cutter like a toy, the two men like dolls, smashing them onto the cobbles, and washing the shattered remains into the cove.

Those around the fire had leaped to their feet as the icy water surged up the steep beach to within a few feet of where they stood, expending its final fury on the sand berm behind which they had built the fire to keep it out of the wind. As the echoes of crashing ice and water reverberated across the cove and its surface surged back and forth in ever decreasing crests, Darwin and the rest stood frozen in awe and horror. He felt a warm wetness and realized he had urinated in fear. Of Ley and Williams he could see nothing. The cutter and all its gear had disappeared into the cove.

As the immediate danger subsided, Wickham and the other eight assessed the degree of their bad luck, consequences of their carelessness, and chances for surviving long enough for the *Beagle* to find them. Nearly nothing of their original fortnight's provisions remained. Everyone had his firearm and knife and the few items not yet loaded into the cutter such as some tin cups, the billycan, and an axe. Everything else had disappeared along with the cutter, Ley, and Williams. The rendezvous date remained three days off, and Fitzroy would probably not search for them right away. At minimum they needed to survive for a week in this cove. Several miniscule rivulets flowed down the cliff and lost themselves among the boulders and stunted beeches of the footslope but had provided enough water for coffee and would suffice indefinitely for the nine of them. Driftwood was plentiful and dry enough for fires. Beech boughs and leaves would make for snug wigwams, Fuegian style. The only real problem was food.

After looking around and noting the absence of any animal, even sea birds, Wickham turned to York, who was whittling something from a piece of driftwood.

"No Yamana will come to trade here because this is neutral land, between two tribes of Mountain-Valley Channel. But as soon as tide falls, we have p'enty of food. I show you how to make c'am rakes and baskets."

The seamen, all handy at whittling, readily copied the clam rake that York made from several pieces of wood. Once done, he showed them how to weave baskets from beech withes.

By the time the equipment was ready and stomachs were rumbling, the tide was beginning to fall. In pairs, the men, with a watchful eye on the ice cliff even though they could never out run another wave, spread out along the beach where the cobbles gave way to a muddy flat. One of the pair would pull the rake through the top few inches of mud to catch the clams on the tines; the other would scrape them into the basket and periodically rinse the mud off in the retreating surf.

Within an hour, the four pairs of men had gathered hundreds of clams and brought them up to the cooking pit York had dug in the dry sand of the upper beach. He lined the bottom and sides of the pit with the flattest cobbles he could find and then built a fire of dry driftwood inside. After allowing it to burn down to coals and ashes, he raked them from the red-hot stones and covered them with several layers of wet seaweed. Quickly but carefully discarding any open, dead clams, he placed the rest in the pit and covered them with more wet seaweed and sand. An hour later, they were enjoying a feast of steamed clams.

Afterwards, singly and in pairs, they policed the surf as the tide came back in, hoping for some sign of Ley or Williams. But the cove gave back nothing but a few broken planks from the cutter.

Over the next two days, York showed the crew how to vary the clams with other food. Where the rivulets lost themselves among the boulders in the shade of the beeches, a thick carpet of moss had developed. Hidden underneath the moss grew berries that York called belacamaim, meaning rain berries. They looked and somewhat tasted like a small raspberry. The only clue to their presence was the minute green starflowers that grew almost level with the moss. Finding the flowers and following their stems resulted in a bounty of fruit in a place that Darwin at first would have though contained none at all. A fungus that grew on the beech trunks was more obvious but less appealing. Although the taste was slightly sweet and relished by York, the others only learned to appreciate its mucilaginous texture once the diet of clams and berries had become completely monotonous.

175

On the morning of the fifth day of being marooned, the crew awoke to a gunshot. Wickham, with the worries of command, had awaked early and spotted some vultures eating something in the surf. He shot one and, as the others scuttled away down the surf line, slowly lifting off the ground and screaming in fury, ran down to where they had been feasting. Darwin, bleary eyed, watched from the opening of the wigwam but could only see a black form half afloat in the surf. He though it must be the corpse of Williams or Ley.

But when Wickham returned, holding the dead vulture by its legs, he was smiling. "Meat tonight, lads!," he announced. "It's the corpse of a seal and fresh enough for the girls we go with."

Despite the drizzle, morale was high as they feasted on roast seal and vulture around a roaring fire. When Darwin offered York a piece of vulture breast, though, the Yamana refused.

"We do not eat vulture. It eats dead peop'e. What if ear'ier this one ate someone from my tribe who had become lost and died without cremation? Eating that would then be like eating f'esh from one of my own peop'e."

"But...," replied Darwin, startled, "I thought you did eat your dead. That boy, Pin, at Woollya told us so! He said you hold the grandparents' faces in the smoke to suffocate them and then eat them."

"Ah, Char'es, that boy was great joker. Remember story about Okoko and matches? You cannot believe everything you hear, not even everything you see. We do not kill our grandparents, and when one dies we burn the corpse and scatter the ashes over the sea. And we do not eat vulture flesh."

Fitzroy had regretted his decision to survey the outer islands immediately upon rounding Cape False. The shelter of Nassau Bay had belied the force of the westerly blowing up the Drake Passage, and the *Beagle* labored to make even minimal westing. Then the wind veered to the southwest and blew up into such a gale that he no longer even dared retreat. To leeward, the welter of reefs around Cape Horn waited to add the *Beagle* to a long inventory of wrecks already

claimed. He ordered Chaffers to come around to the south and head
into the open polar sea.

Five days passed under close-reefed topsails and double-reefed
courses, the topgallant masts secured on deck. Rain alternated with
hail. The pumps clanked watch after watch. The boatswain's crew
battened down the hatches with the care of those who knew the coffin
brigs' reputation.

Fitzroy stayed on deck except to sleep a few hours at a time, and
even then refusing to go to his cabin below, instead napping in Darwin's hammock in the chartroom, just behind the wheel. There also,
at the big table, he would make entries in the logbook, laboriously
timing his writing with the corkscrew pitching of the deck.

"February 20. Southwesterly whole gale. Southerly heading. Position unknown."

"February 21. As yesterday. Crew resolute. Quo me cumque rapit
tempestas deferor hospes."

During those times alone, recording a day's danger in a line or
two, he sometimes felt despair flood in, like a sea washing over him
and dragging him down into the deep. Only on deck, occupied with
the immediacy of keeping the tossing *Beagle* afloat in the maelstrom,
could he focus enough to beat back the panic of being driven further
and further from land into the polar sea. He even had Fuller bring him
such cold meals as were possible to where he stationed himself on the
quarterdeck.

On the sixth day, during the forenoon watch, the gale increased to
storm force and the masts began to bend and quiver so much that Fitzroy ordered the canvas reduced to storm trysails and the forestaysail.
MacCurdy, one of the better foretop men, his hands frozen stiff, lost
his grip on the icy rigging while taking in sail. He pitched overboard
headfirst. Before anyone even had time to throw him a line, he disappeared beneath the foaming waves.

The logbook reduced the terror to an even more terrible simplicity:
"February 22. Blew up to storm during the forenoon. Crew weary.
MacCurdy lost overboard while taking in canvas."

Even with so little canvas, the *Beagle* maintained steerageway,
and Fitzroy was standing beside the two quartermasters at the wheel

when three giant rollers approached in close succession, their sides walls of black water, their crests snarling with teeth of white foam. The *Beagle* met the first roller and rose over it, righting herself as she gushed water from the lee scuppers. But the second roller hit before she could regain more than half a point of her heading, completely deadened all steerage way, throwing her so far off the wind that the third roller hit right abeam. She went over until three feet of water covered the lee bulwark from the cathead to the stern davits, the whaleboat hanging there full of water, its weight threatening to capsize the *Beagle*.

Fitzroy and Bennett, one of the quartermasters, grabbed axes to cut the swamped boat away. They half swam and half fell across the quarterdeck toward the davits. Each attacked one davit, awkwardly hacking at the soaking ropes with one arm while trying to keep a grip on anything solid with the other.

During that interminable moment while the *Beagle* teetered on a knife-edge of black water, her keel and masts competing to come up first, everyone aboard consigned their souls to the deep. But as the whaleboat and Bennett disappeared in the foam to stern, she slowly rolled back onto her keel. Half a fathom of water covered the deck, and Fitzroy had to fight his way back to the wheel to help the other quartermaster wrestle the bow back into the wind so that she met the next wave with the water streaming from the scuppers.

Thereafter the wind began to slacken and the sea fall, almost as if out of amazement that the tiny brig had survived. Two of the crew had been lost: MacCurdy and Bennett. A whaleboat was gone. The delicate mechanism of one chronometer had not survived the pounding. But those seemed small losses relative to what would have happened if Bennett and Fitzroy had not managed to cut the whaleboat lose or if a fourth giant roller had hit. The *Beagle* and her crew would have joined the many other coffin brigs in Davy Jones Locker.

Overnight the wind decreased further, but so did the temperature. Spindrift coated everything above deck with a film of ice, and Fitzroy suspected they were far south in the polar sea. He ordered a sharp lookout for floating ice, but thick clag hid everything beyond the small patch of black water that had become their world. Nonetheless, he set a course to the north and had topsails and courses set. The mist and drizzle would clear well before approaching the rocky islands off Tierra del Fuego, he hoped, as he led the entire crew in the hymn of thanksgiving.

"O come, let us give thanks unto the Lord, for he is gracious: and his mercy endureth forever."

"Great is the Lord, and greatly to be praised; let the redeemed of the Lord say so: whom he hath delivered from the merciless rage of the sea."

"The Lord is gracious and full of compassion: slow to anger, and of great mercy."

"He hath not dealt with us according to our sins: neither rewarded us according to our iniquities."

"But as the heaven is high above the earth: so great hath been his mercy towards us."

"We found trouble and heaviness: we were even at death's door."

"The waters of the sea had well-nigh covered us: the proud waters had well-nigh gone over our soul."

"The sea roared: and the stormy wind lifted up the waves thereof."

"We were carried up as it were to heaven, and then down again into the deep: our soul melted within us, because of trouble."

"Then cried we unto thee, O Lord: and thou didst deliver us out of our distress."

"Blessed be thy Name, who didst not despise the prayer of thy servants: but didst hear our cry, and hast saved us."

"Thou didst send forth thy commandment: and the windy storm ceased, and was turned into a calm."

"O let us therefore praise the Lord for his goodness: and declare the wonders that he hath done, and still doeth for the children of men."

"Praised be the Lord daily: even the Lord that helpeth us, and poureth his benefits upon us."

"He is our God, even the God of whom cometh salvation: God is the Lord by whom we have escaped death."

"Thou, Lord, hast made us glad through the operation of thy hands: and we will triumph in thy praise."

"Blessed be the Lord God: even the Lord God, who only doeth wondrous things."

"And blessed be the Name of his Majesty forever: and let every one of us say, Amen, Amen."

"Glory be to the Father, and to the Son: and to the Holy Ghost."

"As it was in the beginning, is now, and ever shall be: world without end. Amen."

The clag did clear as the *Beagle* approached the outer line of islands between Cape False and Cook Bay, at the head of which the Beagle Channel emerged. The islands, facing into the prevailing westerlies blowing out of the open Pacific, were the barren and desolate seasonal homes of hair and fur seals, sea lions, and penguins. Already a day late for the rendezvous with Wickham, Fitzroy hurried north toward Delta Island.

Dusk and mist had already obscured the cove by the time Wickham finished rationing out the last of the seal meat. No one spoke, everything possible having been repeated several times over during the eleven days since the glacier had marooned them. The date set for the rendezvous at Delta Island had passed three days ago, and the prospect of an interminable clam diet lay ahead. Only the blazing driftwood kept the chill of the glacier at bay. As they swallowed the last of their meager portions, despondency settled over the small group on the lonely beach.

Suddenly York stood up and said, "Hush, p'ease, misters. I think I hear sailboat."

And then, as others heard sails flapping in the slight breeze, a cheer went up around the fire. A moment later, the whiteness of two spritsails emerged out of the darkness.

Sullivan had seen the smoke of the fire from out in the channel and, as dusk descended, used the firelight to navigate the yawl toward the encampment. He was ready to haul off if the fire proved to belong to Fuegians, but when he saw Sullivan, Darwin, and the others who had rushed down to water's edge, everyone shouted in joy at once.

But the hand shaking and back clapping proved nothing compared to the uproarious feast that followed. When Fitzroy had not found the cutter waiting at Delta Island, he had waited a day and then sent his second lieutenant up the Beagle Channel in the yawl with three men as crew. And Sullivan, expecting that the crew of the cutter would be short on provisions when he hopefully found them, had brought plenty of biscuit, canned meat and vegetables, rum, and tobacco.

When Sullivan heard that the calving of a glacier had wrecked the cutter, though, he interrupted the celebration to have the yawl hauled up the steep beach beyond the sand berm. Thereafter, the party continued long into the night, and after a short night's sleep, all were glad to sail out of Glacier Cove at dawn. As they passed out into the channel, Wickham dubbed the western and eastern promontories Ley Point and Williams Point.

The arrival at the *Beagle* was much less pleasant than anticipated, though, because Fitzroy was so openly critical of Wickham for his loss of the cutter and two men, almost flying into a public rage instead of welcoming the lieutenant back at the gangway. Darwin thought Fitzroy unreasonable, especially considering that he had himself lost two men and a whaleboat in the Drake Passage and, very nearly, the entire crew and *Beagle* as well. Besides, no one could have predicted that nearly the entire leading edge of the glacier would break away all at once. He could still clearly remember the thunderous crack, the blue ice plunging into the sea, the sheet of foaming water, the enormous wave surging across the cove and curling up into an enormous breaker as it hit the beach. Ley and Williams had not even had time to scream before the water knocked the breath out of them, picked them up, smashed them onto the cobbles, and washed their shattered bodies out into the cove with the splintered boat.

Perhaps the complete lack of survey results since leaving Woollya upset Fitzroy as much as anything. The storm had ensured that he had accomplished nothing. And Wickham's work on the *Beagle* Channel had been lost with the cutter. At least he had confirmed that the channel indeed connected the Atlantic to the Pacific. It was much narrower and further south than the Strait of Magellan but also much shorter and straighter. Fitzroy expected more, though, of his officers and of himself.

And Old Hot Coffee's mood did not improve. The winds continued strong and the seas high through the narrow channels of the exposed western archipelago of Tierra del Fuego. The *Beagle* spent most days rolling and pitching while at anchor, bottled up in one cove or another among the many small islands.

Some of the coves also contained sealing camps. The area teemed with hair and fur seals, not to mention penguins and whales. Spouting and breaching whales became so common that Darwin no longer ran to the side every time the lookout shouted, "Whale ho!" Once the lookout warned of a reef close on the weather bow, but changed his opinion when he noticed that the waves lifted the dark mass instead of breaking over it. On approaching, brownish gray rock resolved into the putrid mass of a dead whale, buoyed up by the gas of its own decomposition. Weeds and barnacles covered the thick epidermis, a large flock of gulls ripping at it with great determination while a halo of sharks tore at the flanks.

Yamana hunters killed the seals with clubs by sneaking up on the places where their colonies carpeted the rocky islets. Those that fled into the sea became the prey of other hunters waiting just offshore in canoes. Their harpoons had a barbed bone point nearly two feet long that was set loosely into a groove in the end of fifteen-foot wooden shaft. When the harpoonist speared a seal, the shaft would pull lose and, attached to the point by a sinew thong about a yard long, drag perpendicularly through the water. The seal, slowed and unable to dive, thus became easy prey for another thrust and, finally, the deathblow with a club.

Given the limitations that the weather seemed intent to place on surveying, Fitzroy used York to extract as much geographical information as possible from the Yamana sealers. Every time the *Beagle* anchored near one of their camps, Fitzroy went ashore with York and came back with a sketch map showing the local coastline and the names of its many coves and points. Fitzroy was not happy, especially after he found out that Teke-uneka, the toponym he had marked on his master chart for several places, translated as "difficult to say for sure." But he persevered as best he could given the weather and incrementally filled in the blanks on the chart.

At one sealing camp along the ragged shore of New Year's Sound, York recognized a family in one of the canoes that came to trade. With a whoop, he was over the side in a moment and hugged the man and woman, all of them shouting and crying and smiling at the same time. Only later, when York came back on board to announce that he was leaving the *Beagle*, did any of the crew realize that the two nearly naked savages waiting in the canoe were his parents. In ten minutes he had collected his few possessions and said his farewells. He would join his family at their sealing camp for a few weeks before they all went home to Woollya around the time the *Beagle* would also return there.

As Darwin watched the three figures in the fragile canoe paddle away toward the rocky shore he marveled that people could live here with so little protection from the harsh elements. York's people were, of course, no different than any of the other Yamana tribes, despite his protestations. They had few possessions and looked, to Darwin, about as close to animals as possible while still being recognizably human. Glacier Bay had proven that this coast could easily kill most Europeans. Yet the Fuegians seemed to thrive by moving between the poles of their winter and summer camps.

Other sealers, a polyglot mix that made up the crews of mainly American ships, were also busy in the area. They worked from bases in coves, where they could skin the pelts from the seals and render their blubber into oil over fires ashore. The sealers would make forays to their killing grounds by whaleboat to hunt seals, and haul the carcasses back to base. A rough crowd, besmeared with the gore of their trade, they would scowl up from their whaleboats at the crew of the *Beagle* when they passed near enough. But mainly they avoided the *Beagle* altogether. Fitzroy was just glad to avoid them as much as possible, the sealers having a reputation for attacking the camps of the Fuegians to rob them of their furs.

Only on one occasion did a sealer seek out the *Beagle*. Captain Ebenezer Coffin of the barque Acushnet out of Nantucket sent a boat over one morning to ask for the help of a surgeon. Apparently two of his men had been badly burned when they accidentally overheated a rendering cauldron and it split open, dousing them with hot oil.

Fitzroy agreed to send MacCormick but first warned him not to reveal any information to the sealers about the survey, particularly the locations of Yamana sealing camps. As usual when given a direct order, MacCormick bristled. He considered Fitzroy's "Indian charts," as he called them, a waste of time. Over the past week, he had told anyone who would listen that, in his opinion, the *Beagle* would be employed more usefully in the sheltered waters of the Strait of Magellan. As the Yankee boat pushed off from the side, the surgeon steadfastly avoided looking toward the *Beagle*. And when he returned from the Acushnet in late afternoon, he said little but that while he had had to amputate an infected leg, the two sealers would no doubt survive, albeit horribly scarred and one a cripple. In appreciation, captain Coffin had sent over two bottles of bourbon for the officers' mess, earning MacCormick an increment of credit among his peers.

The novelty of American whisky did a little to cheer what had become a discouraging effort to survey the western archipelago, so discouraging that Fitzroy decided to abandon the effort and sail for Woollya. After checking on the mission, he reasoned, he would sail for the Strait of Magellan to continue that aspect of the survey.

First, though, he had Chaffers make for the sealing camp belonging to York's family. The alacrity with which York had joined his parents in their canoe had caused Fitzroy to worry whether MacCormick might be right about the Fuegian capacity for retaining the lessons learned in England. Better for all concerned to return York to civilized company as soon as possible, first to the *Beagle* and then directly to the mission at Woollya.

The camp was abandoned, though, with little left but piles of seal bones among which the gulls foraged for scraps of flesh. The other camps in the area were also abandoned, as if the Yamana had all decided to return eastward together.

As the *Beagle* sailed south through New Year's Sound, the reason for that exodus became clear. On islet after islet, in cove after cove, at each of the camps Fitzroy had mapped, those Yamana sealers who had not left had been massacred. The gulls fiercely contested the bloody corpses. Some of them lay within wigwams frames, charred black. Holed canoes littered the shore. The killers had taken the summer's harvest of seal pelts and left no witnesses alive.

Nothing could be proven. And, in any case, nothing could be done so far beyond the pale of any country's justice. But Fitzroy made no secret of his suspicion that, while aboard the Acushnet, MacCormick had told the sealers about the Yamana camps in New Year's Sound. Sickened by the murders and more determined than ever to quit the desolate and unproductive archipelago, Fitzroy ordered Chaffers to make for Woollya to see if York had returned there.

On approaching the strait between Cape False and Cape Horn, though, the weather blew up so fiercely that Fitzroy abandoned the planned stop at Woollya. Instead of attempting to gain the shelter of Nassau Bay, he had Chaffers set a course to double the cape and then make for the eastern entrance to the Strait of Magellan. The bitterly cold, northwest wind and clag made a misery of handling the sheets and reefing the topsails. With the wind abaft the beam, though, the *Beagle* sailed comfortably within sight of Cape Horn's jagged black teeth. Just seventy-five miles beyond them lay Woollya and the mission, where, Darwin and Fitzroy fervently reassured one another, all must be well with Matthews and York.

9

AS THE *BEAGLE* PROCEEDED past Dungeness Point, those on watch noted how much it looked like its namesake at the entrance to the Strait of Dover and felt a twinge of homesickness. Despite bucking a fresh west wind, the floodtide carried them up the Strait of Magellan and into the First Narrow, where the shores approached to within two miles of one another. The opposition of tide and wind in the narrow passage caused such a hollow sea that the *Beagle* had to struggle ahead under just enough canvas to maintain steerageway, corkscrewing across large standing waves that broke over the weather side. With little room to maneuver, Chaffers wore ship every ten minutes, but even such tedious effort resulted in little progress. And when the tide turned and further headway became impossible, Fitzroy ordered retreat to an anchorage just east of the First Narrow. There the *Beagle* pitched and rolled between her cables, awaiting a spring tide that could carry her through the full dozen miles of the narrows.

Five days after the failed attempt, two days after the full moon, the tide reached its peak and Fitzroy ordered another attempt. Only three quarters of the way through, though, at noon, the crew soaked and sore with effort, the ebb once again forced a retreat. The next morning, Fitzroy stole a march by ordering the anchor weighed before the tide turned. By the time the flood began, the *Beagle* was already positioned within the entrance to the narrows. Beating against the wind, wearing ship every ten minutes while nearly awash, water breaking over forecastle and poop, Chaffers managed to clear the First Narrow.

Darwin heard the cheer go up from the crew as they realized they were through, and he briefly staggered onto deck to share in the celebration and see the famous strait. The treeless, rolling country stretching inland from both shores reminded him of the Patagonian plains further north. On the mainland, to the north, several large herds of guanaco grazed undisturbed, signaling that the local Tehuelches were elsewhere. On the large island of Tierra del Fuego, though, to the south, the Ona had noted the *Beagle* and gathered to light fires and wave their mantles. But Fitzroy, anxious to realize his objectives and still leave Tierra del Fuego before winter began, would not stop to trade.

At the Second Narrow, just as long but twice as wide as the first and therefore a much easier passage, scattered trees began to dot the landscape.

And by Port Famine, the strait had opened up into a broad sound and the country and weather had become more typical of Tierra del Fuego. Mountains cloaked in trees rose directly from the shore. Cloud hid the sun. And rain fell at least once every day.

Darwin could well understand how Port Famine had long promised seamen a safe haven and then betrayed them with desolation. The anchorage seemed well protected by rocky peninsulas and large enough to anchor a squadron of ships of the line. The land immediately along the shore was more level and the forest more open than usual for Tierra del Fuego. Streams of sweet water descended from the surrounding mountains. And plenty of driftwood littered the beach for a ready fuel supply. But to Darwin the overall prospect seemed bleak. A near constant drizzle made the mountains, already piebald with snow and cloaked in dark forest, seem as cheerless as possible. The only relief came on the infrequent occasions when the clouds briefly parted to reveal Mount Sarmiento many miles due south. Its peak was so regular in outline and the snow that covered it reflected all the dim light without the least shadow, that it presented a near perfectly triangular profile: a massive, sublime white pyramid in the distance.

Pedro Sarmiento had been the first to succumb to Port Famine's duplicity. According to the account Darwin had read while lying sick in his hammock, Sarmiento had established the town of San Felipe on the shores of the bay to bar English access to the Pacific. A few years before, Francis Drake had entered the Pacific via the Strait of Magellan and gone on to raid Spanish colonies from Chile to Mexico. King Phillip of Spain intended that Sarmiento's San Felipe would prevent anymore such raids. The Dutch would not discover the passage around Cape Horn for another quarter century, the Strait of Magellan was only ten miles wide at San Felipe, and so the Spanish plan seemed sound enough.

Sarmiento established the fledgling town in 1584 with four hundred people and then sailed for Spain to arrange a supply ship. But that ship never came. The French captured Sarmiento in mid Atlantic, and he spent the next several years in a prison. With no advocate at Phillip's court, San Felipe became another forgotten detail in the complexity of the sprawling Spanish Empire. Meanwhile, at San Felipe, the failure of the crops, the snow and cold of the first winter, the constant overcast, the long nights, and the failure of the supply ship created such deprivation that many of the settlers had died by spring. After another winter during which more people starved, twenty of the survivors tried to walk overland to Buenos Aires to find out why Sarmiento had not returned with fresh supplies. They disappeared somewhere in the Patagonian desert. By the third year, more people occupied the graveyard than the town, and the few dozen survivors decided to walk eastward along the northern shore of the strait in the hope of encountering ships at the narrows. After losing more people to a battle with the Tehuelches, the last survivors established a crude camp at the entrance to the First Narrow and waited. Any ship trying to pass from Atlantic to Pacific would sail within sight.

Within a week, with seemingly miraculous timing, a flotilla of three vessels arrived. But the commander was none other than Thomas Cavendish, one of Drake's compatriots, on a mission to again pillage Spain's Pacific colonies. At first Cavendish mistook the ragged band of Spaniards for a tribe of Tehuelches. He took one aboard to interrogate, though, and soon learned everything he wanted to know. He weighed anchor, ignoring the pleas of the Spaniards ashore, and sailed for San Felipe. There the privateers loaded the six cannons that Sarmiento had intended for the battlements of the town, burned the crude houses, and then sailed on to raid Valparaiso. Two and a half centuries later, only the vestiges of the Spanish cemetery remained. Cavendish had even changed the name to Port Famine in order to obliterate the Spaniards' efforts.

Pringle Stokes had been Port Famine's most recent victim, and Fitzroy intended to erect a headstone over his grave. From the moment the *Beagle* had dropped anchor and Darwin had emerged on deck, he began to hear rumors about what had happened during that winter. Of those who had actually lived through it, Fitzroy and Mac-Cormick would say nothing. Rowlett confided that, "It wore colder'n a weetch's teet, it wore." Chaffers told Darwin the most.

Stokes had made Port Famine his base camp during his survey of the Strait of Magellan. That strategy seemed to offer several benefits. Quarters built ashore permitted more comfort than on board. Ready access to the driftwood that littered the beaches made large and constant fires possible for heating the huts. Lightening the *Beagle* by unloading most of the provisions increased her utility for survey in confined waters. Establishment of a semi-permanent celestial and meteorological observatory allowed a record of observations throughout the year. And no time would be wasted in having the *Beagle* sail back and forth to Buenos Aires every year to re-victualate. Instead, Stokes had contracted with a Scottish merchant in Buenos Aires to send a supply ship in the spring.

In May, the *Beagle* and its boats returned from surveying to winter at Port Famine. The nightly snows started in June, and by the solstice three feet obscured the ground. A constant thick overcast pressed down on the camp so that the six hours of daylight seemed only slightly less oppressive than the long nights. Frequent snow squalls forced drifts of snow into the rough huts of driftwood and canvas. The gloom, the cold, the monotony created a general despondency.

Despite the constant fires that warded off the cold and damp, or perhaps because of their smoke, an increasing number of men suffered pulmonic ills, catarrhal afflictions, and rheumatic pains. With little besides tinned and salted preserves, people sickened further. By July, scurvy had gripped the camp, and men already weakened by other ills weakened further. Stokes had assumed that hunting would provide enough fresh meat to ward off that particular disease, the bane of all sailors. But the guanaco and waterfowl had left with the first snow, and travel in the forest became so difficult that no one went further than to gather firewood along the beach. Just when trade

189

for fresh food with the Fuegians would be welcome, they too had disappeared from the country.

As the winter dragged on, Stokes grew increasingly frustrated with MacCormick. Apparently the surgeon had underestimated the amount of limejuice required and had run out. None of the other antiscorbutics available had enough of an effect to improve the condition of those beset by scurvy. Neither pickles, dried cranberries, Winter's bark, nor wild celery cured the bleeding gums and anemia. They did not lack food, only fresh food.

Stokes considered abandoning his plan to stay the winter and sail for Buenos Aires, but beyond the protection of the bay, gale after gale tore up the strait. With so many of the crew bedridden or nearly so, he could not chance sailing until spring brought better weather. The best alternative seemed to be to send those healthy enough overland to the drier, lower country near the eastern entrance to the strait in the hope of finding Tehuelches willing to supply fresh guanaco meat. At eighty miles just to the Second Narrow, and considering the rough going along the coast for at least the first half of that distance, the party could be gone a couple of weeks before returning with any meat. And even that hopeful estimate depended on quick contact with Tehuelches willing to trade and able to find guanacos.

Fitzroy lead the victualating party of a dozen of the healthiest seamen and marines. Stokes also sent MacCormick. He had little confidence in the surgeon, but with rumors circulating that a secret stash of limejuice was keeping him healthy, he had become worse than useless at Port Famine. Everyone who had the energy came out to watch the departure of the little column that embodied their hopes. All were heavily armed and carried packs of trade goods. Chaffers could still vividly picture how they had disappeared into the dawn mist along the narrow strip of brown beach that the tide kept clear between the gray water and the white snow.

Chaffers did not know all the details of what had happened to the victualating party. Fitzroy had never said anything, nor had MacCormick. But the seamen told Chaffers some of what had happened. After a tough two days along cliffy shores and through wet snow and gloomy forest, the party had reached the Patagonian plain near the

Second Narrow. They rejoiced because the ground was bare and they could see smoke from Tehuelche fires rising in the distance.

The next morning, eight Tehuelches rode into camp before the sky had fully lightened. The watch had seen them coming and everyone had guns loaded and ready for any trouble. Chuzos sprouted from the tight cluster of painted men and horses that rode right up to the fireside as if it were their own. Across the fire where vapor rose from the boiling billycan, Fitzroy stood backed by the semicircle of his dozen men, guns pointing aloft but ready to drop their muzzles if necessary. But that should not happen, of course, because the Tehuelches wanted copper and cloth and beads, and the English wanted fresh meat.

The roar of a musket froze time. A cloud of powder smoke rose from behind Fitzroy. The chest of the leading Tehuelche spurted blood into the smoldering fire. Every man on both sides of the fire gapped at the smoke, at the shattered chest, at the blood sputtering and steaming among the coals.

Then chuzos and bolas began to quiver and whir overhead and horses wheel around and wild whoops sound in anger and fear. Fitzroy instinctively stepped back among his men and was enveloped in the acrid smoke and orange flash of a volley that smashed into the Tehuelches.

Bodies with close-range, gapping bullet holes tumbled from the backs of rearing horses. While his men reloaded, Fitzroy looked for any threat to fire his pistol at but found none left. All eight Tehuelches were on the ground or tangled among the panicking horses. Fitzroy did not panic. He leaped across the fire and grabbed at the bridle of one horse, shouting back to his men to catch as many of the others as they could. Only one escaped, another lay dead, a bullet in its brain, and so did six of the Tehuelches. The other two had taken bullets in their stomachs and died by the time the provisioning party had slaughtered the dead horse, loaded the live ones, and began its trek back to Port Famine.

Fitzroy could not bear to say anything to MacCormick, just relieve him of his rifle in grim silence. The surgeon had with that single panicked shot ended all chances of trade with the Tehuelches, even all chance of hunting guanaco for themselves.

By evening the column was well into the trees and the snow again. Fitzroy, reasonably certain the Tehuelches would not follow into the gloom of the forest, ordered camp made and a double watch set. They would bring back the meat of seven horses, little enough for the three-score men left at Port Famine but perhaps enough to eke out survival through the remainder of the winter.

In the meantime, Chaffers continued to recall while Darwin silently struggled to comprehend the horror of the story thus far, those at Port Famine most affected by the scurvy had begun to die. First one, a few days later two, then the next day three stopped breathing. The stiff corpses accumulated in a snow cave Stokes ordered dug as a mortuary.

But then, as they waited for the provisioning party to return, Stokes returned from a hunting foray with some meat, a liver, and ordered it cooked and apportioned among the sickest. While the slices sizzled in the pan, no one much listened to Stokes's story of meeting a Fuegian in the forest and trading some copper buttons for the liver of a bear. The next day he returned with another liver and, a day later, with two more. The men relished the meat and began to strengthen somewhat.

When Fitzroy returned, Stokes ordered the horses slaughtered and rationed out among the sick but became increasingly withdrawn, leaving daily matters to Fitzroy. He had the horsemeat stored in the chilly morgue beside the plank boxes of the nine who had died. He also ordered the carpenter to nail the coffin lids more securely and posted a marine at the door.

The slim proceeds of the victualating expedition proved to be sufficient to improve the strength and spirit of many of the crew. Others remained weak, but no one else died. When the supply ship arrived in September, the jars of limejuice and other stores soon revived the entire crew.

Captain Stokes, however, never seemed to recover his spirit, and while on one of his solitary walks along the beach he shot himself in the head. By the time the crack of the shot echoed across the bay to those at the camp, they had seen him fall, first to his knees and then onto his face. The bullet had destroyed his left eye and blown off the back of his skull, spattering brain into the sand. The old Spanish graveyard, its mounds of rocks still discernable through the rank grass, received Stokes and the other nine dead as if it had been patiently awaiting them for more than two centuries.

"My God, man," whispered Darwin after Chaffers had not spoken for a full minute, "ten dead.... I had no idea.... There are no bears anywhere much south of the equator,...not this far south...."

"Aye, lad, so they say," muttered Chaffers, never meeting Darwin's eye before standing up and walking away.

Darwin now understood the distance between the officers who had lived through that hell together and those who had joined the *Beagle* more recently. None of the seamen who had over wintered at Port Famine had rejoined the *Beagle*. But Fitzroy, MacCormick, Chaffers, and Rowlett had come again. Yet Darwin had noted how they had grown less communicative with the other officers upon approaching Port Famine. Chaffers had clearly felt the need to share the burden, but with Darwin rather than with another officer. Now Darwin also understood why Fitzroy so detested MacCormick, even more than might be attributable to the surgeon's, and Fitzroy's, abrasive personalities. And he well understood why Fitzroy refused to winter in Tierra del Fuego. After Chaffer's tale, Darwin was himself very thankful for that mercy.

Fitzroy had all ten of the graves in the old cemetery tended and the granite headstone erected over Stokes's body but did not linger at Port Famine. As the *Beagle* sailed out into the straight, her cannons fired in succession to salute her former captain and those of his crew who would never leave Port Famine.

From Port Famine, Fitzroy planned to head for Gallant Bay to check Stokes's survey of the western Strait of Magellan. Doing so required doubling Cape Forward, the southernmost point of the South American mainland, however, and to do so Chaffers had to beat determinedly to windward against the westerlies that blew through the strait with such constancy. With shores so bold, the boards could stretch right across the full width of the strait, but progress was so minimal, even under a heavy press of sail, that Chaffers tried to find a westward setting tide by tacking more closely along the shores. From the previous voyage, he knew that the strength of the westerlies caused a current of about two knots to set to the eastward in mid channel. The tides exerted the most influence near the shores and sometimes set up one side and down the other. Chaffers thus hoped to find a westward current along one shore or the other to help double the cape. Tacking along the north shore offered nothing but sudden squalls that blew down from its high mountain peaks. But a tide along the south shore provided the necessary assistance. The only disadvantage was the indraught along various narrow channels and low valleys that cut through to the open Pacific beyond.

Nonetheless, after as tough a sixteen hour's beat to windward as the crew had ever made, requiring forty-one tacks, with the indraughts scarcely allowing the men to have the ropes out of their hands for a minute, the *Beagle* sailed into Gallant Bay. Once at anchor in that snug harbor, most of the crew took a well-earned rest, except for those detailed to accompanied Fitzroy to the summit of Cerro de la Cruz.

Even for Darwin, who carried nothing more than his rucksack, the climb was a marathon. The first third of the ascent followed a ravine through forest and required a tough scramble up wet, loose stones. The edges of the ravine provided no better alternative, being covered with spongy moss and saturated with water. The men who carried the theodolite and other instruments slipped many times, taking bruisings in an effort to protect their delicate burdens. Above the forest, upward of a thousand feet elevation, even steeper slopes forced the climbers to use the stunted, straggling arbutus and beech shrubs to forcibly pull themselves upward. Even along the more level stretches, the spreading branches, none more than a foot above the rock, were densely entangled with wild cranberry and formed an elastic carpet that forced scrambling rather than walking. The bare rock of the last two hundred feet, a loose pile of frost-shattered greenstone with large hornblende phenocrysts among the feldspar, thus came as a relief even though the men had to pass the instruments up from hand to hand.

While Fitzroy leveled and oriented the theodolite, Darwin and Syms examined the small cairn at the summit. Someone had piled up a cone of the sharply fractured stones and inside, as Darwin discovered once Syms had removed some of them, placed a tin box containing a corked bottle with a piece of paper rolled inside. Using a pair of forceps he carried to pick up insects, Darwin carefully pulled the paper out of the bottle. Damp had destroyed much of the text, but a few moments were enough to reveal the author and the date: Louis Antoine de Bougainville had written it in 1766.

Darwin brought the paper over to Fitzroy and, heedless of the consequences of disturbing him at his work, held the paper under his nose without comment.

Fitzroy started from his concentration over the theodolite and just stared at Darwin and the paper he held so carefully between his fingertips. Then he slowly reached out and took the paper. Sitting down on a stone, he read what dampness had not already destroyed.

"Viatori Benevolo salus...que a periculose admodum naviga...Brasilie Bonarve et insularum...incertis freti Magellanici portubus...historia astronomia...Bougainville...Duclos et de la Giaranda 2 navium...Primaris...Comerson...Doct med naturalista Regio accu...m. Veron astronomo de Romainville hidrographio...a rege Christianissimo demandans...Landais Lavan Fontaine navium Loco tenentibus et Vexillariis...itineris locus DD Dervi Lemoyne...Riouffe voluntariis...vives...scriba...Anno MDCCLXVI."

Fitzroy and Darwin sat staring at the paper for a full minute before the former pronounced, "Amazing, Chawes; simply amazing. He stood in this exact spot the best part of a century ago."

Darwin just took the pages back and began to copy the Latin into his notebook with a lead pencil.

"That's right, Chawes. Just copy it out and we'll take the original to the British Museum, were it belongs."

Darwin added another page with the names of the officers of the *Beagle* and the date. Then he placed both sheets in the bottle, corked it, and had Syms replace it inside the cairn.

That evening, Fitzroy and Darwin played chess after dinner for the first time in a year. Fitzroy in particular was well satisfied with the eight-hour trip up Cerro de la Cruz. The weather had been unusually clear and he had been able to sight on many of the prominent peaks and capes along the reach of the strait below. Stokes had constructed his chart by triangulating among those landmarks. That each azimuth now traced a sharp line on that chart between the summit and those landmarks proved Stokes's diligence. That was satisfaction enough, and Fitzroy toasted his former captain and teacher. Darwin, in turn, toasted Bougainville. That venerable French soldier, navigator, and scientist had left his testament in that cairn at the ends of the earth in 1766. Their finding it two-thirds of a century later seemed miraculous. Maybe in a hundred years someone would find their own testament to their work in this desolate land.

Their satisfaction only increased when they heard the lookout yell out that a ship had just entered the bay and Mellersh came down to tell them that a side-wheeler flying the red ensign of the Hudson's Bay Company had just steamed into the anchorage. Abandoning their chess game, Darwin and Fitzroy ascended to the deck just in time to see a messenger rowing over. The note invited "Captain Fitzroy and Mr. Darwin" for a drink and cigars aboard the SS *Beaver* and was signed "Capt. Holmes."

The riddle of how a Hudson's Bay Company captain would know who was aboard the *Beagle* resolved itself the moment they stepped onto the deck of the *Beaver*. Ambassador Ian Douglas, his white muttonchops and broad grin gleaming against his dark skin, held out his hand to welcome them aboard just as if he were at home in his embassy in Rio de Janeiro.

"Gentlemen," he roared, "permit me to welcome you aboard the *Beaver* and present Captain Holmes of the Hudson's Bay Company!"

Once all had settled into Douglas's cabin and he had offered some Madeira and cigars, he proceeded to expound on what they had been missing while surveying the ends of the earth. "It's become a damned tricky situation in Buenos Aires these days. I had a report just before leaving Rio. With Rosas away on his Desert Campaign against the savages, the Unitarios talked the bloody French into supporting them against Doña María, Rosas's wife, don't you know. Well, she left for the provinces, where Rosas's friends Estanislao López and Juan Facundo Quiroga control things. They will never give into the Unitarios plan to carve up their estates. My sense is she welcomed the Unitarios and French showing their hand. Just as they are getting comfortable, believing they are really in charge, Rosas will return and together with López and Quiroga slaughter every last Unitario once and for all. That's my..."

"And Lucy...?," interjected Darwin, who had quietly, anxiously been thinking of nothing else since Douglas had welcomed them aboard.

"Oh, Lucinda is fine, as always.... But you'll never guess were I'm headed now. So I'll tell you. Fort Vancouver on the lower Columbia River, gentlemen, that's where. And why...? To settle a damnable boundary dispute with the Americans. This steamer will be the first on that coast and go a long way toward reinforcing Hudson's Bay Company control. It's perfect for that sort of coast. A lot like Tierra del Fuego, actually, with lots of narrow channels that sailing vessels find impossible in contrary winds. Lots of wood to fuel her as well! From Gravesend to Rio and then to here she's been underway no more than three months, eh? Captain Holmes?"

"Right you are, ambassador," replied the tall, thin Hudson's Bay man, who like the rest had sat mostly silent through Douglas's pontifications. "She steams at nearly eight knots but is a decent sailing brig as well. We've really only been under steam since Dungeness Point. Made quick work of the First Narrow, I must say. Couldn't be happier with this command. What say I give you a tour, gentlemen? My chief engineer'll be glad to join us."

So, leaving Douglas to turn in with the promise to call aboard the *Beagle* in the morning, Holmes passed the word for his chief engineer and led the way forward to the engine room. Mister Archer joined them at the companionway and welcomed them to the smell of oil and smoke and steam. His lantern revealed a seeming jumble of tanks and levers that only began to make sense as he patiently pointed out what each did and how it connected to the others. Built and rigged as a brig by Green and Wigram at Blackwall on Thames, above deck the *Bea-*

ver looked much like the *Beagle* had before the addition of the miz-zen mast. The main differences were the funnel and the paddlewheel housings that jutted out from the hull just abaft the mainmast. But that similarity belied the differences below decks. There, twin steam engines by the Watts Company filled the long, low engine room. Two vertical cylinders with a stroke and bore of about a yard each produced thirty-five horsepower. A complex system of cranks and levers connected the pistons to the wheels, each thirteen feet in diameter, to drive them at thirty revolutions per minute when at top speed. Past the cylinders, the lantern light glinted off an enormous iron boiler resting on a series of brick furnaces. Behind the boiler, stacks of cord wood filled much of the rest of what on the *Beagle* would have been the crew's quarters and mess. Luckily the *Beaver* required a much smaller crew, only thirty-one, including four stokers and thirteen woodcutters, about half those normally required to sail a brig. She burned a lot of wood, explained Arthur, when Fitzroy whistled at the number of woodcutters aboard. A day's travel of about a hundred miles required cutting wood for two days. Both Holmes and Arthur therefore expressed a distinct preference for coal, whenever available. Holmes had, in fact, pulled into Gallant Bay to replenish his wood supply and was much appreciative when Fitzroy offered to detail some of his men to help with the cutting.

While a line of boats ferried a steady stream of cordwood to the *Beaver* the next day, Douglas visited. Over a long lunch with the officers in their mess he related every detail of the Pacific Northwest boundary dispute. The basics were already well known to any officer in the Royal Navy with an interest in international politics. Britain wanted the border to follow the Columbia River westward from where it crossed the forty-ninth parallel near the Rocky Mountains. The Americans wanted to use the forty-ninth parallel as the border all the way to the Pacific. At least the reasonable ones did. The most jingoistic wanted to control everything up to the Russian Tsar's territory at fifty-four degrees, forty minutes north. Douglas explained his own task as an assessment of the relationship between the Hudson's Bay Company, which controlled western British North America by Crown charter, and the American pioneers starting to flood into the Oregon

Territory south of the Columbia River. If the dispute were not settled before too many more pioneers established an indisputable American presence both north and south of the river, Britain and the Company might have to retreat to the Fraser River, the next major valley to the north. "Maybe that will be your next mission, gentlemen," finished Douglas, "to survey the coast between Fort Vancouver and Alaska? If so, though, you'll probably be doing it aboard a steamship, eh? That's the future, both for the Company and the Navy."

The officers enjoyed the visit, not only as an excuse to break out every delicacy they had been hording but for feeling that their tedious survey work was somehow connected to weighty international boundary negotiations. None of them, though, having long trained for a life under sail, was willing to believe the prediction that steam would supplant canvas any time soon.

Fitzroy's satisfaction at the clear weather that had allowed the observations from Cerro de la Cruz did not last. The *Beagle* left Gallant Bay in the wake of the *Beaver* but instead of turning north headed for the entrance to the Barbara Canal. It was one of several narrow channels connecting the Strait of Magellan to the Pacific, and Fitzroy wanted to obtain precise soundings around the many islets that choked the eastern end of the canal. But heavy gales and torrential rains soon thwarted that goal. Instead of surveying, the *Beagle* spent most days pitching and rolling at anchor. Darwin remained sick in his hammock, sipping laudanum and, more and more after the meeting with Ambassador Douglas, thinking about Lucy.

On one of the few days when sounding was possible, trusting too much in the rule that kelp always marks shoaling hard bottom, the *Beagle* ran onto a rock at about five knots. It lifted her forward and heeled her over with a ripping shudder and crash that all aboard felt through to their bones. Then she plunged downwards and, before anyone could take action, was scudding along as before. Wickham, the officer of the watch, quickly ordered the pumps manned and the carpenter below to inspect the hull. Fitzroy paced the quarterdeck awaiting the damage report but by the time Jonathan May emerged on deck again, the pumps had already emptied the bilges and the sucking of air revealed the lack of serious damage. The survey proceeded while all exhaled with relief at what was a near escape from serious consequences.

While Fitzroy was not particularly worried that the grounding had seriously breached the bottom, he did want to check it as soon as possible. Also, winter was approaching, with darkness inexorably expanding its dominion to sixteen hours per day and the snowline creeping down the mountain slopes. And doing justice to the survey of Tierra del Fuego demanded another full summer. So he decided to return to Buenos Aires to refit and re-victualate. The Pacific would wait another year. Some of the crew would be disappointed to extend the voyage, but science demanded patience.

So Fitzroy ordered Chaffers to make for the mouth of the Rio Santa Cruz, on the coast of Patagonia a hundred and fifty miles north of Dungeness Point. The Santa Cruz discharged into a sheltered cove with a steep beach of muddy shingle that, at this time of year, had tides of forty feet or more and would be an excellent place to careen the *Beagle*. More than that, beyond the survey of the cove that Stokes had previously completed, the Santa Cruz remained an intriguing mystery: the only river between the Rio Negro and the Strait of Magellan with a discharge substantial enough to suggest that it drained the slopes of the Andes themselves. The narrowness of Patagonia so far south supported that inference and also promised the possibility of a transcontinental route, no more than a couple of hundred miles long, along the Santa Cruz valley.

While Fitzroy saw to repairing the bottom of the *Beagle* and draughting presentable copies of the working charts completed over the summer, a small expedition could explore up the Santa Cruz. That way, rather than again wasting valuable time on draughting while otherwise idle in Buenos Aires, he could work on his charts while his lieutenants and Darwin extended his explorations. He was not particularly happy with the amount of work accomplished in Tierra del Fuego but remained confident that with time and effort he would realize all his objectives.

10

DARWIN SAT ATOP ONE of the driftwood logs that littered the beach along the northwest shore of the cove and looked across it with his telescope. Behind him, well above the reach of the high tide lapping at the log, an encampment of sailcloth tents surrounded the enormous pile of crates and casks that the crew had so laboriously unloaded the day before.

Fitzroy was directing the warping of the lightened *Beagle*, floating high, against the steep beach along the other shore of the cove. As the tide ran out again, the larboard bilges settled against the muddy gravel of the beach and the carpenter's crew used spare spars to shore up the careened hull. Meanwhile, Boatswain Sorrell directed his men to rig additional cables to the anchors they had so laboriously buried in the beach.

Darwin could see the three red-coated marines patrolling along the top of the low cliff that rose directly behind the *Beagle*, keeping watch for Indians and, somewhat less likely, pirates. A mile to the right of the redcoats, the mouth of the Rio Santa Cruz interrupted the cliff. Below the marines, the *Beagle* revealed the bottom of her hull. He could clearly see how the encounter with the rock had torn a large section out of the keel and ripped off a swath of the copper sheets from stem to beam. The exposed fir sheathing looked a little splintered but not much damaged. A foot or two less water over that reef, he shuddered, and they might all be at the bottom.

He was ecstatic that Fitzroy planned to stay with the *Beagle* to supervise the repairs while he would accompany an expedition under Sullivan's command up the river into unknown territory. The discharge of the Santa Cruz was so suggestive of Andean headwaters that, perhaps hoped Darwin, they might even reach one of the lakes rumored to abut the eastern slopes of that fabled mountain range.

Greatly satisfied with that prospect, he reversed his position on the log to look over the camp to the plain beyond. No cliff rose from the beach along this shore. In the foreground, marines stood around the six pounders that they had emplaced around the perimeter of the camp. Like him, they were looking out at the Patagonian plain that stretched inland, a landscape even more arid than the one he had crossed between the Negro and Colorado rivers. He found the desolation strangely inspiring, perhaps because it seemed the epitome of a sterile wasteland. Dry, sandy soil with plentiful gravel and shell fragments showed everywhere among the widely scattered bunches of yellowish brown, wiry grass. Not a tuft of green showed anywhere. On the horizon, a dark line marked the escarpment that stepped up to another, identical plain. He and Syms had walked there while the crew was unloading the *Beagle* and discovered that at least three such plains ascended from the shore as if a series of terraces. The first one sloped gently up toward the next and was separated from it by a hilly rise of about forty feet. Further inland, they had discerned another such escarpment.

He had also noted that the shells that littered the plain were broken but not rounded, just as Fitzroy had described them so long ago in his cabin while anchored at Plymouth. Some even retained vestiges of pigmentation. During the long walk back from the escarpment he had, he thought, developed an explanation Lyell would approve of. Clearly, Fitzroy was wrong about the cause being the Deluge. Rather, thought Darwin, using his knife to score some diagrams in the bleached surface of the log, the same slow, natural process that was currently forming this coast easily explained the stepped plain and its broken shells.

"Let us suppose," he muttered to himself while sketching with the point of his knife, "that southern Patagonia emerged from the sea at a nearly equable, slow rate, yet sufficiently quick to prevent the waves quite removing each part as soon as it was brought up. In that case, every portion of the former bed of the sea successively formed a beach, and from being exposed to a like action was similarly affected. It cannot matter to what height the tides rose, even if to forty feet as they do here now, for they would have acted with equal force and in like manner on each successive line of beach. Hence there is no difficulty in the fact of this plain sloping up to the foot of the escarpment and yet having no marks of any one particular beach-line on it be-

cause the whole surface has been a beach at some point." He paused
to rest the knife's point against the intersection of two of the lines he
had scored in the log, one indicating the sloping plain, the other current sea level. "I cannot pretend to follow out the precise action of the
surf during the land's elevation, slow yet sufficiently rapid to prevent
denudation, except when sufficient slowing occurred to create a line
of cliffs, now marked by the series of escarpments. But if it be analo-
gous to what takes place on protected parts of the present coast, where
gravel is now accumulating in large quantities, an inclined surface,
thickly capped by well-rounded pebbles of about the same size, would
be ultimately left. On the gravel now accumulating, the waves, aided
by the wind, sometimes throw up a thin covering of sand and mud,
together with shells. Shells thus cast up by the strongest gales during
the highest tides, would, during an elevatory period, never again be
touched by the sea. Hence, on this view of a slow and gradual rising
of the land, interrupted by periods of rest and denudation, we can understand the pebbles being of about the same size over the entire
width of the step-like plains, the occasional thin covering of sandy
earth, and the presence of shells, broken by being cast up in storms
and not subsequently rolled or rounded by the action of surf."

A year ago he might have been tempted to try out such an idea on
Fitzroy. But now he was content to let him and others believe that the
plain was a reliquiae diluvianae, if they so wished. As the camp settled down to sleep under the tents and the watch stoked the fires
against the chill, he quietly set down his conclusions in a notebook.

The expedition left on the next day's flood tide, the men at the oars in
each of the three whaleboats pulling with all possible strength to get
as far upriver as possible before the ebb. Near the mouth, gargantuan
sea lions lifted their shaggy necks and lazily peered at the passing
boats, sniffing the air before bellowing and returning to their sunbath-
ing. As the boats ascended to the limits of the reach of the sea, the
current strengthened to some seven miles per hour and became a
milky blue torrent some three hundred yards wide and more than a
fathom deep in mid channel, as if they were already within sight of

the melting ice that must feed it. Exhausted, they pulled the boats ashore to make camp.

The next day they towed the boats upstream. A rope connected the boats stem to stern and, with canvas halters, to the crew of men who toiled along the bank. Two men remained in each boat to fend off the logs grounded in the shallows. Two shifts of ten men each spelled one another on the rope hour by hour. The idle shift and officers scouted ahead and behind, always at the ready with firearms in case of Indians. The towpath was clear enough and the gravel provided reasonable footing, but whenever the river turned across the valley, a steep cut-bank obstructed progress and they had to cross over to the point-bar on the other side. The forced crossings, the rapid current, and the logs restricted progress to between fifteen and twenty miles per day, which amounted to no more than ten miles westward progress because the river meandered so much.

The days were just warm enough to be comfortable, and the sky was a constant blue. Each day at sunset the expedition stopped at the first likely spot to set up camp. The nights were starry and freezing, but the tents provided some warmth, especially with gravel banked along the bottom edges of the canvas to keep out the bitter wind that blew down the valley around dawn. Fortunately, fuel abounded and the watch could keep the fires blazing through the night. The few shrubs provided almost no firewood and most of the reddish brown trunks of trees, ground smooth by their journey from the Andes and stranded in the shallows, were so waterlogged that they would not burn. But guanaco frequented the river and defecated, as was their habit, in well-defined piles. Some of them were as large as eight feet in diameter, and the dry dung burned well. By morning the air had usually cooled so much that the river, itself quite cold, steamed until the sun had fully risen. After a quick breakfast around the fires, the men eagerly jumped to the towrope to warm up.

In such a monotonous country with such slow progress, they watched for even the most trivial sign of change. The least bit of bark remaining on the drifted trunk of a tree elicited long debate about the distance remaining to the Andean foothills. But the river and its valley continued much the same day after day. The river remained the same torrent that reached nearly to the sea, its roar so constant that they no longer noticed. They encountered no tributaries, no lakes, no placid reaches. The channel continued to meander across the valley floor, itself generally from one to five miles wide, trending straight westward, and covered in large gravel like that found on the bounding plains and on the beaches. In places, floods had left behind patches of mud and sand that pioneering shrubs occupied with the only green in sight. Bounding the valley to north and south, pairs of corresponding terraces stepped up to the plain five hundred feet above the river. Except for the occasional shrubs, the tracks of pumas, and the broken skeletons of their guanaco prey, the valley seemed sterile. Darwin saw fewer than a dozen birds in a week. He could find no minnows in the shallows and could catch no fish. Even insects were scarce, although a swarm of a type of horsefly found them on the third day and followed them persistently thereafter. They came and went with the sun, eliciting a curse whenever someone lost a bite out of his neck.

Despite the seeming desolation, though, thin lines of smoke rising into the blue sky from the plain above signaled the presence of Tehuelches. On the eight day, a patch of mud preserved the footprints of dozens of people and horses that had recently forded the river. Syms pointed out were they had trailed their chuzos in the mud, the lines still sharply defined. Cairns built on nearly every promontory overlooking the valley provided evidence of the antiquity of Tehuelche occupance, or perhaps that of some tribe of predecessors. The feeling never left Darwin that he was being watched, but no matter how often he scanned the rimrock, he never saw the watchers.

The slow pace of the expedition did allow Darwin and Syms to explore back and forth across the valley in search of life. Sullivan had ordered them not to stray too far but allowed considerable latitude. They found little life, though, and most of the cairns seemed to be no more than piles of flat river cobbles. One stood out, though, in part because of the regularity of its courses of stones and in part because of its size. The Tehuelches, or perhaps a more ancient tribe, had built a low wall of rocks around the edge of a ledge in a cliff and paved the top of the resulting enclosure with flat stones. Underneath the stones, earth, well mixed with red ochre, filled what Darwin increasingly believed was a sepulcher. Faulkner, after all, had written of the use of red ochre in Tehuelche burials. Syms used one of the flat stones to dig through the earth but the body had nearly entirely decomposed. Only a few fragments of bone, some teeth, and a stone spear point remained. Given the aridity of the climate, Darwin reasoned, the grave must be thousands of years old to have left so little. The spear point was incredible, fully eight inches long, carefully chipped from a piece of dark-brown volcanic glass, fluted where it would have hafted to the shaft, and still sharp as a razor.

He held it up to the sky and the translucent edge, as thin as a sheet of paper, turned from dark brown to blood red. "Incredible, Syms," he whispered in awe. "Look at the workmanship. Imagine the size of the game."

"Not a bird, sir, that's sure."

"More like a *Megatherium*, I'd say."

Syms made no reply as he wrapped the point and the teeth in pieces of cloth and put them inside his coat in preparation for the scramble back down the cliff to catch up with the boats.

As the expedition continued upstream, Darwin began to find fragments of cellular basalt that he surmised to be lava from an Andean volcano. At first he noted only a few pebbles, but each day the stones became larger and more numerous. By the second week, large, jagged, black blocks of basalt littered the channel, and the expedition reached their source: an immense lava flow covering the plain through which the valley cut. From the river, the lava appeared as a black cliff rising two hundred feet above the highest gravel terrace. The unseen plain above, speculated Darwin, must look like the worn anvil of a leviathan blacksmith king. In some places, columnar basalt suggested the ramparts of his castle. Springs emerged at the line where the lava flow and gravel met, the porous basalt acting as a reservoir for the scant rains, each seep marked by a tiny burst of green. Darwin had already thought about how long it had taken for the river to erode down through the gravel. Now, astounded, he had to add this immense thickness of much harder basalt to his calculations. And clearly, that erosion had occurred with pauses and starts, as indicated by the terraces that bounded the valley floor and seemed to correspond in time to the stepped terraces of the surrounding plain he had observed near the coast.

At the lava flow, all sign of Tehuelches, guanacos, and pumas disappeared, the plain above forming a jagged, impassable barrier. The horseflies persisted, though. And condors began to appear. They roosted on the steep, basaltic cliffs. As the sun warmed the air and created updrafts, the immense birds would soar up out of the valley to search for food on the plain beyond the lava. By climbing to a perch near one of the nests, Syms was able to shoot a large male when it returned in the late afternoon. The bird tumbled with an echoing scream to where Darwin waited below to recover the corpse. It weighed thirty-six pounds and measured nine feet eight inches from wingtip to wingtip. After Syms had skinned it, Sullivan had it roasted and portioned out to the men. No one got very much, but fresh meat brought welcome relief from two weeks of tinned beef and vegetables.

By the time they saw the Andes on the seventeenth day, the river was more than a thousand feet below the level of the plain and its channel choked with boulders. The valley had broadened to ten miles or so, and a stationary bank of dense white clouds had been visible in the east for the entire day. Since noon, various hopefuls had been pointing out imagined snowy peaks among the clouds. But at sunset, they finally all saw the summits they had been hoping for, the sun silhouetting the peaks amid haloes of luminous cloud. Sullivan led the expedition in a prayer of thanks.

The next morning, Sullivan led a small party up a ravine to the surface of the plain. Supplies were low, and he hoped to discern what lay ahead to decide whether to go on another day or turn back. The lava flow turned out to be even more daunting than imagined: jagged, black, lifeless. The lack of a vantage point precluded determining anything more than that the valley seemed to continue roughly westward. So at noon Sullivan took final readings with sextant, chronometer, and barometer to determine location and elevation. They would not be able to complete the final calculations until comparison with the reference instruments aboard the *Beagle*, but the average of the three chronometers made the time forty-seven minutes and twenty seconds past four in the afternoon, Greenwich time. Sullivan made the calculation, with each minute of time equal to 15 angular minutes, and announced they were at 71 degrees, 50 minutes, and 0 seconds west longitude, about 140 miles from the Atlantic. He also announced that although the Andean peaks appeared to be only some seventy-five miles further westward, supplies were too short to proceed any further. After Sullivan shot the azimuths of the visible peaks with the transit, the party returned down the ravine to the boats.

Disappointed at not having reached the hoped for lake at the foot of snow clad peaks, they turned the boats around that afternoon in preparation for an early departure the next morning. After the agonizing upstream pace, the speed of the descent was frightening. They almost lost boats a few times, either stove in by rocks or swamped by cross currents. But the seasoned men at the oars took each reach in stride and saw them through. At the most dangerous rapids, where the current accelerated through narrow chutes between boulders, the oarsmen turned around and rowed against the current to slow the descent to a manageable speed.

Darwin saw nearly as little life on the descent as he had on the ascent but could not shake the feeling that Tehuelches watched from where the sky met the rim of the valley. Once past the basalt country, fires on the plain above again sent pencils of gray smoke straight up into the blue sky. And as they approach the ford where they had seen the many footprints on the banks, they maintained an anxious watch.

The lead boat first raised the alarm, and then everyone saw the dark figures crossing the stream ahead. With apprehension, Sullivan ordered the oars backed to slow their decent, and those not so occupied to check their guns. But then the first silhouette, by now more clearly discernable, reached the bank and rose up onto stilt legs, revealing itself to be an ostrich. By the time the boats rushed by, six ostriches, perched between curiosity and fear, stared from the bank at what they must have thought three extremely strange amphibious beasts. In an instant, the gawking birds fell to their knees in a blast of sound, lead, powder smoke, and feathers.

That evening the crew was well satisfied with their luck at a meal of fresh meat, the first since Syms's condor and much more substantial. Darwin took additional satisfaction in eating what he thought might be a drumstick from another new species. The ostrich of northern Patagonia and the pampas was quite small, much smaller than the African ostrich. But this ostrich of southern Patagonia was even smaller than its northern cousin. Moreover, its plumage was darker and mottled, its legs shorter and feathered further down, as if leggings to guard against the cold. As far as Darwin could tell, this southern Patagonian ostrich was an entirely new species of *Struthioniformes*. He made sure that Syms carefully stored the skin of one, complete with feet and head, for forwarding to Henslow. In the meantime, until the avian experts had made a determination, he would refer to them in his notes as the lesser and greater Patagonian ostriches.

After a descent of less than four days, the ebb tide shot the three boats out into the cove from between the cliffs of the Rio Santa Cruz. The *Beagle* lay at anchor nearby, all repairs finalized, provisions reloaded, fully watered, awaiting the return of the river expedition. Fitzroy had barely congratulated Sullivan on his safe return before ordering the boats secured and the anchor weighed.

Darwin's only respite from seasickness on the voyage back to Buenos Aires came when Fitzroy put in at Port San Julian, discovered and named by Magellan himself. It was one of the few decent anchorages south of the Rio Negro, and Stokes had already surveyed it. Fitzroy merely wanted to check its longitude.

While Fitzroy went ashore with his instruments, Darwin came on deck to look at the desolate landscape. Drake had wintered here, naming the two small islands to starboard the Isle of True Justice and Execution Island. A long, narrow peninsula nicely enclosed the bay, protecting it from all but the fiercest storms, but Darwin could see no source of freshwater and little vegetation. According to the accounts he had read, Drake's men, and Magellan's before them, had dug shallow wells in the sand. But even with a source of water, the prospect of spending months in this forbidding place would have been a grim one, and Darwin, especially after having heard Chaffer's account of the winter at Port Famine, could well understand how mutiny and death had overtaken both Magellan and Drake.

Magellan, a Portuguese sailing for Spain, was in command of a fleet of five ships captained by Spaniards. At the end of March 1520 a storm battered the ships with hail, coating the rigging with ice and forcing Magellan to take shelter in Port San Julian. Dismayed at the prospect of even colder latitudes further south, he decided to stay the winter.

By April, discouraged by the desolation and bitter weather, three of the captains mutinied with the intention of sailing back to Spain. Magellan managed to gain control of three of the ships to blockade the entrance of the bay. After a fight, he regained full control and, after a perfunctory trial, had the mutinous captains drawn and quartered, the pieces hung from gibbets erected on the shore.

Just as he was again firmly in control, though, while the crew was building houses and transferring supplies ashore, Magellan discovered that Portuguese agents had sabotaged his provisions. He had only half what he expected. Hunting helped stretch out the food but brought them into conflict with the Tehuelches. Magellan was so impressed with their stature that he called them Patagones, after an ogre who featured in a play of the day. Patagonia thus got its name. But with the Tehuelches becoming actively hostile as Magellan's men hunted ever further a field, the admiral decided to leave Port San Julian. His fleet left in the spring and sailed on to discover the strait named for him.

When Drake reached the bay a little more than half a century later, Magellan's gibbets still lined the shore, a testament to Patagonia's aridity. Like Magellan, Drake also commanded a fleet of five ships, sailing on their mission to destroy Spanish colonies along the Pacific coast. Unknown to Drake, one of those aboard was an agent of elements in the Privy Council who opposed the plot hatched by the Queen and Drake, fearing that it would provoke the Spaniards to invade England. Drake had thought Thomas Doughty a friend, but during the Atlantic crossing he had begun fomenting mutiny. Plagued by storms and treachery, Drake had decided to winter at Port San Julian. With Doughty becoming more openly mutinous in his activities, Drake charged him with witchcraft, accusing him of causing the storms. A trial found him guilty of mutiny, although not of witchcraft, and Drake had him beheaded and his body hung from one of Magellan's gibbets.

The gibbets were long gone now, thought Darwin, as he watched Fitzroy and some others on the shore. But the gray cliffs and desolate beaches that rimmed the bay were as forbidding now as they must have been three centuries ago. And those ancient ships had been tiny caravels. Even Drake's flagship, the Golden Hinde, was smaller than the *Beagle*. Yet Drake went on to plunder the Spanish ports and circumnavigate the globe, as Magellan's ships had before him. Both of those momentous expeditions crossed paths in this otherwise inconsequential place, reflected Darwin, spitting over the taffrail, and if Doughty or the Spanish mutineers had prevailed, either expedition could have ended here too.

And what was his role in this place, he wondered? Was he inconsequential, or would his decision to join the voyage of the *Beagle* amount to something worthwhile? Did he have any regrets? Would he have lost his virginity anyway? To Fanny or to Emma or to someone else? Probably. Then he thought about Lucy and worried about whether she was safe in Buenos Aires. If he had not accepted the offer to join the *Beagle*, he would probably be enjoying better company, he thought with a grim chuckle, that's for sure. Especially now that Matthews and York were no longer aboard. Fitzroy had as yet not displayed any of the suicidal tendencies Darwin had worried about in Plymouth, but Old Hot Coffee was far from the most pleasant companion. And if he had turned down the offer to join the *Beagle*, at least he wouldn't be sick all the time—so desperately, pukingly sick. But, on the positive side of the ledger, he smiled broadly, he had seen as much natural history as many of his friends at Cambridge could dream of seeing in a lifetime. And he thought that his ideas were sound, that he was really onto something big about the origins of species. If he could only fill in the missing logic.

He saw nothing moving ashore except the surveying party, not even an ostrich. He had been thinking about ostriches since enjoying that roasted drumstick on the bank of the Rio Santa Cruz. Two nearly identical but clearly distinct species occupied adjacent areas of Patagonia at the same time, which reminded him of the fauna at Fossil

Point. There, similar species, all toothless Edentates, occupied the same region but at different times. Formerly they had been sloths. Now they were armadillos. But all were Edentates. Clearly the shift over time from sloths to armadillos was related in some way to changes in the environment. That much was clear because the sloths needed trees. In the same way, the shift in ostrich species from north to south, from greater ostrich to lesser ostrich, must relate in some way to environment. Somehow the lesser ostrich thrived better than its greater cousin in the deserts of southern Patagonia. Why did the lesser ostrich not also occur in the more humid environment of the pampas, though? Could it be that the same mechanism pertained to both the emergence of new species over time, as former species became extinct and new ones became dominant, as to the dominance of particular species in particular regions at the same time? In general, that mechanism must, the best he could see, be the same one through which one generation gives rise to the next. Of that principle he had become convinced. But what gave that mechanism its direction? What was the connection among environment, reproduction, and the emergence of species, each with its wondrous internal homogeneity and perfection, each with its amazing organization relative to other species, each with its geographical distribution? Perhaps, he concluded his still nebulous thoughts, by studying the spatial variation of living species, he could understand the temporal variation of fossil species?

The frigate HMS *Ganges* intercepted the *Beagle* just off Montevideo and relayed the news that Rosas was besieging Buenos Aires. Captain Cockburne of the *Ganges*, confirmed what Douglas had already relayed. With French help, the Unitarios had recently evicted Rosas's wife and the other leading Federalists from the city. Reportedly, Doña María had left vowing bloody revenge: "I will execute justice with my own hands! I will leave nothing standing that is not for Rosas!" Officially, Britain was staying out of it, but only, speculated Cockburne, because Palmerston fully expected Rosas to prevail by himself. He had returned from slaughtering Indians in the south and together with López and Quiroga had encircled the city with their gaucho armies. So far the Unitarios were surviving, but poorly, and only because the French were resupplying them. In any case, Hood, the consul at Montevideo, advised Fitzroy to keep clear of Buenos Aires.

Fitzroy complied, but unhappily. He had foreseen a stay of a month at most, and that only because of the need to replace the two wrecked boats. At Montevideo, he worried, obstructionism by the Frogs would probably delay sailing until late August.

Darwin was also unhappy. In Buenos Aires he might at least have hoped to hear news of Lucy from his friend Lumb.

The mail awaiting him at the Montevideo consulate was some consolation, though, and he settled into the front room of his hotel to catch up on news beyond the *Beagle*. One thick letter was from Emma, and out of anxiety he shuffled it to the bottom of the pile. His sisters had all written, bringing him up to date on Shrewsbury news. Apparently Fanny's marriage was not the happiest, but he felt no emotion one way or the other about that news. They also spoke glowingly of Emma, as if they suspected something might be brewing, the thought of which elicited an involuntary smile. Henslow had also written, a short but highly complimentary letter about the fossils, especially the *Toxodon* and the horse. He read and re-read Henslow's letter, luxuriating in the approval. Then Darwin again fingered Emma's letter but placed it aside to try first to relax by reading the back issues of *The Times*.

He was pleased to see that with the reformation in Parliament, a bill had finally passed that abolished slavery everywhere in the British Empire. Predictably, the Boers, West Indian planters, and many others opposed emancipation but could do nothing much to thwart it. Captain John Ross had returned from his search for a passage through the Arctic. Unsuccessful in that attempt, the ship stuck in the ice for months, he had nonetheless discovered the magnetic north pole. Darwin also noted that one of his former professors at Edinburgh, something of a curmudgeon, had published a book entitled *On the Adaptation of External Nature to the Moral and Intellectual Constitution of Man*. The brief notice did not comment on the contents, but he could imagine the sort of dogmatic thinking involved. He also noted the stir created by a woman named Elizabeth Barrett publishing a translation of *Prometheus Bound*. He could still remember the somnolent gaze of Mister Chesworth, the Greek tutor at Shrewsbury School, when Darwin and his chums had had to recite the complete trilogy. As far as he was concerned, he hoped that Miss Barrett would in time translate them all so no other schoolboys would have to suffer so.

Only after having finished the papers did he feel like his emotions at first seeing Emma's letter had subsided enough to open it. He returned to his room and slowly opened the envelope, steeling himself against rejection as he read the several pages. But she had sent just the opposite. At least he thought he could read her affection between the lines of family news: her friends were marrying, she despaired of ever meeting anyone, her family adored him, he was so brave for sailing on the *Beagle*, and so on.

Emma was as sweet now as when they had been children together on holidays, he smiled to himself. For a few moments he tried to imagine what she would look like naked. Her breasts would be white and soft with rosy nipples. He hardened as he imagined slipping between her smooth thighs and entering her soft, wet, warmth while he fondled her breasts and kissed her lips. Rubbing himself through his pants he ejaculated with a stifled moan of pleasure and then fell asleep in his clothes.

In the morning while breakfasting in the hotel's front room, Earle came in and sat down across from him, smiling.

"Augustus! God, man, you're alive! The rumors...? I thought...."

"As you can see, Charles, I'm quite all right," he replied. "So please don't make a fuss."

Earle explained that he had reached Buenos Aires last winter and spent the past year "taking care of some business." Now he was about to leave for Santa Fe, a couple of hundred miles upriver from Buenos Aires, and proposed that Darwin accompany him. "Lucy is there, and two guns are better than one on the roads around here." Earle left promising to call an hour before dawn the next day. If he did not see Darwin, he would go alone.

Darwin spent the rest of the morning debating his matrimonial options, as distant as they might be. He wondered whether he would marry anyone at all upon returning to England. The possibility of marrying Lucy was remote, not that she had given any sign that she would ever want to. How would he introduce her to his father? As one of Palmerston's mulatta spies? His family would never approve, not as they would of Emma. Emma offered all the familiar comforts that Lucy could not, but none of the exotic romance. Yet, why even worry about marriage at this point? The *Beagle* might wreck when next in Tierra del Fuego. He would go to Santa Fe, he decided, and worry about his future life in England when he returned to England.

First he went to the *Beagle* and told Fitzroy about the plan to go to Santa Fe but was waved away with an admonition to be back in no more than seven weeks. So Darwin checked his guns, returned to the hotel, arranged for a horse, and turned in early.

By noon the next day, Earle and Darwin were miles beyond Montevideo's walls, safely out of reach of any interference by the Colorados. In the countryside, Oribe and his Blancos ruled and guarded Rosas's flank. The only real threat was the usual one of banditry, but Earle and Darwin each carried a rifle and a pistol. Their best guard was the level, open landscape that precluded the sudden approach of other riders. It was monotonous country, somewhat more undulating but otherwise similar to that around Buenos Aires: a grassy, treeless plain full of cattle and horses and sheep and isolated ranch houses.

The cool, dry winter weather allowed a fast pace to the Rio Uruguay, and on the third day Earle and Darwin left their horses at a ranch on the riverbank and boarded a small coastal scow. It was no more than a hundred tons, with a single raggedy lugsail and paint so badly worn that no more than a few flakes lingered in protected corners. The faded lettering across the stern was indecipherable. Worse than the poor repair, something of a shock to Darwin after the care taken of the *Beagle*, overpowering barnyard and maritime odors mixed to force him to the weather rail. Only the master inspired less confidence than the vessel. Reluctant to talk, even to give his name, his girth nearly equaled his height. Not a single hair disrupted the rough brown hide of his body, which showed amply through gapping rents in his shirt and made Darwin think of the illustration of a rhinoceros he had seen in Cuvier. If the crew of two were of any race, they were of all; and they talked even less than their master. Only when Earle placed some coins in the master's palm would he venture even as much as, "Santa Fe. Una semana."

Darwin and Earle retreated to the weather bulwark, staying as far upwind as possible while still remaining on board, and watched the delta of the Rio Parana approach. Its many channels disgorged muddy, reddish water into the black of the Rio Uruguay. But Darwin, between bouts of retching over the rail, could not distinguish any gap in the low line of trees along the horizon until within half a mile of the mouth of the main channel.

The many low, wooded islands and bare mud banks in the broad swath of brown river demanded frequent turns, but the master seemed to know just when to change course to avoid running aground. The banks and islands were of the same reddish pampaean mud exposed at Fossil Point. A tangle of willows, shrubs, and creepers obscured everything beyond the sloughs and marshes that bounded the main channel. In infrequent clearings, the houses of woodcutters and smugglers rose on stilts, now high above the river but, Darwin conjectured, submerged to the porches during the rainy season. In summer, the humidity, heat, and mosquitoes would probably make this trip unbearable. Now, a pleasant breeze pushed the scow upstream so smoothly that his stomach felt as settled as possible given the stench that rose from the hold.

One day graded into the next, scarcely without noticing. Other scows passed them on their way downstream, but the master steered well clear of them, seemingly determined to reach Santa Fe without any communication beyond the orders to his crew.

The promised single week stretched into a second, but each afternoon, well before dusk, the master still insisted on anchoring in the shadow of some islet. Seemingly committed to a wholly fluvial life, the crew never once went ashore, fish and water from the river and a cask of stale bread sustaining their needs. Nor did Earl, content to spend his days smoking and sketching, desire an excursion ashore. So one evening after anchoring near a large island, Darwin rowed himself over to where a small beach seemed to offer access to the interior. Repelled by the density of the vegetation, though, and by the many jaguar tracks, he retreated aboard before dark and thereafter contented himself with making observations from the deck.

Although Earle remained as reticent as ever, for the first time he cooperated with Darwin by agreeing to sketch the many birds that lived along the river. Black scissor-beaks—*Rhynchops nigra*, thought Darwin—skimmed the water in small flocks at dusk, their lower bills just beneath the surface, plowing up fish fry. *Ceryle americana* sounded their low notes from the riverbanks, and *Conurus murinus* screeched down from the treetops, reminding him of his first day ashore in the tropics. He carefully counted the months since that day in the Cape Verdes and was surprised to sum only eighteen. In that year and a half he felt he had learned more, both about himself and about natural history, than in all his years in school.

As the scow ascended the river toward Santa Fe, the banks began to rise into bluffs, nearly sixty feet high by the time they passed the town of Rosario. The bluffs were of reddish, clayey earth but graded into indurated marl at the base, the whole sometimes slumped into irregular hillocks covered with cacti and mimosas. In several places Darwin saw fossil bones of mastodons and other large quadrupeds projecting, but the master refused to stop for a closer examination.

Darwin could see enough from the deck, though, to congratulate himself on the theory he had developed at Bahia Blanca. The pampas used to be a bay of saltwater, subsequently filled in with estuarine sediments as the ancient Rio Parana built its delta into the sea. The tons upon tons of sediments that made up the bluffs derived from the rocks of Brazil, thus explaining the exfoliation he had seen around Rio de Janeiro. The rock of Sugar Loaf Mountain and the many other tors must indeed have formed under great pressure, far beneath the surface. Over millions of years, erosion had removed the overlying strata while rivers like the Parana carried the detritus away, relieving the pressure and causing the layers to peel off the tors like the skins of so many onions. The resulting sediments, ground ever finer as water carried them downslope eventually became the mud swept downstream by the Parana. The river also carried the bodies of dead animals, just like the bloated corpses of cattle he had seen choking the Rio Salado, until interring them in the delta that formed where the flow of the river slackened upon reaching the sea. The mud and car-casses settled to the bottom, forming an immense sepulcher. As the whole delta gradually emerged from the sea, the river cut downward, re-exposing in the cliffs the bones of the corpses it had buried so long ago. And, if he were correct, he would find the fossils of extinct ma-rine species in the marl stratum that underlay the estuarine mud, rep-resenting the bottom of the ancient embayment of the sea. If only, he grumbled to Earle, the damn master would agree to pull into the main bank for an hour.

But, eventually, after two full weeks on the river, they reached the pier at Santa Fe. A high bluff formed the other riverbank, but the western shore onto which they disembarked stretched level to the ho-rizon. The town was a short cart ride from its harbor and hemmed in on all sides by sloughs, marsh, and grassland full of the immense herds typical of the pampas.

The loquacious cart driver talked about the exploits of Estanislao López, the federalist governor who ruled Santa Fe province. He was a great Indian fighter who just last summer had pursued a band of fifty to their haunt in the Gran Chaco, slaughtered them, and sold their children in front of the town's cathedral. But now, of course, he was helping Rosas at the siege of Buenos Aires. In the garrulous driver's opinion, once the Unitarios were done away with, Rosas would re-ward López with the vice presidency of the republic.

By the time Darwin had washed up at the hotel, Earle had disap-peared. The desk clerk knew nothing, and Darwin had no idea how to find Lucy by himself. So he left a note in case Earle returned and went for a stroll in the plaza to see what he could find out. Every time he saw a tall young woman he snuck a hopeful look at her face but really had no hope of being that fortunate. By dusk, somewhat dis-gusted with his own helplessness, he retreated to a café under an ar-cade.

After the privations of the river scow, both the passable local wine and the beef were very agreeable, and he began to feel more con-tented with his situation. As he ate, vendors passed on their rounds, selling everything from candles and bibles to ponchos and hats. One sold him some fossilized shark teeth that, apparently, had come from the base of the bluff across the river. Darwin gleefully tucked them into his pocket, thinking that they alone made the trip worthwhile.

He also became more hopeful that Lucy would show up at the hotel because the same boy who had sold him the teeth passed on the rumor that the siege of Buenos Aires had ended. Rosas and his allies were victorious over the Unitarios and had agreed to the Pacto Federal, confederating the provinces into a united Republic of Argentina of which Buenos Aires would be the capital but in which each province would retain substantial autonomy. Rosas had again become governor of Buenos Aires, and López was returning to Santa Fe. The Federal Pact guaranteed that the estates of the cattle barons would not be divided up into farms and that the provinces would not pay taxes to Buenos Aires, which is what Sarmiento and the other Unitarios now fleeing into exile had wanted.

Darwin spent the next several days exploring the bluffs across the river from Santa Fe. He did not find any better specimens of shark teeth than he had bought, but he did confirm their presence in the basal marl. He also found some fossil clamshells that further confirmed his theory. In the evenings he sat at a table in the front room of the hotel and wrote replies to the letters he had received in Montevideo.

He also decided to write a long letter outlining his ideas about natural history to his elder brother Erasmus, who more than anyone else might appreciate them. Erasmus had been traveling in Europe for several years and his letters had been sporadic, to their father's regret. But despite his brother's seeming lack of direction, he was the one who had setup the chemistry laboratory in the garden shed. He was the one who had taught Darwin the basic principles of scientific experimentation, a welcome relief form the drudgery of learning the classics by rote at Shrewsbury School. The two brothers had also always shared a love of collecting everything from bugs to birds and while at Edinburgh together one year had spent many days at the Firth of Forth. Now, supported in idleness by their disappointed father, Erasmus was probably traveling somewhere on the continent. Or maybe he had finally returned to England, perhaps even home to

Shrewsbury. In any case, if 'Ras thought his little brother's ideas too wild, he would say so but keep them to himself.

One evening, while concentrating on the long letter to his brother, Lucy appeared at the hotel. They coupled twice before sleeping and then again in the morning, Darwin for the first time entering from the rear and feeling the deliciously full contact of her buttocks against his hips. After breakfast, they lay on the bed chatting, mainly about Darwin's geological theories because she refused to say anything about her own activities.

He told her about his feeling of awe at the hundreds of millions of years that must have passed to erode the rocks of Brazil, until the granite that had formed deep under ground, under the enormous pressure of the overlying strata, became exposed as the exfoliating dome of Pão de Açúcar. She smiled and asked if he recalled the story about the woman who had thrown herself from the top of the tor to the meadow in which they had eaten lunch on the way to the fazenda. Then she told him that he was a genius and asked whether they would find fossil shark teeth even among the strata exposed in the highest Andean passes between Argentina and Chile.

Afterwards he lay quiet beside her and thought about whether Emma would be as desirable. And he wondered what Lucy was thinking but had learned not to ask.

In the afternoon, the streets and newspaper were full of the news of López's death. On the way back from Buenos Aires, assassins had ambushed him and his lieutenants as they crossed the Arroyo Seco. Women were in tears. Groups of men tore up and down the streets on horses, shouting that they would catch the assassins. But no one knew where to find them. Then word came from Buenos Aires that Rosas had granted López the posthumous title of "Glorious Hero of the Confederation of the United Provinces of the Argentine Republic." Joy mitigated grief, and the vigilantes, sure that the guilty Unitarios and their French conspirators would try to escape westward over the Andes, to exile in Chile, rode off up the road to Cordoba. There they planned to join forces with those of Quiroga, El Tigre de las Pampas, to hunt down the assassins before they escaped toward Mendoza and over the Chilean frontier.

The next morning, Darwin awoke alone. Although he hoped, he knew what the desk clerk would tell him. The woman had left with the other English man, the tall one, before dawn. More than that, he did not know or would not say. With no clue as to the direction Lucy and Earle had taken, Darwin had little choice but to return downstream by river scow and rejoin the *Beagle* before she sailed.

Lucy had left two envelopes in the inside pocket of his coat, one addressed to Consul Hood and the other to Fitzroy, but none to Darwin. During the trip downriver, he several times nearly opened the envelopes, hopeful that they might contain a clue as to where Lucy had gone. But he could not bring himself to violate her trust so decided to deliver them as addressed.

And, perhaps, he thought, he did not want to confirm what he suspected: that she and Earle had been involved in the assassination of López at the Arroyo Seco ambush. When Darwin had heard the news the day before, he immediately recalled Lumb's Machiavellian prediction. Once the Unitarios were eliminated Rosas would not need López anymore, and therefore neither would Palmerston. Britain would be able to manipulate all Argentina through its alliance with one man: Rosas.

On the way downriver Darwin had made several attempts to write Emma a reply, but each one seemed wrong and he watched the crumpled sheets of paper disappear astern, slowly soaking up the brown water and sinking out of sight. As the *Beagle* sailed from Montevideo, he resolved to write her a letter before reaching Valparaiso, which would be the next opportunity to send mail.

11

ALL ALONG THE SOUTH SHORE of Windhond Island, canoes followed the *Beagle*. As usual, the interminable cry and insatiable demand was, "Yammarschooner, yammarschooner,...." But, not at all as usual, and worrying to Darwin and others, many of the Yamana wore strips of colorful cloth around their limbs and foreheads—cloth that looked like it had come from among Matthews's possessions.

As the *Beagle* sailed into Woollya Bay, all glasses fixed on the mission: the house and wigwams still stood, but no one seemed to be around. Closer inspection by the shore party, led by Fitzroy himself and including Sergeant Beareley and five of his marines, did not find anyone either. All the goods provided by the Church Missionary Society were gone. Not a stick of furniture or scrap of cloth remained in the house or its cellar. Grass had overgrown the garden. The only hope that Matthews remained alive was the absence of any sign of violence.

No Fuegians had followed the shore party up the slope to the mission, but a whole crowd of them now watched from the cluster of wigwams half a mile away. Fitzroy, furious and fearful for Matthews at the same time, ordered the marines to keep their muskets at the ready while he led them over to confront the prime suspects in Matthews's disappearance and the looting of the mission. Without a translator, Fitzroy despaired at uncovering what had happened at Woollya over the winter but, if necessary, was determined to search every wigwam for any clue.

By the time the little column reached the wigwams, the Yamana had fled into the forest. The marines were just about to start a search when York stepped out from the forest edge and came forward. He was as naked as any Fuegian, his hair long and face so covered in paint that, until he spoke, Fitzroy did not even recognize him. But once Fitzroy realized who the savage in front of him was, he demand to know what had happened to Matthews.

"He with Fuegia at Ukurh, on north side of island."

And then, with only a little prodding by Fitzroy, York related what had happened. His English had deteriorated a little, but his story was clear enough.

From what York had heard, after the *Beagle* and cutter had left Woollya, one party of natives after another had come to the mission to see what they could get from Matthews. They would badger him all day with their yammarschoonering, even threatening him with clubs and stones until he relented and gave them some copper buttons or strips of cloth. Jeremy had become so discouraged at the situation that when his family returned from the sealing grounds, he had left the mission to live with them. Fuegia had also left with her people, to live in the village called Ukurh.

Just as she was leaving Woollya, the canoes of her family loaded full of things donated by the Church Missionary Society, York had returned with his own family. They had joined the exodus from the sealing grounds when the crew of the Acushnet began massacring and robbing the Yamana seal hunters.

At Woollya, York had found Matthews alone and in great distress, constantly besieged by demands for the last of his possessions. York had tried to help, but no one would listen to his demands that they leave Matthews in peace. Instead, they had taken turns making loud noises so that Matthews and York could not sleep for several days. Then, when both of them had collapsed from exhaustion, the thieves stripped the mission to the bare planks.

Fuegia and her parents had returned the day after that final ransacking. They had taken the despondent Matthews back to Ukurh, where her father, now rich, was the chief. York had since heard that Fuegia and Matthews were married and that she was pregnant.

Later that winter, York's father and mother had both died in an attack by Ona men. Just before the first snow fell, they had crossed the Mountain-Valley Channel in canoes stolen from a Yamana village on its north shore. Then the Ona raiders had crossed the island to attack Woollya, probably having heard about the mission and all of Matthews's goods. Many Yamana escaped in canoes or hid in the forest, but York's parents had died in their wigwam at the beginning of the attack. York, fishing from his canoe out in the bay, had watched help-lessly as the Ona men sacked and burned his village. They had killed as many men as possible and enslaved those women and children who did not escape into the forest or by canoe. The Ona had stolen any-thing not buried in caches in the forest, forcing the Yamana women and children to carry the seal pelts and other possessions back to Ona country.

While York was giving his account, the marines had searched the wigwams. Beareley confirmed that the people at Woollya had no more than a few of Matthews's things. Most, apparently, had either gone to Ukurh with Fuegia, had been traded from one end of the *Beagle* Channel to the other, or had become Ona plunder.

That evening over dinner, Fitzroy spoke more than he had for months previous. He was livid. Darwin realized the futility of doing anything more than listen as Fitzroy vented his frustrations.

"How could that bloody idiot have been so incompetent and weak, Chawes! He was surely not unprepared for his circumstance. Did we not provide everything a missionary could hope for? A house. Trans-lators. Tools. Has he fallen a pawn to Fuegia and her family's ambi-tions? Is that it, Chawes? Manipulated by a woman, forsaking his ob-ligations?"

Darwin inwardly rejoiced when Fitzroy relented in his criticism of Matthews long enough to decide to rescue him from Ukurh. No mat-ter the circumstances, Darwin could not contemplate Matthews living out his life among Fuegians. To be a missionary with responsibility for a flock was one thing. To live among them as just another sav-age—as a husband, as a father to a Fuegian child—was quite another matter. Darwin could not imagine such a life being anything but hor-rible, and he readily voiced his appreciation of the rescue plan.

Fitzroy, once determined on a course of action, took York aboard the next morning and ordered him to bathe and dress. York seemed only too glad to comply. With his closest family dead, he seemed ea-ger to rejoin the *Beagle*, perhaps even return to England. When he emerged on deck, dressed in breaches and a coat, shoes on his feet and a smile on his face, he once again looked like the York that Dar-win had gotten to know over the past year.

Over a chart on the big table in Darwin's cabin, Fitzroy and York conceived a plan. From Woollya, Ukurh was twenty-five miles around the shore of Windhond Island, sheltered in a small bay on its northcoast. But York pointed out an overland route, little used by the Yamana, who hated to travel by any mode but canoe. The trail cut strait across a low pass between two valleys and halved the distance from Woollya to Ukurh. Fitzroy knew that the Yamana would have buried most of their possessions, including their booty from the mission, in secret caches in the forest and would flee there themselves as soon as they saw the *Beagle*. To follow them among the dense trees would risk an arrow in the back. So he planned to send the marines and a dozen seamen overland under command of Beareley and Wickham. They would encircle Ukurh on the landward side. On the seaward side, the *Beagle* would approach until close enough to send the boats ashore undercover of darkness. At first light, Fitzroy would spring the trap by rowing onto the beach and destroying the Yamana canoes.

Now Darwin, who had accompanied the overland party, crouched behind a mossy log within sight of the silhouettes of the wigwams of Ukurh. York had led the party along the trail that climbed up one of the streams that crossed the meadow at Woollya. After a tough slog to the crest of the pass, Wickham had ordered a halt until the moon rose and they could move stealthily to within sight of the wigwams. After settling in behind the stumps and fallen trunks of trees, the temperature dropped until frost formed on every surface. Darwin buried his face between his lapels to keep his teeth from chattering and tried not to think about Matthews.

With the first pale light of day, a breeze from the bay began to rustle the leaves of the beeches. And, in a moment, the village dogs caught the scent of strangers and began barking their warning. As the Yamana tumbled out of the wigwams, they heard the boats rushing onto the beach with a great splashing of oars and so turned to run in among the trees. But Beareley ordered his men to fire into the air, and the Yamana realized they were trapped. On one side, Fitzroy's men were axing the bottoms of canoes. On the other side, muzzle flashes exploded in the darkness among the trees and heavy lead balls crashed and whined through the foliage.

The Yamana, desperate, fled eastward along the shore, scrambling across a streambed that cut across the beach. As the marines blocked the way west and torched the wigwams, the sailors gave chase with pistols and cutlasses. Those who had landed in boats and those who were hidden along the forest edge tried to trap the Yamana between them.

Darwin, in trying to jump across the streambed, slipped and fell in just where two women were concealed under the cutbank. They leaped on top of him and beat his skull with sharp stones. He shielded his head with his forearms but felt the stone cut into his flesh to the bone. The women were screaming at him, pounding and kicking him, their hatred palpable in the darkness of dawn. He wanted to fight back but was afraid that if he took his arms away from his head for even an instant, his skull would be bashed in. He could feel the hot wetness of his blood running down his face and filling his eyes. As the flames flared higher among the wigwams, his sight filled with the redness of fire seen though blood.

He regained consciousness hunched in the sheets of one of the whale-boats as its crew pulled for the *Beagle*. The sun had risen fully above the horizon and he could see dozens of dead and dying Yamana prostrate on the beach. The trail of bodies lead from the still burning wigwams to the forest edge. There Darwin could clearly see Matthews and Fuegia among those who had escaped. None of the *Beagle* crew remained on the beach, and the Yamana were shouting and gesticulating towards the retreating boasts as they came back down the beach toward their dead and wounded kin.

Back aboard the *Beagle*, after a hot breakfast, Fitzroy recorded the results of the morning's action: "Matthews not found at Ukurh. Several Fuegians died while obstructing search. 11 men injured, none fatally."

Having spent months confined in narrow channels, among dark mountainsides and blinding glaciers, between gray water and gray cloud, the *Beagle* sailed between the East and West Furies out onto the broad Pacific as if delivered from Erebus.

Despite despondency over the failure of Matthews's mission and interminably foul weather ever since, Fitzroy had stubbornly persisted with the survey of Tierra del Fuego. He had probed to the end of every fjord of the Brecknock Peninsula in case any penetrated through to the Strait of Magellan. He had surveyed every channel among the many islands around Cook Bay and Whaleboat Sound. And he had sounded nearly every possible anchorage. But as the days began to grow ever shorter after the fall equinox, the increasing grumbling of malcontents, beginning but not ending with MacCormick, had worn down even the most stalwart. Fitzroy had relented and ordered Chaffers to set a course for Valparaiso. Beaufort at the Admiralty would be pleased with what he had accomplished.

In the weeks immediately following the attack on Ukurh, Darwin thought that Fitzroy was trying to reconcile their differences. Fitzroy had come to visit often and seemed somewhat more amicable than usual. He never mentioned the failure of the Anglican mission, instead talking nearly incessantly about England and how much both of them would enjoy returning. After a few weeks, though, he stopped coming to the cabin unless he needed to work on a chart, and then he always demanded complete silence while he concentrated on his work.

Darwin actually preferred the silence, attributing the temporary lapse in their mutual antipathy to Fitzroy being shaken up by Matthews going native. The killing at Ukurh would not in itself have so disturbed Fitzroy, concluded Darwin, only the inexplicable manner in which the mission had gone so badly wrong. Fitzroy had wanted to reaffirm his own cultural affiliations with the only other gentleman aboard.

As usual while underway, Darwin had spent much of the time in his hammock alone in his cabin, this time for an even longer stretch than during the Atlantic crossing and with his head and arms bandaged until they healed. He had forced himself to exercise by stumbling about the deck once per day but preferred to remain horizontal as much as possible. Nonetheless, the laudanum had helped him to spend the time productively, reviewing and consolidating his note-books. Every morning he had dictated a few pages to Syms. By the time the *Beagle* entered the Pacific, the official account of the voyage thus far filled eleven chapters under the working title of "Researches into Natural History and Geology During the Voyage of H.M.S. *Beagle*."

And, because he also felt the need to record what he dared not include in "Researches...," he had begun a private account as well. Once his arms had healed sufficiently to write by himself, the inkbottle and paper balanced on a short plank across the hammock, he had begun to spend a few hours each afternoon working on that personal record of the voyage. He had no idea what he would do with it, certainly not attempt to find a publisher, but felt compelled to record even what he did not intend to share with others.

He was both disappointed and pleased with how the voyage had gone thus far. It had already exceeded by six months the agreed on two years, his seasickness had not improved, and MacCormick and Fitzroy were two of the most arrogant asses he had ever met. They were not half as smart as they supposed. Fitzroy thought that might made right. MacCormick thought that age did so. And neither seemed capable of an honest intellectual discussion rooted in facts and logic. At least Fitzroy was proving to be of sterner stuff than his ancestry predicted, and he had promised to return home as directly as possible via the Pacific. Perhaps, Darwin hoped, he would be in Shrewsbury for Christmas. As for his stomach, which if anything had grown more sensitive since leaving Plymouth, he planned to continue the strategy of spending as much time ashore as possible. The laudanum helped while aboard and had, in fact, become a necessity for him. He would need to stock up in Valparaiso. He had survived thus far, he concluded and congratulated himself, and would survive another six months—just as long as the *Beagle* continued to defy her reputation as a coffin brig.

In fact, he deliberated, he would probably look back on the voyage in a few years and judge it the best undertaking he had ever agreed to. What he had observed so far had already completely converted his thinking about geology. Every formation he had encountered was un-

lerstandable in terms of Lyell's principles, without recourse to supernatural explanations. Most exciting of all, he was able to use those
principles to predict what he would find in places he had never been
before, like the presence of marine fossils in the basal stratum at
Santa Fe. He fully expected that his theory of Patagonia's emergence
from the sea would be borne out by what he would see in Chile. If he
had a chance to ride up into the Andes behind Valparaiso, he predicted that the sedimentary strata he found there, no matter how tilted,
buckled, and metamorphosed by the subterranean forces that had
pushed them upwards, would contain marine fossils.

And, just as exciting, those steep mountain slopes might provide
just the sort of natural laboratory in which to observe the gradation of
closely related, contemporaneous species, something like the two
Patagonian ostriches but over a shorter distance. The strong environmental gradients that Humboldt had described for the Andes were just
the sort of situation that might provide clues as to the biological ge-
netic principles that must complement Lyell's geological ones. Then,
Darwin repeatedly contemplated while lying in his hammock, he
would be able to explain the mechanisms that connected the emergence of new species to reproduction and environmental change. He
might even become the "Charles Lyell of biology," although he
barely admitted that ambition even to himself.

Besides the letter to his brother, Lucy was the only one he had discussed his ideas with. He still marveled that she had understood him
well enough to predict that he would find marine fossils exposed in
the Andean passes. Unlike MacCormick and Fitzroy, she was secure
enough in her own identity that she could openly discuss any topic
(excepting her spy work for Palmerston, and not that exactly because
of the nature of the need to keep that identity secret). Every time he
took a sip of laudanum he thought about her. He counted up the times
they had copulated. Nine, he was quite certain after having reviewed
the delicious memories many times. He wondered what orders she
had gone to carry out when she had abandoned him the last time. Had
Palmerston ordered her and Earle to assassinate another of Rosas's
allies who had outlived his usefulness? But he mainly wondered

whether he would ever see her again. Probably not, he concluded, with a complex amalgam of regret and relief.

He would see Emma though, back in Shropshire, perhaps as soon as the coming Christmas. Both their families would be ecstatic if a relationship blossomed. Yet he did not know if he even desired the married life. Before the voyage he would have been more certain, but now he was thinking that a family might take too much time away from his research. He could have pictured himself and Emma in some parsonage, but he now had no intention to pursue a clerical career, no matter the disappointment his father would feel. He would need to discuss everything with his brother, who seemed to have become a confirmed bachelor. Hopefully 'Ras would be at Shrewsbury for Christmas and would advise him as to the pros and cons, not only on marriage but whether his natural history ideas were even worth pursuing. Darwin retained few doubts on that score anymore, however. Whether or not he eventually solved the mystery of mysteries or not, his passion for serious natural history had become too great to abandon.

When Syms had come to announce that the *Beagle* was about to pass between the Fury Rocks and into the Pacific, Darwin had been thinking about Matthews and York.

He could not understand how the missionary could have married a Fuegian, not under any circumstances. He and Matthews had so much in common. Neither fit well the world of the Royal Navy. Their ages were similar, as was their resentment toward Fitzroy, as was the choice they had faced regarding a spiritual vocation. Yet Matthews must at base be very different to have made such a choice. Perhaps his utter lack of intellectual interests allowed him to contemplate a life among savages? And certainly the commitment required to carry out the mission required great love for the Fuegians. Still, to choose to live among them as one of them was so inexplicable to Darwin that he concluded that even Matthews could probably not explain, at least not with any degree of conviction, his own actions. And after the disaster at Ukurh, it seemed unlikely that Matthews would ever have the opportunity to explain himself.

Just consider York, reflected Darwin, suddenly appreciating the
irony. How different the Fuegian was from Matthews. York sometimes came to visit Darwin in his hammock to talk about what his
future in England might be like. He had no desire to talk about Matthews, Fuegia, Jeremy, or anything that had happened at Woollya or
Ukurh. He thought only of improving himself and would, judged
Darwin, do very well. He was even contemplating employing York in
some capacity. So, wondered Darwin, how could a Fuegian, albeit
much improved by education, have made the more rational decision
than a born Englishman, who had bound himself in a marriage that
was anathema to his own society?

But as the *Beagle* sailed out onto the Pacific, Darwin left those
thoughts to digest and dragged himself on deck for the occasion.
Standing at the lee bulwark, he marveled too much at the scene to feel
his stomach: white cumulus clouds fringed the brilliant blue dome
that fell to a horizon that had suddenly become infinite. Fitzroy came
over and, without a word, handed over a small envelope.

After retreating to his hammock, Darwin read the note inside: "My
sweet Charley. Thank you for delivering my letters. Robert will give
you this when you reach the Pacific. I'll cross the Andes from Santa
Fe by land and see you in Valparaiso. L."

Printed in the United Kingdom
by Lightning Source UK Ltd.
117375UKS00001B/133

7.5×10^{18}
The number of grains of sand on Earth.

70%
The percentage of the Earth's surface which is covered with water. Only around 3% of this is fresh (and drinkable).

365.2564 days
The length of a year on Earth (the extra .2564 creates the need for leap years).

8.6 million
The number of lightning strikes on Earth every single day.

200,000
The approximate number of people born every day (but 2 people die every second).

2414 km
The width of the solid iron ball which lies at the centre of the Earth.

Adam Spencer's

WORLD
of Numbers

NUMBERS. THEY'RE EVERYWHERE.

XOUM PUBLISHING

Sydney

XOUM

First published by Xoum in 2015

Xoum Publishing
PO Box Q324, QVB Post Office,
NSW 1230, Australia
www.xoum.com.au

ISBN 978-1-921134-86-9 (print)
ISBN 978-1-921134-87-6 (digital)

Front endpaper credit: NASA Goddard Space Flight Center Image by Reto Stöckli
(land surface, shallow water, clouds). Enhancements by Robert Simmon
(ocean color, compositing, 3D globes, animation). Data and technical
support: MODIS Land Group; MODIS Science Data Support Team; MODIS
Atmosphere Group; MODIS Ocean Group Additional data: USGS EROS Data
Center (topography); USGS Terrestrial Remote Sensing Flagstaff Field Center
(Antarctica); Defense Meteorological Satellite Program (city lights).
[Image has been cropped.]

Back endpaper credit: Gregory H. Revera under the Creative Commons
Attribution-Share Alike 3.0 Unported license. [Image has been cropped.]

The moral right of the author has been asserted.

Cataloguing-in-Publication data is available from the National Library of Australia

Cover design, text design and typesetting by Xou Creative, www.xou.com.au
Author photograph by David Stefanoff
Printed and bound by Asia Pacific Offset

Hello number lovers!

To those of you who bought last year's book, welcome back. To those of you joining this nerd-ageddon for the first time, it's great to have you along for the ride (and please go and buy last year's book ;-)

A lot has happened in 12 months. On the science front, we've taken incredible images of Pluto and its moon Charon; we've ramped up the Large Hadron Collider and quite possibly found incredible new stuff; and in the world of research, new discoveries abound and humans continue to ask 'why', often with spectacular results.

On a more personal level, I've learnt one of the great rules in life – publish a book that sells pretty well and people will lean on you, saying, 'Where's your next one?'

Well, here it is, *Adam Spencer's World of Numbers*.

The philosophy is similar to the *Big Book of Numbers*. The world is an incredible place – full of amazing things to know – and at the heart of both understanding the world and in describing what we know to each other, are numbers. Measuring temperature, length, speed, age, just counting things or exploring the beautiful intricacies of numbers themselves is, IMHO, one of the things that makes us human. It's also got to be one of the most enjoyable things you can possibly do while you're on this orb moving at 107,000 km/h through the Milky Way. So that is what the *World of Numbers* is all about: a good hearty slice of stuff we know and the ability of numbers to convey that knowledge.

I should point out there is nothing definitive about this book. To be honest, it represents a grab bag of stuff I thought was really interesting at any given time. So please don't get bogged down asking, 'Why didn't you include XYZ?'. Just sit back and marvel at how box jellyfish see, how fast a 92-year-old woman can run, or the threat to biodiversity that feral cats pose in Australia. And while you're at it, isn't it mindblowing how many different ways 70 people can line up?

Many of these 'facts' will be superseded as technology improves, ignorance is pushed back and we come to understand more about our world. I welcome sections of this book becoming out of date because that simply means we've learnt more – and that is never a bad thing.

One thing has changed significantly in the last 12 months. I've come to realise how much it can help calling upon the assistance of others in compiling a book like this. Whether it's specialists like Professor Fred Watson, the marine biologists at James Cook University, smell-meister Alex Russell, lifelong friend and science guru Dr Karl Kruszelnicki, the surfing scientist Dr Ruben Meerman, or FIDE chess master Brett Tindall, this book is all the more crammed with accurate information for their efforts.

Similarly, the web pages NumberADay, @Derektionary, jimwilder.com, ThisDayInMath and Wolfram MathWorld were invaluable for fact-checking our calendars and calculations. And the *QI* books, Brian Gaensler's *Extreme Cosmos* and John Emsley's *Nature's Building Blocks* make for brilliant and informative reading.

And while relying on specialists for the occasional inquiry, this pales in comparison to the efforts of similar curious minds as mine who helped me by providing a deluge of data and pursuing particular peculiarities that took my fancy. Thank you to Yael Bornstein, Alex Downie, Kate Hewson, Julian Ingham, Liam Scarratt and my two math-nerd-brothers-for-life, Sean Gardiner and Gareth White ... this simply could not have happened without your application but, more importantly, your lust for learning. Kudos.

Having praised these wonderful people, I should stop to clarify that any errors or omissions are, as the young people say these days, 'my bad'.

This book proudly wears the Xoum logo. If you ever want to publish something and want the assistance of three of the most amazing publishers around, pop into Xoum. Rod and Jon will greet you warmly ... and Roy will wander in around midday and produce his special genius. Thanks guys.

And to Mel, Ellie and Olivia, thank you. A life-defining year for the three of us and I could not love you more.

So, strap yourself in for the ride – absorb and be inspired – and, as always, contact me at book@adamspencer.com.au with any questions, comments or ... eeeerrrr misprints.

I really hope you enjoy my *World of Numbers*.

Adam S

V

The measure of us

well, the way we measure, at least ...

Trust me ...

0.999... = 1.

This freaks some people out but all it's saying is that however close to 1 you wish to get, you can go far enough along the sequence 0.9, 0.99, 0.999, 0.9999 ... to get that close. So when the 9s go on infinitely we are at 1.

But if people still don't believe you, point out 0.9999... must be fairly close to 1. How much would they like you to add to get to 1? Clearly you need to add nothing!

You could actually survive for around 9 seconds at 1000°C without suffering lasting injury ...

(please, please, *please* just take my word for that!)

2

Itty bitty primes

A prime number is a whole number greater than 1 that cannot be written as 2 whole numbers multiplied together except for 1 and itself. So 6 = 2 × 3 and hence 6 is not prime. But 7 is prime because it can be written as 1 × 7 but not as the product of any other factors. Two is the smallest prime number, and the only even prime.

Euler's theorem

Euler's beautiful theorem: V + F – E = 2 for convex poly-hedra shows that for a shape like this cube, the number of vertices (corners) V, plus the number of faces F, minus the number of edges E, equals 2.

A few cool things about hot

You know how, when it gets hot, we often say 'the mercury is rising'?

We say this because, since 1714, the mercury element has been used in glass thermometers in order to determine the temperature. Mercury is liquid at room temperature and its volume changes slightly as it is heated or cooled, so a small variation makes the mercury expand and move up the tube. Here are some places where the mercury has *really* gotten moving, or in some cases would have literally boiled:

Hottest air temperature on Earth: 56.7°C at Furnace Creek Ranch, in the romantically named Death Valley, California, USA, 10 July 1913

Hottest surface temperature on Earth: 70.7°C at Gandom Beryan in the Lut Desert, Kerman province, Iran, in 2005

Hottest ground temperature on Earth: 93.9°C again at Furnace Creek Ranch, Death Valley, California, USA, 15 July 1972

When it is very hot, the temperature beneath the surface of the soil can far exceed that of the surface or air, because any cooling wind takes a long time to penetrate the soil.

Hip to be square

The number after 3 is 4 and 4 = 2 × 2. That in itself may not seem all that impressive, but it is actually the only example of a prime number that is followed by a square.

e = 2.71828...

Three is the closest whole number to the 2 non-whole numbers that most mathematicians would consider most important. They are π = 3.14159... which you've probably heard of and e = 2.71828... which may well still be a mystery to you.

3

The 3rd day of the year is January 3

Hot places

Australia comes in at number 8 when ranking countries by highest recorded temperatures, thanks to a 50.7°C achieved by Oodnadatta, South Australia, on 2 January 1960.

Incidentally, the 'winning' countries are USA (56.7°C), Tunisia (55°C), Kuwait (53.6°C), while the 'losers' unsurprisingly are Antarctica (17.5°C(!)), Greenland (25.9°C), Iceland (30.5°C).

In Australia, state by state, the hottest recorded temperatures have been in:

South Australia: 50.7°C in Oodnadatta, 2 January 1960

Western Australia: 50.5°C in Mardie, 19 February 1998

NSW: 49.7°C in Menindee, 10 January 1939

Queensland: 49.5°C in Birdsville, 24 December 1972

Victoria: 48.8°C in Hopetoun, 7 February 2009

Northern Territory: 48.3°C in Finke, 1 & 2 January 1960

Tasmania: 42.2°C in Scamander, 30 January 2009

Finally, the place with the most consecutive days above 100 degrees Fahrenheit, or 37.8°C, is Marble Bar in Western Australia (31 October 1923–7 April 1924). Congrats, Marbs!

4

The 4th day of the year is January 4

The number four

is the smallest composite number. A composite number is a positive integer that has at least 1 positive divisor other than 1 or the number itself. In other words, a composite number is any integer greater than 1 that is not a prime number.

Our first square

Four being 2 × 2 is also referred to as '2 squared' making 4 the smallest interesting square (of course, I'm ignoring the trivial examples of 0 and 1. Don't worry, they won't take offence).

Hot (and cold) spaces

Below are the average temperatures of planets and other objects in our solar system (all °C):

The Sun: 5505
Mercury: 167
Venus: 464
Earth: 15
Earth's Moon: –20
Mars: –65
Jupiter: –110
Saturn: –140
Uranus: –195
Neptune: –200
Pluto: –225

The brightest known natural stellar system in the Universe is Eta Carinae, about 7500 light years from our Sun. Its temperature is 36,000–40,000°C. This amazing image of the blue hypergiant star comes from NASA's Hubble Space Telescope.

One of Hubble's stunning images of the gas and dust clouds of the supermassive star Eta Carinae. Source: Public domain

Solidly Platonic

There are 5 'Platonic solids'. What are they? Well, I'm sure you're familiar with a cube, probably the best-known Platonic solid. To describe a cube in fancy-pants maths talk we say, 'A cube is a 3-dimensional shape with each face the same polygon, [namely a square] and all the faces meeting the same way at each vertex [corner]'.

Platonic solids get their name from the famous ancient Greek philosopher and extremely clever dude, Plato.

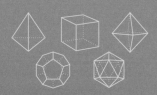

5

*The **5th** day of the year is **January 5***

Check out these amazing numbers (not quite to scale, obviously!)

−273.15°C

Absolute zero. The coldest possible temperature at which atoms theoretically stop moving. Pack accordingly. Scientists also call this temperature 0 degrees kelvin (K) and kelvin units go up at the same rate as Celsius. As you'll see on page 10, we've come incredibly close to this temperature in the lab.

−40°C/F

The point at which the Celsius and Fahrenheit scales intersect.

−273°C

The lowest temperature survived by a living creature – the tardigrade. Check out pages 118–119 for more about these amazingly rugged little invertebrates.

0°

The melting

−183°C

The boiling point of oxygen. Below this, oxygen is in liquid form. Liquid oxygen is used for everything from medical devices to treating waste water to launching rocket ships. At −219°C liquid oxygen freezes.

6

e 6th day of the
r is January 6

Perfectly six

Take the divisors of 6 apart from 6 itself (we call these the 'aliquot' divisors or 'proper' factors) and add them together. You get 1 + 2 + 3 = 6. It doesn't happen very often that the sum of the aliquot divisors of a number add up to the number. The Greeks christened them 'perfect' numbers and 6 is the smallest perfect number.

There is only 1 other 'perfec day' in a calendar year. Can you guess what it is? Hint: It falls in the month of January.

12.7°C

The lowest recorded human body temperature survived – by a 2-year-old Polish boy in 2014.

100°C

The boiling temperature of water (at sea level).

46.5°C

The highest recorded human body temperature survived – one Willie Jones, in 1980.

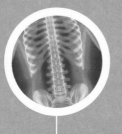

36°C

The approximate melting temperature of butter.

70.7°C

The hottest recorded surface temperature on Earth – in the Lut Desert, Iran, 2005.

37°C

The normal average body temperature of you (presuming you're a human being).

7! minute week

When we multiply a whole number by all the whole numbers less than it all the way down to 1, we get what mathematicians call a 'factorial', which we denote with an exclamation mark. So 4! = 4 × 3 × 2 × 1 = 24.

Convince yourself that 2 × 7! is the exact number of minutes in a 7-day week and that there are 10! seconds in 6 weeks.

7

*The **7th** day of the year is January 7*

1027°C

The maximum temperature of the flame produced by burning wood.

151°C

The highest temperature survived by a living creature – take a bow, once again, the incredible tardigrade!

1400°C

The hottest part of a wax candle's flame.

101°C

The average temperature during the daytime on the surface of the Earth's Moon. Not ideal picnic weather, to say the least.

1200°C

The temperature of volcanic lava (when erupting).

357°C

The boiling temperature of mercury.

8

The **8th** *day of the year is* **January 8**

F_6

The number 8 is a Fibonacci number. The Fibonacci numbers – 1, 1, 2, 3, 5, 8, 13, and so on – are found by adding 2 consecutive numbers to get the next one.

As you can see, 8 is the 6th Fibonacci number – hence we sometimes write it as F_6.

Lucky 8

The number 8 is considered especially auspicious in China because its Cantonese pronunciation, 'ba', sounds very simlar to 'fa' – meaning good fortune.

Conversely, the number 4 sounds like the word 'si' – meaning death. Needless to say, it's *not* considered lucky.

5555°C

The boiling point of tungsten. The highest boiling point of any element.

$1.416785 \times 10^{32}\,°C$

Absolute hot. The highest theoretical, or 'Planck Temperature'. Don't bother packing a water bottle – not only will you and it have vaporised, the entire laws of conventional physics will also have broken down!

5,500,000,000,000°C

The hottest manmade temperature (that's 5.5 *trillion*°C/K or 5.5×10^{12}°C) which came to us courtesy of the Large Hadron Collider in August 2012.

10,000,000°C

The peak temperature inside a nuclear explosion fireball (inital X-ray blast).

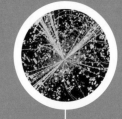

15,000,000°C

The temperature of the Sun's core. To make writing massive numbers like this easier, we can write 1.5×10^7. Here 1×10^7 would be the number 1 with 7 zeros after it.

Consecutive powers

The numbers 8 and 9 (2^3 and 3^2) are the only consecutive powers of integers.

Sure, that's pretty nifty, but if you want to sound fancier, you could also say:

'$x^p - y^q = 1$ has only 1 solution for integers p and q both greater than 1.'

This was first conjectured in 1844 by the legendary French (and Belgian) mathematician Eugène Catalan – and proved some 160 years later by Romanian gun Preda Mihăilescu.

A few hot things about cool

Now, Marble Bar locals might reach for their beanies when temperatures drop below 20°C, but suffice to say, it gets properly cold in other parts of our planet ...

In fact, the coldest air temperature on Earth in recorded history was –89.2°C on 21 July 1983 at Vostok Station, Antarctica. More recently, on 10 August 2010 at Dome Argus, Antarctica, –93.2°C was recorded, but this is yet to be certified.

While that's enough to make you want to pack another pair of socks, the coldest known natural temperature in the Universe is around 3 degrees kelvin or 3°C above the absolute coldest it can get in relatively empty areas of space. In April 2015, a group of scientists from Stanford University announced they had cooled an arrangement of rubidium molecules to just 0.00000000005 of a degree above absolute zero.

The winners in the category of 'countries with the lowest temperatures ever recorded' reads as follows: Antarctica (–89.2°C), Russia (–68°C) and Greenland (–66.1°C), while the losers include Malaysia (7.8°C), the Philippines (6.3°C) and Puerto Rico (4.4°C).

10

The **10th** *day of the* *year is* **January 10**

Pandigital

The 10 decimal digits 0, 1, 2, 3, 4, 5, 6, 7, 8, 9 can form 3,265,920 10-digit pandigital numbers, which is a number where each digit appears at least once; for example, 4,356,012,879; 6,037,428,951, and so on. How many of them are prime?

Despite our amazing, scorching Australian summers, we've got some respectable efforts in the winter months, too. The coldest places ever measured by state are:

NSW: –23.0°C in Charlotte Pass, 29 June 1994

Tasmania: –13.0°C in Butlers Gorge, Shannon, and Tarraleah, 30 June 1983

Victoria: –11.7°C in Omeo, 15 June 1965 and in Falls Creek, 3 July 1970

Queensland: –10.6°C in Stanthorpe, 23 June 1961 and in The Hermitage, 12 July 1965

South Australia: –8.2°C in Yongala, 20 July 1976

Northern Territory: –7.5°C in Alice Springs, 17 July 1976

Western Australia: –7.2°C in Eyre, 17 August 2008

Double the anagrams

Not only is $11 + 2 = 12 + 1$, but 'eleven plus two' is an anagram of 'twelve plus one'.

Eleven

is the first 2-digit prime number and $11 \times 11^{11} + 11^{11} - 1$ is a prime number whose expression uses 11 ones.

11

The 11th day of the year is January 11

61 things we know exist (and a few we really hope do)

Everything around us – our bodies, our food, even the air we breathe – is made up of 'atoms': the elemental building blocks of the Universe.

However, if we zoom in, we find that atoms can be broken down further into electrons, protons and neutrons. One of the greatest journeys of the 20th century was when scientists went *inside* these building blocks. It turns out that if you zoom in further you get … go on … have a guess … that's right, even *smaller* particles!

These are what's known as fundamental particles.

What we know about fundamental particles today blows my mind – not just *how* much we know, but how *quickly* we've come to know it. As recently as 1932, all we knew was that an atom had a nucleus at its centre made up of protons and neutrons, with electrons 'orbiting' around it. This was thanks to the great physicists J. J. Thomson (electron, 1897); Ernest Rutherford (nucleus, 1911, proton, 1919) and James Chadwick (neutron, 1932). Their discoveries gave us the basic shape of an atom, but that was it.

And then the predictions started coming thick and fast. But as great as the theories were, we just didn't have the machinery to test them out. A mere 80 years later, the list of 3 fundamental particles has grown to 61. And it's only going to grow further. In

Homer's Last Theorem?

In the 1995 *Simpsons* Halloween episode, it's claimed that $1782^{12} + 1841^{12} = 1922^{12}$. Now, if this were true, it would show that one of the world's most famous pieces of mathematics – Fermat's Last Theorem – was in fact wrong. Relax, $1782^{12} + 1841^{12}$ does *not* equal 1922^{12}, but it comes very close. In fact, $1782^{12} + 1841^{12} = 1921.99999995...^{12}$.

This is just one of the hundreds of mathematical in-jokes that the writers of *The Simpsons* have inserted into the cartoon series. British author Simon Singh wrote a great book called *The Simpsons and Their Mathematical Secrets* on this very topic.

fact, physicists lick their lips at this the most exciting of times.

So what are these 61 fundamental particles? Let's get the most complicated ones out of the way first.

'Quarks' are incredibly small particles and are the building blocks of protons and neutrons. Think of the nucleus of an atom as the Sun, the surrounding electrons as the planets, and the quarks as the elements that make up the Sun. The interaction between quarks in protons and neutrons plays a vital role in holding the nucleus together.

Just in case you were thinking, 'Hey, this is pretty simple' there are 6 types – or flavours – of quark: up, down, strange, charm, top and bottom. For each of these flavours there is an antiparticle called an 'antiquark', taking us to 12 objects. But the way quarks interact depends on something we call their 'colour' and each quark has one of 3 possible colours (red, green or blue). This gives us a grand total of $6 \times 2 \times 3 = 36$ types of quark! Phew. Trust me, that's the nastiest bit.

One of the discoverers of the quark, Murray Gell-Mann, based the spelling of 'quark' on this passage from James Joyce's classic *Finnegans Wake*:

Three quarks for Muster Mark!
Sure he has not got much of a bark
And sure any he has it's all beside the mark

Next, meet the 'leptons'. There are 12 types of leptons. These fundamental particles don't interact the same way as quarks

---

Solid, Archimedes, solid

There are 13 Archimedean solids. An Archimedean solid is a highly symmetric, semi-regular convex polyhedron composed of 2 or more types of regular polygons that meet in identical vertices. The solid shown here is a *truncated icosahedron*. They are different from Platonic solids (which we met earlier), which are composed of only 1 type of polygon meeting in identical vertices.

Archimedean solids get their name from the ancient Greek mathematician, inventor, physicist, engineer and astronomer Archimedes. He really was a maths machine.

13

The 13th day of the year is January 13

– instead, they do really cool things like form the outer shell of atoms. It's only when atoms 'see' each other's outer shells that they can get together and do really amazing chemistry stuff.

The remaining 13 fundamental particles are called 'bosons'. Bosons are vital for the interactions between the other particles. For example, when light hits a solar panel, the boson called a photon helps us understand how the light generates energy.

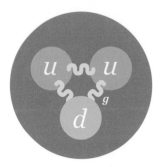

A proton contains 2 'up' quarks, 1 'down' quark and a boson called a gluon to help hold it all together.

Scientists are looking deep into space for things called 'axions' that might explain dark matter; deep underground for insights into the forces at play in the Universe and all sorts of other amazing places. What we call the 'standard model' of particle physics is continuing to evolve as we make more breakthroughs in understanding what constitutes our world.

In just 80 years the number of fundamental particles we know about has grown from 3 to 61. But right now we're cranking up the Large Hadron Collider (LHC) in Switzerland on the hunt for even more particles of greater energy and mass. We were very excited in 2012 to confirm the discovery of the Higgs boson,

14

*The **14th** day of the year is January 14*

Plus or minus?

By selecting one of + or – in front of each number, there are 14 solutions to $\pm 1 \pm 2 \pm 3 \pm 4 \pm 5 \pm 6 \pm 7 \pm 8 = 0$.

For example:

$+1 + 2 + 3 + 4 - 5 - 6 - 7 + 8 = 0$

Can you find them all?

which has a mass of about 126 protons, but the energy level we found it at strongly suggests that there must be more. There might even be 5 types of Higgs boson. In mid-2015 the team at the LHC seemed to confirm an arrangement of 5 quarks in an array called a 'pentaquark'. Now that's awesome. The message here is, 'watch this space' ... get it, space!

Most authors fear that a reference in their book might be out of date in a few years time. I'm excited that in a decade or so, our list of 61 fundamental particles will have been superseded!

The W⁻boson carries away the negative charge and transforms the electron into an electron neutrino.

When an electron decays into an electron neutrino the W-boson carries away the negative charge.

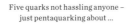

Five quarks not hassling anyone – just pentaquarking about ...

Triangular numbers

$1 + 2 + 3 + 4 + 5 = 15$. We call 15 the fifth 'triangular' number. Triangular numbers can be represented in the form of a triangular grid of points where the first row contains a single element and each subsequent row contains one more element than the previous one.

15

*The **15th** day of the year is **January 15***

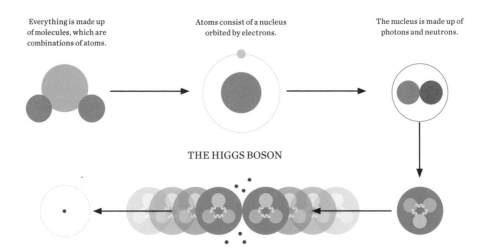

Everything is made up of molecules, which are combinations of atoms.

Atoms consist of a nucleus orbited by electrons.

The nucleus is made up of photons and neutrons.

THE HIGGS BOSON

Higgs boson particles have a field called the Higgs Field which acts like a 'syrup'. It plays a crucial role in slowing down protons so they 'clot', forming matter.

To prove the theory, protons were smashed into each other at very high speeds in the Large Hadron Collider. Little particles called Higgs boson became measurable from these collisions.

Protons are composed of quarks and gluons. Nobody knew why protons stuck together instead of flying around at the speed of light, but they had a theory.

When an electron and its antiparticle – a positron – are smashed into each other at massively fast speeds, they annihilate each other and produce electromagnetic radiation in the form of photons. Some of these photons will decay into types of leptons called muons and anti-muons.

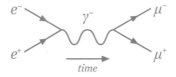

16

*The **16th** day of the year is **January 16***

$16 = 2^4 = 4^2$

In fact, 16 is the only number that can be written as $a^b = b^a$ when a and b are not equal. This was proven to be the case by Leonhard Euler, without doubt the greatest mathematical gun of all time.

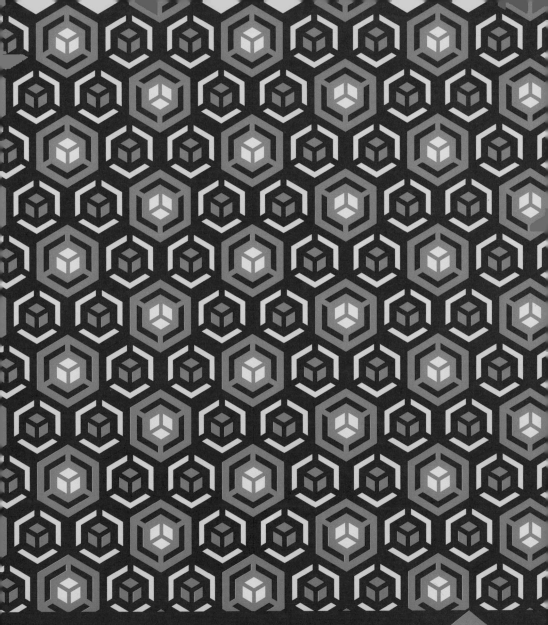

Wallpaper groups

Wallpaper groups, also known as a plane symmetry group or special tessellation, is a type of 2-dimensional repetitive pattern, based on the symmetries in the pattern. Such patterns occur frequently in architecture and decorative art. There are 17 distinct wallpaper groups. The example above belongs to the group *p3m1*.

Oh, and by the way:

An English haiku
Has seventeen syllables
Flowing through three lines

On this day in 1905 Mathematician D.R. Kaprekar was born, 199 years after Benjamin Franklin

Brian Cox, who works at the Large Hadron Collider on the Atlas project, is also one of the hottest objects in the known Universe.

18

Cute cube

If you consider both the cube of 18 and the cube of the sum of its digits, you stumble across this cute little fact:

$18 = 5 + 8 + 3 + 2$ and

$18^3 = (5 + 8 + 3 + 2)^3 = 5832.$

Apart from the trivial case of 0, 18 is the only number equal to twice the sum of its digits, that is, $18 = 2 \times (1 + 8)$.

Firkin awesome!

What are kilderkins, butts, firkins and hogsheads, I hear you ask? And what about virgates, alqueires, oxgangs and hides? Wonder no more.

No, they're not those weird friends of your dad's who come over on weekends and disappear into the man cave. Nor are they members of that obscure Swedish death metal band your cousin is obsessed with.

Kilderkins, butts, firkins and hogsheads are all imperial measurements and many are still used today, mostly in the food and beverage industry. A firkin is just over 40 litres, 2 firkins make a kilderkin and 3 kilderkins make a hogshead.

But Adam, what of the virgates, alqueires, oxgangs and hides? Glad you asked. They're all units of area. But while an oxgang (15 acres, the amount an ox could plough in one season), a virgate (2 oxgang) and a hide (4 virgate) all date back to the English field system of the Middle Ages, an alqueire is a traditional unit of land area in Portugal and in Brazil where it is still in use today.

Hop to it!

$19^5 + 19^2 + 19^1 + 19^3 + 19^5 + 19^6 + 19^4 + 19^0 = 52,135,640$ (the powers here are the digits of 52,135,640 in order). To test your addition skills, work out the powers with a calculator then add them together by hand! You can do this, young grasshopper.

(Note you may have to ask Mum or Dad about the 'grasshopper' reference – even better, watch the television series *Kung Fu* and the movie *The Karate Kid* ... now!)

19

The 19th day of the year is January 19

SYDNEY
by numbers

48,000
The capacity of the historic Sydney Cricket Ground. Sydney's ANZ Stadium holds closer to 83,500.

31.7%
The estimated number of Sydney residents who were born overseas. The overall figure for Australia is around 22.2%.

4,293,000
The estimated population of Sydney, making it the nation's most populous city.

1222.7 mm
The annual rainfall in Sydney. About 90% of that seems to fall while I'm outside watching the footy.

1988
The year in which the loan for the Sydney Harbour Bridge was finally paid off. It cost about £10 million in 1937 – about $1.5 billion in today's coin. Mind you, we're still paying a toll ...

20
The 20th day of the year is January 20

Euler pie

The very important mathematical constants e and π are closely related to the number 20 through the equation $e^{\pi} - \pi \approx 20$ (actually it's 19.999099979...).

12

The number of personnel in Sydney's
(and therefore Australia's) first police force.
It was comprised of well-behaved convicts.
What could possibly go wrong?

4,840,600

The official population of Sydney as of
June 2014. That's almost 21% of the
total Aussie population.

1788

The year in which the Brits arrived
in Sydney. But that's nothing compared to the
estimated settlement by Indigenous Australians,
who have been here for at least 40,000 years.

180 mm

The reported variation in the height of the
Sydney Harbour Bridge due to expansion and
contraction (depending on the weather).

1,056,006

The number of tiles on the
Sydney Opera House.

21 squares

To tile a larger square using
only smaller squares whose
side lengths are all different
whole numbers requires
a minimum of 21 smaller
squares.

The larger square is of size 112
× 112, the smallest square, the
little one near the middle, is
2 × 2 and the biggest one, top
left, is 50 × 50.

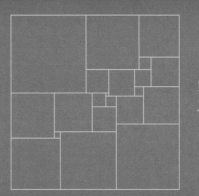

21

*The **21st** day of the
year is January 21*

Dude! Where's my chaldron?

The phrase 'don't hide your light under a bushel' goes all the way back to the King James Bible.

In Matthew 5:15, among other places, it is said, *'Neither do men light a candle, and put it under a bushel, but on a candlestick; and it giveth light unto all that are in the house.'*

Although the phrase has come to mean 'if you're good at something, don't be shy telling people all about it', there's always a backstory! The bushel wasn't just a measure, it was also applied to the basket or pot into which a bushel's worth of stuff would fit – thus the biblical phrase referred to hiding the light under this pot, not burying it in wheat.

The word bushel had been around since the mid-1200s and may well have come from the French word *buissiel* meaning 'little box'. It's a measure of dry goods equal to 4 pecks. How big is a peck? A British peck was 2 gallons while its US cousin was 8 quarts.

If you had more than a bushel of stuff, lucky you: you might have had a 'strike' (2 imperial bushels), a 'coomb' (4 bushels), a 'quarter' (8 bushels), or, if you were really planning to party with your dry commodities, perhaps you had a 'load' – 40 bushels of stuff!

And if the stuff you were carting around was coal, you might have had what I consider one of the cooler terms for volume ... a whole 'chaldron', or 36 bushels. Word to the wise, though – a chaldron's not going to fit in your average backpack.

22

The 22nd day of the year is January 22

There is around 10 'African elephants' worth of paint on the Eiffel Tower ...

In other words: 60 tonnes! It's been repainted 18 times in its life, about once every 7 years. It takes 18 months for a team of 25 specialist painters suspended by 50 kilometres of safety lines. They go through 1500 brushes, 1500 aprons and 1000 pairs of leather gloves as they spruce up the tower by hand, the same way as it's always been done.

The Birthday Problem

How large does a group of people have to be before there is a better than 50% chance that somewhere in the group is a shared birthday? The answer to this classic piece of maths, 'The Birthday Problem', is a surprisingly small 23 people.

#$%! you right back

Yesterday we noted that 22! has 22 digits. Well, it turns out 23! is equal to 25852016738884976640000, which has 23 digits. Can you guess how many digits 24! has ... yes, 24! = 620448401733239439360000, has 24! digits. This pattern stops here.

23

The 23rd day of the year is January 23

On this day in 1912 Mathematician David Hilbert was born

How big's a bottle?

Okay, your average wine bottle almost always holds ¾ of a litre, or 750 ml. But why?

In Roman times, wine was generally stored in clay vessels, however by the 1500s, as glass-blowing technology improved, well-heeled households would use glass bottles to tap a ration from wooden barrels.

By the 17th century, bottles were able to be produced in more consistent quantities, sizes and shapes and over time the 'standard' cylindrical wine bottle shape we know today evolved.

Bottle sizes varied for the next few centuries (in fact, they weren't standardised at 750 ml until the 1970s) however they mostly fell between about 600 ml and 800 ml during that time. Why? Well, there are a few different theories floating about. The most boring, though perhaps most pragmatic explanation, is that it was simply a convenient size – and easy to carry.

Personally, I like these other plausible options: that the range (around 750 ml) happened to be the average capacity of a glass-blower's lungs (and thus that's the biggest bottle they could blow); or, according to some, it was considered the 'proper' ration for a grown man with his meal. Sure, the alcohol content of wines back then was probably lower, around 10%, but that's still a pretty hefty drink!

24

The **24th** *day of the year is* **January 24**

$4! = 4 \times 3 \times 2 \times 1 = 24$

which means that 4 people could line up 24 different ways. That might not be all that impressive, but 62 people can line up in 62! ways, which is more ways than there are fundamental particles in the entire observable Universe!

Pyramid²

Did you know that, apart from the trivial case of 1,

$$1^2 + 2^2 + ... + 24^2 = 70^2$$

is the only non-trivial 'pyramidal' number that is a square? You do now!

100 things ...

(or more) you (probably) didn't know *about the first 100 elements*

I reckon it's fair to say that of any single set of numbers humankind has compiled, the Periodic Table of the elements sheds the greatest light on our understanding of the Universe.

The elements in the Periodic Table are arranged by their atomic number, that is, the number of protons in the nucleus – if you will, the heart of the atom.

So from 1 to 100, from hydrogen (H) to fermium (Fm), throughout this book you'll find 100 (or more) things you (probably) didn't know about the first 100 elements.

Let's kick things off at number 1 with everyone's hugely abundant, Sun-fuelling favourite ...

Sum of 2 squares

Twenty-five is the smallest square that can be written as a sum of 2 positive squares:

$25 = 5^2 = 3^2 + 4^2$.

What are the next couple?

On the topic of cool things involving the sum of 2 squares, $24^2 + 25^2$ is prime as is $25^2 + 26^2$.

25

Hydrogen

Hydrogen is the most abundant element in the Universe: a staggering 88% of *all* atoms are hydrogen. It fuels stars like our Sun, in the centre of which the temperature gets as high as 15,000,000°C (wear a hat!). At this sort of temperature the protons in hydrogen fuse to form the nuclei of helium atoms. In doing so they release massive amounts of energy. This takes about a million years to reach the Sun's surface after which it takes only 8 minutes for the light produced to reach the Earth.

1234567891011121314151617181920212223242526272829303132333435363738394041424344454647484950515253
5455565758596061626364656667686970717273747576777879808182838485868788899091929394959697989910100

26

*The **26th** day of the year is **January 26***

Fermat's sandwich

Fermat's sandwich theorem states that 26 is the only number sandwiched between a perfect square $5^2 = 25$ and a perfect cube $3^3 = 27$. According to Simon Singh (1997), after challenging other mathematicians to establish this result while not revealing his own proof, Fermat took particular delight in taunting the English mathematicians Wallis and Digby with their inability to prove the result.

Helium

Helium and hydrogen account for a mind-blowing 99% of the Universe's elemental mass! However, there are 8 times as many hydrogen atoms as there are helium atoms. Helium has the lowest boiling and melting points of any element.

Many of us have inhaled helium and spoken in a funny voice. This happens because the sounds leave your vocal cords in the usual way, but then they pass through a different medium – helium – so different (and often hilarious) sounds emerge.

1234567891011121314151617181920212223242526272829303132333435363738394041424344454647484950515253
5455565758596061626364656667686970717273747576777879808182838485868788899091929394959697989910

$27^3 = 19,683$

which has a digit sum of 27. There is no larger number for which the sum of the digits of the cube is equal to the number. Can you find the 6 smaller numbers for which this is the case? Hint: Two of the answers are 'trivial'.

27

Lithium

Lithium is the third element on the Periodic Table and is a soft, silver-white metal. Along with hydrogen and helium, lithium was produced in the Big Bang, but in much smaller amounts. Lithium is found in tiny quantities in plenty of living creatures but we don't quite know why as it doesn't seem to serve any special biological function. However, it does have medical benefits: the lithium ion Li^+ is sometimes given to people as a mood-stabilising drug in the treatment of bipolar disorder.

28

The 28th day of the year is January 28

A perfect day ...

The proper factors of 28 are 1, 2, 4, 7 and 14. Further, we have $28 = 1 + 2 + 4 + 7 + 14$.

So 28 is the second perfect number (a number which is the sum of its proper factors) and the last year day that will be perfect.

Like all the perfect numbers except for 6, it is the sum of the cubes of consecutive odd numbers starting from 1, that is, $28 = 1^3 + 3^3$.

Convince yourself that 496 is a perfect number and find the sum of consecutive odd cubes starting from 1 to give you 496.

Beryllium

The only elements formed at the Big Bang party way back when were hydrogen, helium and lithium. Beryllium is the first element on the Periodic Table *not* formed in the Big Bang.

Even though it has no BB street cred, beryllium is still an important element. In 1932, the Nobel-winning English physicist James Chadwick bombarded a sample of beryllium with alpha-rays from radium and in doing so discovered the neutron. Cool.

... and my birthday!

Happy birthday, me!

2^{29} = 536,870,912 is a 9-digit number with no digit repeated.

All the numbers from 2 up to 29 are either prime or have at most 2 prime factors. For example, $12 = 2 \times 2 \times 3$ so its prime factors are 2 and 3. This run stops tomorrow at day $30 = 2 \times 3 \times 5$.

29

*The **29th** day of the year is January 29*

My birthday!

Boron

The word boron comes from the Arabic word *buraq* meaning white, which was the name for borax (or sodium borate), from which boron is commonly obtained. The famous English chemist Humphrey Davy fused the word 'borax' with 'carbon' to get boron.

The very existence of boron might be proof that the Big Bang was *inhomogeneous*! Say what? This just means the Big Bang did not create an even distribution of protons, electrons and neutrons. Simple, yeah?

1234567891011121314151617181920212223242526272829303132333435363738394041424344454647484950515253
5455565758596061626364656667686970717273747576777879808182838485868788899091929394959697989

30

The 30th day of the year is January 30

Dirty Gertie

$1^1 + 2^2 + 3^3 + ... + 30^{30} =$

208492413443704093346554910065262730566475781

is prime. Maybe you'd better take my word for it.

Carbon

The element with 6 protons in its nucleus, carbon, is present in everything from pencils to diamonds and is the most essential element in order for life to exist. Living creatures need carbon for eating and breathing, plant growth, and supporting the structure of our cells.

About ¼ of your entire body mass is carbon. Because of the strong bonds that carbon can form inside our cells – for example, in the amino acids that make up our body tissue – you are officially known as a 'carbon-based life form'.

3456789101112131415161718192021222324252627282930313233343536373839404142434445464748495051525354

555657585960616263646566676869707172737475767778798081828384858687888990919293949596979899100

Mersenne primes

Thirty-one is prime and $31 = 2^5 - 1$. That is, 31 is a prime number of the form $2^p - 1$ with p prime. We call these numbers Mersenne primes and most of the massive prime numbers we've discovered are Mersenne primes. In January 2013, Curtis Cooper discovered the monstrously big $2^{57,885,161} - 1$ which is a prime number over 17 million digits long.

Check out my TED talk on the subject by searching *TED talk Adam Spencer*.

31

*The **31st** day of the year is **January 31st***

Nitrogen

I'm sure you know that without oxygen you'd choke to death. But did you know that the air we breathe is actually made up of 78% nitrogen? Not only that, if the level of nitrogen gets much *above* 78% you could die of asphyxiation (lack of oxygen). Think about that next time you take a deep breath!

Nitrogen gas is used in all sorts of industries. Car airbags, for example, are engaged by the explosive sodium azide, which is a combination of sodium and nitrogen. Kapow!

32

The 32nd day of the year is February 1

Ask the Leyland numbers

$32 = 2^5$ and $32 = 1^1 + 2^2 + 3^3$.

If a number can be written in the form $a^b + b^a$ with neither a nor b equal to 1, it is called a Leyland number. Convince yourself that 32 is a Leyland number.

If you're paying attention to the headings of these calendar entries you'll notice most are just alliteration or bad puns. This one might confuse younger readers who are advised to ask their parents about *The Leyland Brothers* or look them up on YouTube.

Oxygen

While oxygen only comes in at number 8 on the Periodic Table and wasn't present in the Big Bang (only hydrogen, helium and lithium were), it is in fact the third most abundant element in the Universe.

In a typical 70-kg adult (or a massive kid, I guess), about 44 kg of them (63%) is oxygen. This might seem weird because oxygen is a gas, but partnered with hydrogen it forms water. An amazing 60% of an adult's body weight is water.

3456789101112131415161718192021222324252627282930313233343536373839404142434445464748495051525354
5556575859606162636465666768697071727374757677787980818283848586878889909192939495969798991001

Fine young factorials

Convince yourself that:

$33 = 1! + 2! + 3! + 4!$

$33! - 1$ is a (pretty big) prime number. $32! - 1$ is a (not quite as big but still pretty big) prime number. 32 and 33 are the largest known consecutive numbers for which these 'factorials minus ones' are prime.

We call primes of the form $n! + 1$ and $n! - 1$ factorial primes.

So $4! - 1 = 4 \times 3 \times 2 \times 1 - 1 = 23$ is a factorial prime, as is

$3! + 1 = 3 \times 2 \times 1 + 1 = 7.$

The largest factorial prime we currently know is the 712,355-digit monster $150209! + 1$.

33

The 33rd day of the year is February 2

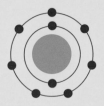

Fluorine

While most of us have heard of, and hopefully have good access to, fluoridated tap water, did you know that fluoride is also present in chicken, pork, eggs, butter, cheese, various types of fish and tea? Teflon, famous for putting the 'non-stick' into non-stick frying pans, is the polymer polytetrafluoroethene. While some people claim that we got non-stick frypans from the space race, it's actually the other way around. Non-stick frypans were available a decade before Teflon was a key part of the design of the 1969 lunar lander.

34

The 34th day of the year is February 3

Primmed and primed

Thirty-four is the smallest integer such that it and both its neighbours are the product of the same number of primes. That is, $33 = 3 \times 11$, $34 = 2 \times 17$ and $35 = 5 \times 7$ are each the product of 2 prime numbers.

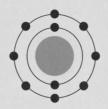

Neon

The fascinating gentleman, mountaineer and professor of organic chemistry, J. Norman Collie, was such a cool dude it's suggested he was the basis for Arthur Conan Doyle's famous detective Sherlock Holmes (who was himself one mean chemist). To add to his stellar list of achievements, Collie claimed to have discovered neon, though this is probably not true. Signs powered by neon might seem, let's be honest, a little gaudy at times, but they are also extremely hardy. A typical neon sign can operate without servicing for up to 20 years.

Hex-travaganza!

Check out these 6 spunky free hexominoes (polyominoes made up of 6 squares).

When I say 'free' I don't mean 'out of prison'. I mean they can't be rotated or reflected to match each other.

There are 35 free hexominoes in all. Try to find them and look up any you miss online.

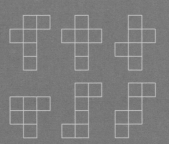

35

*The **35th** day of the year is February 4*

Flying by numbers ...

4.88

The number of metres Australian Lawrence Hargrave flew in his box kite on 12 November 1894. He linked 4 kites together, added a sling seat, and up, up and away he went.

4

The number of brief flights Wilbur and Orville Wright made on 17 December 1903. They achieved the first powered, sustained and controlled aeroplane flight. In the 1890s, the brothers had opened a bike repair and sales shop (the Wright Cycle Exchange, later the Wright Cycle Company), using the bike craze to fund their passion for flight.

14.56

The length, in hours, of Amelia Earhart's 1932 transatlantic solo flight. She intended to fly to Paris to emulate Charles Lindbergh, but after contending with strong northerly winds, icy conditions and mechanical problems, she landed in a pasture at Culmore, north of Derry, in Northern Ireland. When a farmhand asked, 'Have you flown far?', Earhart replied, 'From America'. For the trip, she flew a single-engine Lockheed Vega 5B. It was 8.39 m long, 12.49 m wide (wing-span) and had a height of 2.59 m. In 1937, while attempting to circumnavigate the globe, Earhart disappeared over the central Pacific Ocean near Howland Island.

13,110

The number of passengers carried by the blimp *Graf Zeppelin*, the first aircraft in history to fly over a million miles. It made 590 flights, 144 oceanic crossings and spent 17,177 hours aloft. It flew between 1928–37 but was scrapped in 1940 when German Air Minister Hermann Göring decided its metal should be melted down for reuse by the German military aircraft industry.

36

The number of fatalities of the *Hindenburg* blimp disaster on 6 May 1937. Of the 97 people on board, 35 were killed (along with one person on the ground). During a failed attempt to dock a mooring mast, a fire started in the tail of the airship, igniting leaking hydrogen. While there is some debate about what caused the fire, a plausible theory is static electricity. The incident shattered confidence in airships and marked the end of their era.

36

*The **36th** day of the year is February 5*

Three dozen

Thirty-six is the sum of the first 3 cubes, $1^3 + 2^3 + 3^3 = 36$. The sum of the first n cubes is always a square number and for those who get off on mathematical notation we write this as:

Note that this sequence and its formula were known to (and possibly discovered by) Nicomachus back around 100 CE.

$$\sum_{k=1}^{n} k^3 = \left(\frac{n(n+1)}{2}\right)^2$$

2140

Kilometres per hour – the average cruising speed of the Concorde. By comparison, 1225.044 km/h is the speed of sound. (Airbus A380-800s barely limp along at an average cruising speed of around 900 km/h.) The Concorde flew regular transatlantic flights in less than half the time of other planes. Only 20 were ever built and they were retired in 2003 due to a general downturn in the aviation industry, the only crash of a Concorde in 2000 (Air France Flight 4590), the September 11 attacks, and a decision by Airbus to discontinue maintenance support.

13,804

The distance in kilometres of the world's longest non-stop flight. Qantas QF8 travels from Dallas Fort Worth to Sydney and it takes 16 hours and 50 minutes – that's a lot of episodes of *The Big Bang Theory*! The next Australian entrant on the list is the 20th longest non-stop flight, from Los Angeles to Melbourne. It's 12,748 km, takes 15 hours and 50 minutes, and is flown by Qantas and United Airlines.

1122

The world record for a single-flight passenger load. On 24 May 1991, as part of a transfer of Ethiopian Jews to Israel, an El Al 747 carried 1122 passengers (1087 passengers were registered, but dozens of children hid in their mothers' robes). Multiple babies were born on board the flight.

41,467.46

The distance in kilometres of the longest flight of a non-commercial powered aircraft was set on 12 February 2006 by US businessman and aviator Steve Fossett. Fossett died on 3 September 2007 when a plane he flew over the Great Basin Desert in Nevada failed to return. He was 63.

21,602.22

The distance in kilometres of the longest flight of a commercial aircraft. A Boeing 777-200LR, with pilots Suzanna Darcy-Henneman, Asif Abbas Raza, John Cashman and Mohammed Ilyas Malik, flew from Hong Kong's International Airport to London's Heathrow Airport 'the long way round', taking 22 hours and 22 minutes.

65,000

The amount of time (in hours) that US pilot John Edward Long (1915–99) spent in the air. John made it into *Guinness World Records* for the most flight time … and, I presume, most frequent flyer points!

Role reversal

An amazing reversal: 37 is the 12th prime and 73 make the 21st prime. This enigma is the only known combination and, as you'll find out on March 14, got Sheldon from *The Big Bang Theory* very excited indeed.

Thirty-seven and 38 is the first pair of consecutive numbers *not* divisible by any of their digits.

37

The 37th day of the year is February 6

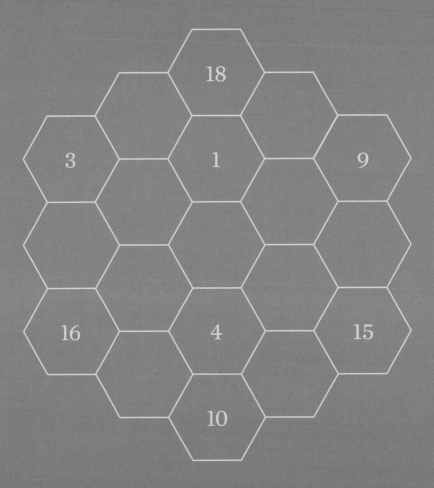

The magic hexagon

38

*The **38th** day of the year is **February 7***

Thirty-eight is the magic constant in the only possible magic hexagon which utilises all the natural integers up to and including 19. It was discovered by Ernst von Haselberg in 1887, W. Radcliffe in 1895, and several others. Eventually, it was also discovered by Clifford W. Adams, who worked on the problem from 1910 to 1957. Cliff was a freight-handler and clerk for the Reading Rail Road in the US and transmitted the solution to the famous maths puzzle setter Martin Gardner in 1963. Gardner sent Adams' magic hexagon to Charles W. Trigg, who by mathematical analysis found that it was unique disregarding rotations and reflections.

55°

Without Whitworth, would screws be screwed?

In 1841, the English engineer Joseph Whitworth created history when he invented the first nationally adopted standard for screw threads. For what?

Well, Whitworth specified that a screw must be shaped with a 55 degree thread angle, a depth of 0.640327p and a radius of 0.137329p (where p is the pitch or distance between 2 ridges of the screw in inches).

By unifying the dimensions of the thread of a screw – which up until then had been random from maker to maker, industry to industry – Whitworth revolutionised manufacturing. Today, many camera tripods, computer components and a whole range of other devices still use Whitworth threads. There's even a reference to Whitworth bolts in the Pixar movie Cars 2!

55°

Armstrong numbers

An Armstrong (or narcissistic or pluperfect digital invariant) number is a number that is the sum of its own digits each raised to the power of the number of digits. For example, the 3-digit number 371 is an Armstrong number, since $3^3 + 7^3 + 1^3 = 371$.

The largest Armstrong number, 115,132,219,018, 763,992,565,095,597,973, 971,522,401, has 39 digits.

This means that $1^{39} + 1^{39} + 5^{39} + ... + 4^{39} + 0^{39} + 1^{39} = 115,132,219,0 18,763,992,565,095,597,973, 971,522,401$. Phew, I'm taking the rest of today off.

39

*The **39th** day of the year is **February 8***

Bizarre weights

Ever wondered to yourself, 'Which is heavier – the heaviest train ever, or a small chunk of the Great Pyramid of Giza?'

1
13,000+ kg Big Ben
hour bell

≈

100,000
delicious oranges

1
99,700 tonne *BHP Iron Ore* train

≈

$1/60$
Great Pyramid of Giza

40

*The **40th** day of the
year is February 9*

*On this day in 1986
We last saw Halley's Comet*

Roaring forties

In English, 'forty' is the only whole number whose letters are in alphabetical order.

On the 2 most commonly used temperature scales, –40 degrees is the same in Fahrenheit and Celsius.

$40^6 + 40^5 + 40^4 + 40^3 + 40^2 + 40 + 1$ is prime, as is $40^4 + 40^3 + 40^2 + 40 + 1$, $40^2 + 1$ and while we're on a roll you can throw in $40^2 - 40 - 1$.

... Well, now you know!

1
adult mouse

≈

40
tasty raisins

1
International Space Station

≈

2
blue whales

Forty-one

can be expressed as the sum of consecutive primes in 2 ways. One of them is 41 = 11 + 13 + 17. Find the other.

41: a power of fun

11^{41} = 4,978,518,112,499,354, 698,647,829,163,838,661,251, 242,411 and is the highest power of 11 we know that doesn't contain a 0.

41

*The **41st** day of the year is February 10*

Sofa, so good

Anyone who has ever moved house has no doubt dealt with the frustration, stress and physical pain of trying to get a lounge around a corner, up a flight of stairs or through a door.

'How the heck did it get in here in the first place ... did they build the house around it?' you scream, exasperated, as you leave another layer of knuckle skin on the wall.

Well, if it's any consolation, this problem has given rise to a lovely piece of recreational mathematics called 'the sofa problem'. This problem asks, 'What is the area of the largest, rigid 2-dimensional shape that can be manoeuvred around an L-shaped corner in a hallway that is 1 unit wide?'

This shape, discovered by John Hammersley, is two quarter circles of radius 1, joined by a rectangle of sides 1 and $4/\pi$ with a semicircle of radius $2/\pi$ removed. So its area is:

$$\pi/4 + 1 \times 4/\pi + \pi/4 - 1/2 \times \pi \times (2/\pi)^2 = \pi/2 + 2/\pi \approx 2.207416$$

42

*The **42nd** day of the year is February 11*

Heronian triangles

We call a triangle 'equable' if its area equals its perimeter and 'Heronian' if its sides and area are all whole numbers. There are only 5 equable, Heronian triangles. This one has perimeter (P) and area (A) equal to 42.

The other 4 are defined by (9, 10, 17; P = A = 36), (6, 25, 29; 60), (5, 12, 13; 30) and (6, 8, 10; 24).

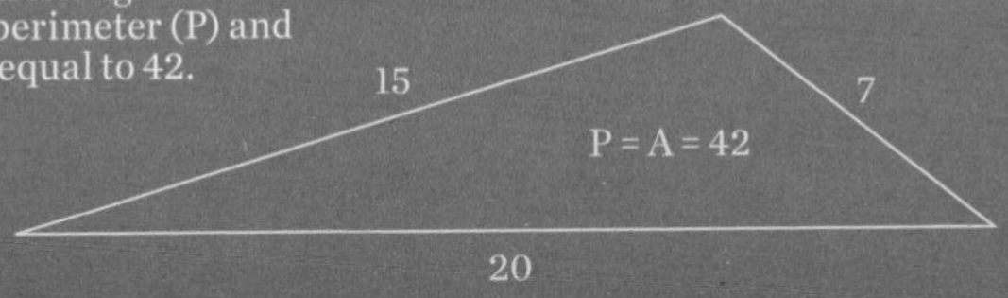

15   7

P = A = 42

20

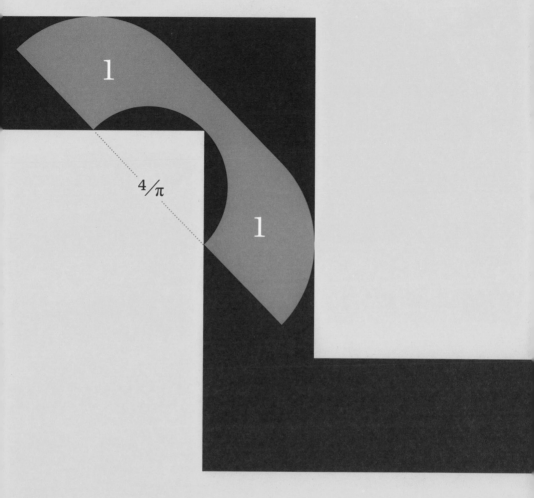

Another mathematician called Joseph Gerver came up with an even more complicated 'sofa' shape made up of 18 arcs, with a larger area A ≈ 2.219532 but, believe me, it really doesn't look very comfy to sit on!

The plays!

In March 1950, the great calculator Claude Shannon proposed that there are roughly 10^{43} possible positions in a chess match. And I've been in a lot of the worst of them!

Incognito in Israel

If you're ever in Israel and want to hide your caller ID from someone, just type *43 before that person's number and ta-da – you're incognito.

43

*The **43rd** day of the year is February 12*

On this day in 1809 Charles Darwin was born

MELBOURNE *by* numbers

1835
The year Melbourne was founded by the 'other' Batman (John the adventurous Tasmanian farmer); for a while the city was actually called Batmania!

6–12
The number of foxes per square kilometre in Melbourne; it's the 'fox capital' of Australia.

121,696
The crowd at the 1970 VFL Grand Final which saw Carlton defeat Collingwood 17.9 (111) to 14.17 (101).

25,000+
The number of bicycle riders in Melbourne (more than any other Australian city).

1
The number of Australian capital cities that celebrate a public holiday for the Melbourne Cup.

44
*The **44th** day of the year is February 13*

Deranged

There are 44 ways to reorder the numbers 1 through 5 so that none of the digits is in its natural place. This is called a 'derangement'. The number of derangements of the numbers 1 to n is given by the scary looking but not-that-bad formula to the right.

$$d(n) = n! \times (1 - \frac{1}{1!} + \frac{1}{2!} - \frac{1}{3!} + \frac{1}{4!} \cdots + \frac{(-1)^n}{n!})$$

So we can derange the numbers 1, 2, 3, 4, 5

$$d(5) = 5! \times (1 - \frac{1}{1!} + \frac{1}{2!} - \frac{1}{3!} + \frac{1}{4!} - \frac{1}{5!})$$

$$= 120 \times (1 - \frac{1}{1} + \frac{1}{2} - \frac{1}{6} + \frac{1}{24} - \frac{1}{120})$$

$$= 120 \times (1 - 1 + \frac{60}{120} - \frac{20}{120} + \frac{5}{120} - \frac{1}{120})$$

$$= 120 \times \frac{44}{120} = 44 \text{ ways.}$$

92

The number of storeys in the Eureka Tower,
Melbourne's tallest building.

312 km/h

The speed limit in the city …
Okay, for certain drivers during
the Australian Grand Prix.

450

The number of trams in Melbourne's
244-kilometre system, the largest
in the world outside Europe.

1912

The year Australia's first traffic
lights were installed (at the intersection
of Collins and Swanston Streets).

928 m^2

The area of the largest stained-glass
window in the world – the ceiling in the National
Gallery of Victoria, created by Leonard
French in the 1960s.

Kaprekar numbers

Forty-five is the third
Kaprekar number. A number
is Kaprekar if when you
square it, split the square into
2 equal or almost equal length
bits and add the bits together
you get the original number.

So $45^2 = 2025$ and $20 + 25 = 45$
making 45 Kaprekar.

Interestingly, 45 is also
'Kaprekar' when cubed or
raised to the fourth power.

$45^2 = 2025$ and $20 + 25 = 45$

$45^3 = 91125$ and $9 + 11 + 25 = 45$

$45^4 = 4100625$ and $4 + 10 + 06
+ 25 = 45$.

45

*The **45th** day of the
year is February 14*

Coin-undrums

Money might not make the world go around in the literal sense, but it's fair to say it's pretty integral to our way of life. But next time you blithely whack down a fiver on the counter, spare a thought for the story behind the money ...

Coins: 5, 10, 20, 50 cents, $1 and $2

The value of the Aussie 5c coin changes depending on the market value of copper and nickel. In 2007, the bullion value of the 5c coin was about 6.5 cents, although base-metal prices have dropped further since and the metals no longer exceed the coin value.

Paying for large goods in coins is possible but it's subject to restrictions. It turns out you can't just walk into a shop with a wheelbarrow full of 5c coins and try to buy a new wheelbarrow! If you've only got 5c, 10c, 20c and 50c coins, a merchant can refuse more than $5 worth. Similarly, if you've got a stack of $1 and $2 coins, you can only offer 10 of either of them before the shopkeeper can say 'no thanks'. Of course, they are allowed to accept more and often will because it's always good to have change around.

There is no such rule in Shenyang, China. In June 2015, a man bought a $140,000 car with 4 tonnes of coins he claimed he had collected over years of working in a petrol station!

46

The **46th** *day of the* *year is* February 15

Chess plus

There are 46 fundamental ways to arrange 9 queens on a 9 × 9 chessboard so that no queen is attacking any other. Working this out isn't hard, but finding a 9 × 9 chessboard lying around may prove a bit more difficult.

On this day in 1564
Galileo Galilei was born

In response to steadily rising prices, Australia removed 1c and 2c coins from circulation in 1992. Lots of these 1c and 2c coins ended up being massively more valuable than they could ever have dreamed when they were melted down to create the bronze medals awarded at the Sydney Olympics.

Notes: 5, 10, 20, 50, 100 … 5000, 10,000

In 1966, a nationwide competition was held to find a new name for the Aussie dollar with a more 'Australian flavour'. Rejected submissions included 'austral', 'boomer', 'kwid' and 'ming' which is a pity, really. 'Hey mate, spare me 10 boomers?' has a great ring to it.

Australia was the first country in the world to develop and use a complete system of banknotes made from plastic (polymer), which provides greater security against counterfeiting. The history of our very colourful polymer notes is itself, very colourful.

In 1967, 2 ordinary Aussies with no experience in counterfeiting decided to forge the new $10 note which had come into circulation on 14 February 1966. 'Decimal day', as it was known, was when Australia relinquished the English pound and took on its own currency. Anyway, Jeffrey Mutton ran a failing suburban Melbourne milk bar and his artist mate Francis Papworth worked at a nearby printing plant. Along with a few other dubious acquaintances, they banged out $800,000 worth of shonky tenners. In today's money that's close to $10 million which buys a lot of milkshakes and hot chips.

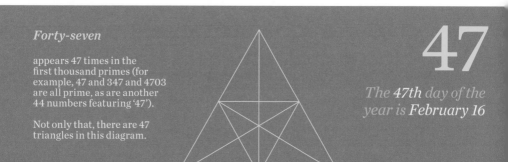

Forty-seven

appears 47 times in the first thousand primes (for example, 47 and 347 and 4703 are all prime, as are another 44 numbers featuring '47').

Not only that, there are 47 triangles in this diagram.

47

*The **47th** day of the year is **February 16***

The notes circulated for years afterwards, creating a distrust of $10 notes. Members of the Amalgamated Engineering Union, for example, refused to accept them as part of their pay packet. As a result of these incidents, Australia's Reserve Bank enlisted the country's chief scientific agency, the CSIRO, to create the world's most secure banknote.

Polymer technology embeds the note with a see-through, plastic panel that exhibits what is known as 'diffraction grating' which splits light into several beams. Today, more than 3 billion polymer notes are in service in 22 countries.

In the US ...

In the 2014 financial year, the US Mint calculated it cost the following amounts to produce 2 of its coins:

- 1.7c to produce a penny
- 8c to produce a nickel (5c coin)

Overall, however, the mint made $289.1 million on 'seigniorage' (the difference between value of a coin and the cost to make it). This was despite a $90.5 million drag from the penny and nickel.

Although the current banknote denominations in print in the US are $1, $2, $5, $10, $20, $50, $100, previously, notes in $500, $1000, $5000 and $10,000 denominations were printed for general use. Although they are still technically legal tender, they were last made in 1945.

48

The **48th** *day of the* *year is* **February 17**

Forty-eight

is the smallest number with exactly 10 divisors.

Find them all.

Changing times

$48 \times 48 = 2304$

and ...

$48 \times 84 = 4032$

Non-decimal currencies

Mauritiania (1 ouguiya = 5 khoums) and Madagascar (1 ariary = 5 iraimbilanja) are the only 2 countries to use non-decimal currencies. However, in both cases the main unit is of such a low value that the sub-unit is too small to be of any practical use.

The official currency of the Soveriegn Military Order of Malta is the scudo, which is subdivided into 12 tari (singular taro), each of 20 grani, with 6 piccioli to the grano.

For a long time, in many Western countries, decimal sub-units were actually the exception rather than the rule. The advantage of non-decimal currencies is that they could be more easily divided (especially by 3 and 8) than decimal currencies, and so were easier for poorly educated people to deal with.

Big bikkies ...

When it comes to big biscuits, the largest denominations you're likely to see on notes in official circulation anywhere in the world include the 500 euro note; a Japanese 10,000 yen bill; and an Indonesian 100,000 rupiah note. Vietnam prints a 500,000 dong note but before you get too excited, it's only worth about $30.

The world's most valuable banknote currently in official circulation is the Brunei $10,000 note. It's worth about 8 times as much as the second most valuable note, the 1000 Swiss Franc. There was a similarly valued $10,000 note in Singapore, but it has been recently withdrawn from circulation because of organised crime concerns.

Please be squareful!

Lots of numbers are 'squareful' (they are divisible by a square number that isn't 1).

For example, 28 = 4 × 7 and 4 = 2^2.

But what's special about the number 49 is that it is the smallest number such that it,

and both its neighbours, are squareful. By this I mean:

49 = 7^2 and is tucked in between 48 = 3 × 4^2 and 50 = 2 × 5^2.

49

The 49th day of the year is February 18

On this day in 1930 Astronomer Clyde Tombaugh discovered Pluto

I do have to make a quick mention of what I think is the biggest of all banknotes. Due to a rule in the UK banking system, every time a Scottish or Northern Irish bank wants to print its own 'local' currency, it has to lodge the same amount in pounds sterling with the Bank of England. To consolidate these massive deposits, over time the Bank of England has printed notes known colloquially as 'titans'. They are the size of an A4 sheet of paper and worth a staggering £100,000,000 each!

Small change ...

Sometimes in a struggling economy prices increase so fantastically fast that the currency becomes worthless. This might happen as a result of war or if an economy is almost entirely reliant on one source of income.

For example, prices rose so quickly in Zimbabwe in the 2000s that by 2009 a 100 trillion dollar ($100,000,000,000,000) note was in circulation. The currency had already been redenominated a few times so this note was actually worth 10,000,000,00 0,000,000,000,000,000 of the original 1980 Zimbabwe dollars!

Other horrid cases of hyperinflation include the German mark after World War I and the Yugoslavian dinar in the early to mid-90s. In just 6 years the highest denomination Yugoslavian banknote grew from the 50,000 dinar in 1988 to 500,000,000,000 dinar in 1994. As part of the currency reform package in 1994, the new 1 dinar note was worth 1,000,000,000 old dinars!

50

The 50th day of the year is February 19

Fifty

is the smallest number that can be written as the sum of 2 positive squares in 2 distinct ways: 50 = 49 + 1 = 25 + 25. If you're wondering about the smallest number that can be written as the sum of 2 squares in 3 distinct ways, you'll be very excited on November 21.

Stop!

The difference in stopping distances if you slam on the brakes at 50 km/h compared to 60 km/h is 35 metres compared to 45 metres. This 10-metre difference is why many Australian roads have a 50 km/h speed limit.

Perhaps the worst ever case of hyperinflation occurred in Hungary in 1945–6 immediately after World War II. The relatively open Hungarian economy had taken a battering on all fronts and by the end of the war the currency was not pegged to a gold standard. At one stage in the middle of 1946 a 100,000,000,000,000,000,000 pengő (a hundred quintillion pengő) note was in circulation. In 1946, when the Hungarian currency was reformed, one new forint was worth 400,000 quardillion of the old pengő.

Here's a brainteaser for you. If I had a pile of 1c, 2c, 5c, 10c, 20c and 50c coins, what combination of coins would give me the greatest amount of money from which I could *not* give you exactly $2.00 change?

Similarly, if I had only 5c, 10c, 20c, 50c and $1 coins, what is the largest amount I could have and *not* be able to give you exactly $4? You'll find the answers to both these coin-undrums at the back of the book.

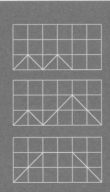

Motzkin numbers

Fifty-one is the number of different paths from (0, 0) to (6, 0) made up of segments connecting lattice points that can only have slopes of 1, 0, or –1 but so that they never go below the x-axis. These are called Motzkin numbers.

51

*The **51st** day of the year is February 20*

72 points about type point sizes

1 point 2.5 point 3 point 3.5 point 4 point 4.5 point 5 point 6 point 7 point 8 point 9 point 10 point 11 point 12 point 13 point 14 point 15 point 16 point 17 point 18 point 19 point 20 point 21 point 22 point 23 point 24 point 25 point 26 point 27 point 28 point 29 point 30 point 31 point 32 point 33 point 34 point 35 point 36 point 37 point 38 point 39 point 40 point 41 point 42 point 43 point 44 point 45 point 46 point 47 point 48 point 49 point 50 point 51 point 52 point 53 point 54 point 55 point 56 point 57 point 58 point 59 point 60 point 61 point 62 point 63 point 64 po

52

The **52nd** day of the year is *February 21*

Prime days

The month and day are simultaneously prime a total of 52 times in a non-leap year. For example, November 19 furnishes both 11 and 19 prime. In a leap year it's 53 because you pick up 29 February.

A note a week?

There are 52 white keys on a standard piano.

Bloodhounds have been known to follow a scent for over 200 km and follow tracks that are 12 days old.

This is because their 'smell centre' is roughly the size of a hankie. Yours and mine? Barely a postage stamp.

No shortage of primes

There are 53 prime numbers less than 250. But more impressively, if you add these 53 primes together, you get 5830, which is divisible by 53.

The nth of days

February 22 is the last time the nth day of the year sees n divide the sum of the first n primes.

53

The 53rd day of the year is February 22

HOBART
by numbers

626 mm
Hobart's average rainfall per year. This makes it the driest capital city in Australia.

206 km
The distance from Hobart to Devonport.

220 km
The distance from Devonport to the mainland.

10,000
The number of years a mighty Huon pine can live to.

54
The 54th day of the year is February 23

Fifty-four
is the smallest number that can be written as the sum of 3 squares in 3 ways. This is not allowing for 0^2 otherwise 41 would steal the crown. (Well, go on, find all 3 ways!)

NBA
When the poor old Utah Jazz of 1998 got towelled up bad by Chicago 96-54, they set an undesired record for the least points ever scored in an NBA play-off game.

1270 m

The height of Mount Wellington which 'towers' above Hobart!

75,000

The number of convicts who passed through Hobart between 1804 and 1877.

698

The seating capacity of Hobart's Theatre Royal, Australia's oldest – which has been running since 1837 and was a favourite of Sir Laurence Olivier.

37

The average age of Hobart's population.

1936

The year in which the last Tasmanian Tiger died at the Hobart Zoo.

2000 km

The distance to Antarctica from Hobart, though when that southerly wind is blowing it feels a lot closer.

Triangular fibs

Fifty-five is the 10th triangular number so we sometimes write it T_{10}. This is also the largest triangular number that appears in the Fibonacci sequence.

0, 1, 1, 2, 3, 5, 8, 13, 21, 34, 55 ...

55

The **55th** *day of the year is* **February 24**

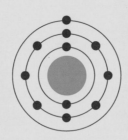

Sodium Na

Lucky legs 11 on the Periodic Table, sodium is the sixth most abundant element in the Earth's crust and is essential for your legs, in fact for all human life – and plenty of plants' lives, too. Sodium is a soft, silver-white, highly reactive metal. Its compounds, such as sodium hydroxide, are used in making soap among countless other things, while sodium chloride is more commonly known as table salt. Salt can enhance the flavours of some foods, but be careful: too much is bad for you!

56

The 56th day of the year is February 25

Latin squares

There are 56 'normalised' (or reduced) 5 × 5 Latin squares. This is a square with the first row and column containing 1, 2, 3, 4 and 5 in order and with no number appearing twice in a row or column.

There are only 4 such 4 × 4 squares. Try to find them.

1	2	3	4	5
2	5	4	1	3
3	4	2	5	1
4	1	5	3	2
5	3	1	2	4

Magnesium

Apart from a few insects who do just fine without it, magnesium is another element that is essential for pretty much all living things. The process by which plants use the Sun's energy to convert carbon dioxide and water into glucose and then make cellulose has at its heart the molecule chlorophyll, which, in turn, has at its heart magnesium. The reason that leaves appear green is that the magnesium-chlorophyll in them absorbs the blue and red shades of sunlight but not the green.

Leyland numbers

$57 = 2^5 + 5^2$ and as such is an example of a Leyland number.

Nearly!

$57 = 1 + 7 + 7^2$ which isn't quite as cute as $1 + 7 + 7^2 + 7^3 = 400$, but we don't have 400 days in the year!

57

*The **57th** day of the year is February 26*

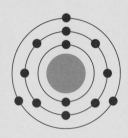

Aluminium

Like it or not, you've got about 60 milligrams of aluminium in your body. In fact, it's found in cheese, sponge cake mixes, lentils, chickpeas and basmati rice, among other things. It's also been used for hundreds of years in papers, dyes and preserving medical concoctions, making it one of the oldest chemical industries.

There are several aluminium oxides. The principal naturally occurring ore is bauxite, the majority of which is comprised of aluminium hydroxide minerals. It's actually significantly cheaper and more energy-efficient to recycle aluminium cans than to mine bauxite from the Earth and process it!

1234567891011121314151617181920212223242526272829303132333435363738394041424344454647484950515253
5455565758596061626364656667686970717273747576777879808182838485868788899091929394959697989991

58

The 58th day of the year is February 27

Fifty-eight, mate

If you take the number 2, square it, and continue to take the sum of the squares of the digits of the previous answer, you get the sequence 2, 4, 16, 37, 58, 89, 145, 42, 20, 4, and then it repeats.

See what happens if you start with other values other than 2, and see if you can find one that doesn't produce 58. Starting from 2, what is the first number you find that bucks this trend?

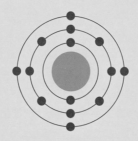

Silicon

Silicon, with its atomic number of 14, is not a metal – although it has some metallic qualities. We call such elements 'metalloids' or semimetals. That's not to say silicon doesn't do some amazing things. It's used a lot in industry and is especially important in the manufacture of integrated circuits, which are at the heart of most computers.

And of course, if you're a cow with bloat (I know you probably wouldn't be reading this book, but go with me here), your vet may well prescribe a silicon-based indigestion tablet that will 'defroth' the gas in your stomachs, allowing it to escape 'harmlessly' into the atmosphere.

Magic primes

The smallest total for the rows and columns of a 3×3 magic square with all prime entries is 177. It has 59 in the middle. Can you find the other 8 prime numbers to fill this magic square?

Hint: Start by finding pairs of prime numbers that add up to $118 = 177 - 59$.

	59	

59

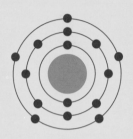

Phosphorus

In 1669, the German alchemist Hennig Brandt made history. He took his own urine, evaporated it and heated the residue. This gave off a vapour, which he collected by condensing it in water. In doing so, he was the first person to isolate the element that would become known as phosphorous. I wish I'd been there at the time so I could have asked him, 'Hennig, whatever made you think to flame your own evaporated urine just to see what would happen?' An atom of phosphorus bonded with 4 oxygen atoms is call phosphate. Your brain tissue is, hopefully, loaded with the stuff.

1234567891011121314**15**1617181920212223242526272829303132333435363738394041424344454647484950515
5455565758596061626364656667686970717273747576777879808182838485868788899091929394959697989

60

*The **60th** day of the year is **March 1** (or sometimes February 29)*

Leaping or marching

It gets a bit confusing in leap years because you have to have each number fact a day earlier, for example, you'd read the fact for June 10 on June 9, but that's not February's fault. Just so we don't offend anyone born on this rarest of days, here's a cute little fact about 29:

$1/3$ is clearly less than 1, as is $1/3 + 1/5$, $1/3 + 1/5 + 1/7$ and $1/3 + 1/5 +$ $1/7 + 1/11$ but if you keep adding the terms $1/p$ where p is prime, (which we call the 'reciprocal' of p) you get to $1/3 + 1/5 + 1/7 + 1/11 + ... + 1/29$ which is finally greater than 1.

Back to 60. There are 4 beautiful Archimedean solids with 60 vertices: the truncated icosahedron, the rhombicosidodecahedron, the snub dodecahedron and the truncated dodecahedron.

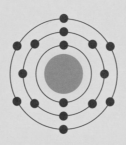

Sulphur

An atom of sulphur has 16 protons in its nucleus, so that's where S sits on the Periodic Table. In ancient times it was also known as brimstone (you've probably heard of 'fire and brimstone'). As the British science writer John Emsley points out in his book, *Nature's Building Blocks*, 'If something smells awful then it probably contains sulphur'. The stink of a skunk is caused by not 1, not 2 but 3 sulphur compounds including 2-butenyl methyl disulphide which, to my ears, smells so bad you can hear it.

345678910111213141516171819202122232425262728293031323334353637383940414243444546474849505152535 5556575859606162636465666768697071727374757677787980818283848586878889909192939495969798991001

0–9 in 13

The 61st Fibonacci number (2,504,730,781,961) is the smallest Fibonacci number which contains all the digits from 0 to 9.

Prime code

If you allocate A = 1, B = 2, C = 3 and so on, the word PRIME = 16 + 18 + 9 + 13 + 5 = 61 and 61 is prime. Cute.

61

The 61st day of the year is March 2

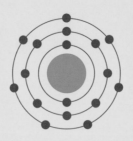

Chlorine

When an atom of chlorine gets friendly with an atom of hydrogen, we get hydrochloric acid. HCl is classified as a toxic substance and you must handle it with gloves and goggles, but it occurs naturally in your stomach where it breaks down food and kills dangerous bacteria.

In World War I, the German Army released deadly chlorine gas at the Battle of Gravenstafel Ridge. The wind blew the gas across into the Allied trenches killing over 5000 mostly French soldiers.

62

The 62nd day of the year is March 3

Sixty-two

is the smallest number that can be written as the sum of 3 distinct non-zero squares in 2 ways. Can you find them?

Need some convincing?

Turning our attention to cubic powers, convince yourself with pen and paper that $62^3 = 238,328$ making 62 the only number whose 6-digit cube contains 3 digits each appearing twice.

On this day in 1845 Mathematician George Cantor was born, 123 years before Professor Brian Cox

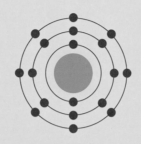

Argon

The word argon is derived from the Greek word *argos*, meaning idle or inactive. It gets its name because of its stable outer shell of 8 electrons, which means it undergoes almost no chemical reactions. What a chilled dude of an element! Argon is what is known as an 'inert' gas, meaning it won't react with other elements. It's so inert that it's used in most kinds of electrical lighting (filament bulbs, fluorescent tubes, and so on) to provide an inert atmosphere and stop it exploding!

345678910111213141516171819202122232425262728293031323334353637383940414243444546474849505152535455565758596061626364656667686970717273747576777879808182838485868788899091929394959697989910 0

LXIII

In Roman numerals, 63 is written as LXIII. If you represent each of these letters by its number in the English alphabet (A = 1, B = 2, C = 3 ...) you get $12 + 24 + 9 + 9 + 9 = 63$.

Did you know ...

Sixty-three is 1 less than 64. Wow, Adam, great stuff. No, bear with me. Sixty-four is a power of 2 ($64 = 2^6$) so this means that 63 will be the sum of all the powers of 2 up to the power below this. Check that $63 = 2^0 + 2^1 + 2^2 + 2^3 + 2^4 + 2^5$.

63

The 63rd day of the year is March 4

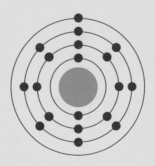

Potassium K

With the names of most elements coming from Greek and Latin, potassium is one of the few that derives from English. The word 'potassium' comes from *pot ash* – the process of soaking plant ashes in a pot of water – a very old-fashioned way of obtaining potassium.

Capital punishment is a controversial practice and one I personally oppose, but I won't get into the ethics of it here. In countries where capital punishment is administered by lethal injection, potassium chloride is one of the most common substances used.

64

The 64th day of the year is March 5

Doubly perfect

Apart from the trivial case of 1, 64 is the first whole number that is both a perfect square and a perfect cube.

Fight!

Sixty-four is also the number of squares on a chessboard which, in my highly biased mind, is just about the most glorious field of battle upon which 2 people can meet.

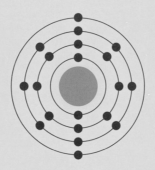

Calcium

You probably know we all have calcium in our bones and our teeth, but did you know you have it in your eyes, too? Calcium helps maintain the stability of your eyes' lens and also helps them handle light.

The description of someone being 'in the limelight' dates back to the 1820s when the Scottish engineer Thomas Drummond invented a light source that could be seen over long distances. TD focused a jet of hydrogen burning in oxygen onto a block of calcium oxide. The brilliant glow that resulted was used in lighthouses and the theatre where it illuminated the stars centre stage.

Magic with 65

Sixty-five is the constant of a 5 × 5 magic square. Can you finish this square which contains the numbers 1 to 25 once each so that each row, column and diagonal adds up to 65?

25			19	7
	9	22	15	3
12	5	18	6	
8				20
4	17		23	11

65

*The **65th** day of the year is **March 6***

66

*The **66th** day of the year is **March 7***

Polyiamonds are a girl's best friend

A collection of equal-sized equilateral triangles arranged with coincident sides is called a poly-iamond (2 triangles form a duo-iamond or diamond). There are 66 different 8-polyiamonds – like the ones you see here:

Life as we know it

(and a few things we're still learning)

Nameless NA,
Anonymous Australia

In the US and Canada if you dial *67 before a number it hides your caller ID from the person you're calling. In Australia, try the prefix 1831 or #31#.

While they try to figure out who you are, why don't you further amuse yourself with this numerical nicety involving 67:

$$2^6 + 2^1 + 2^0 = 26 + 21 + 20 = 67$$

67

The 67th day of the year is March 8

On this day in 1922 Inventor Ralph Henry Baer was born

Take a sample of a hundred people ...

50 would be male

50 would be female

5 would speak English

5 would be from North America

12 would speak Chinese

3 would speak Bengali

3 would speak Portuguese

51 would live in urban areas

49 would live in rural areas

9 would be from Latin America and the Caribbean

15 would be from Africa

30 would be active internet users

62 would speak other languages

3 would speak Arabic

3 would speak Hindi

For more fascinating facts, check out the 100people.org site – an amazing snapshot of the world.

68

The 68th day of the year is March 9

A tasty piece of π

If you searched through the decimal expansion of π for all the 2-digit numbers, the last one you would find is 68. The string 68 begins at position 605 counting from the first digit after the decimal point.

If you're more of a 3-digit person, you may want to know the last such number to be found in the decimal expansion of π is 483 which starts at position 8553 after decimal point; similarly, 6715 rounds out the 4-digit numbers when it begins at decimal place 99846, and 33393 is the last 5-digit number you'll encounter starting at decimal place 1369560.

I could go on all day ... no literally, I could!

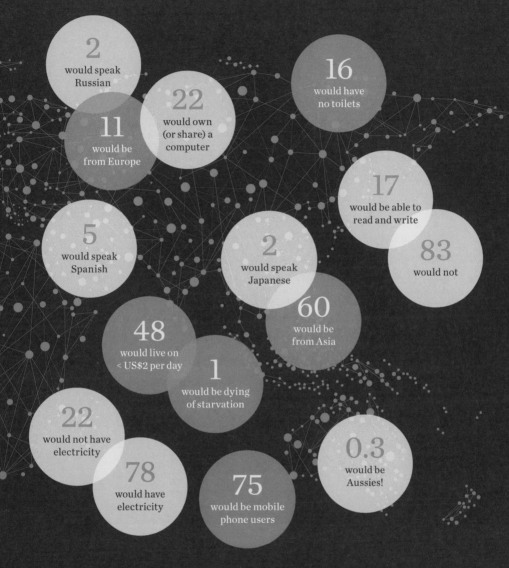

... representing all of humanity

2 would speak Russian

22 would own (or share) a computer

11 would be from Europe

16 would have no toilets

17 would be able to read and write

83 would not

5 would speak Spanish

2 would speak Japanese

60 would be from Asia

48 would live on < US$2 per day

1 would be dying of starvation

22 would not have electricity

78 would have electricity

75 would be mobile phone users

0.3 would be Aussies!

Squares, squares, everywhere!

Show that the square and the cube of 69 together contain all 10 numerals exactly once each.

This will put a smile on your face

$69^{23} + 69^{21} + 69^{19} + 69^{17} + 69^{15} + 69^{13} + 69^{11} + 69^{9} + 69^{7} + 69^{5} + 69^{3} + 69 + 1$ is prime.

69

*The **69th** day of the year is March 10*

On this day in 1876 Alexander Graham Bell made the first electronic telephone call

Body maths

From the smallest parts (the stapes bones in your ear, about 3 × 2.5 mm) to the longest and strongest (your femur or thigh bone, which is about 27% of your height so in someone 175 cm tall is about 47 cm long) the human body is a mathematician's dream!

Right now you're reading this book with your eyes, probably holding it in your hands, processing thoughts in your brain. All bits of your amazing body. But what actually makes up you?

There are about 60 elements floating around in you, including lead, arsenic, uranium and about 0.2 of a milligram of gold. Yep, gold. While its role in your physiological processes was unknown for many years, scientists have recently found that gold is involved in both the health and maintenance of your joints, as well as being a key element in the transmittal of electrical signals. In any given second, about 5000 atoms of potassium are undergoing radioactive decay in your body. You also emit about 500 gamma rays. Lucky you!

But, of course, your body is overwhelmingly made up of 3 elements: oxygen, carbon and hydrogen. Three-fifths of you is water. If someone accuses you of 'being full of hot air' you can now confidently point out, 'No, I'm full of warm water, actually'.

70

The 70th day of the year is March 11

Who's weird?

Seventy is the smallest 'weird' number. This just means the sum of its proper divisors exceeds the number, but no subset of those divisors sums to the number exactly. So, 1 + 2 + 5 + 7 + 10 + 14 + 35 = 74 but you can't get exactly 70 by adding any of the numbers 1, 2, 5, 7, 10, 14 and 35.

AKA sixty-ten

The French do not have a word for seventy. Instead, they refer to it as *soixante-dix* or 'sixty-ten'.

Here are the top 10 components of a 70 kg adult, by mass

Oxygen 44 kg
Carbon 16 kg
(enough to make about 9000 pencils!)
Hydrogen 7 kg
Nitrogen 1.8 kg
Calcium 1 kg
Phosphorus 780 g
Potassium 140 g
Sodium 100 g
Chlorine 95 g
And 19 g of good ol'
magnesium

Seventy-one^{power}

Convince yourself that:

$71^2 = 7! + 1! \ (= 5041)$

The next power of 71 also has a cool property. Can you work it out?

Massive attack

$2^{71} = 2{,}361{,}183{,}241{,}434{,}822{,}606{,}848$ is a power of 2 that doesn't contain the digit 5. In fact, it's the largest such power of 2 of which we know. The same is true if we consider the digit 7. Look, in either case, there may be another one out there, but it must be massive.

71

*The **71st** day of the year is March 12*

ADELAIDE *by* numbers

20 min
The time it takes to get to pretty much all the attractions of the '20 minute city'.

1
The number of tram lines.

228,673
The average number of visitors Adelaide welcomes every day.

529
The number of Christian churches in Adelaide – the moniker 'city of churches' refers more to the lavish architecture rather than the number. Sydney has 1742, Melbourne 1230 and Hobart the most per capita.

72
The 72nd day of the year is March 13

Polyiamond maker

Seventy-two is the smallest number whose fifth power is the sum of 5 positive fifth powers:

$$19^5 + 43^5 + 46^5 + 47^5 + 67^5 = 72^5$$

If you have 72 equilateral triangles lying around, get excited. You can make these twelve 6-polyiamonds!

And what's even cooler, they have names. Across the top row: bar, crook, crown, sphinx, snake, and yacht; and along the bottom row: the chevron, signpost, lobster, hook, hexagon and butterfly.

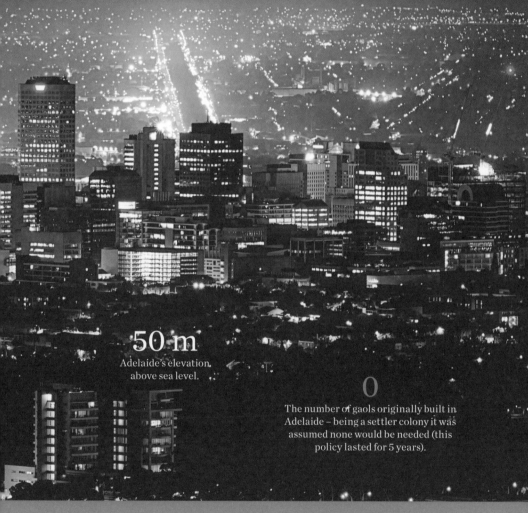

2434

The amount of square metres of toughened glass in the curvilinear roof of the Bicentennial Conservatory at the Botanic Gardens – the southern hemisphere's largest.

1836

The year when the settlement of Adelaide was proclaimed under a gumtree in the seaside suburb of Glenelg.

50 m

Adelaide's elevation above sea level.

0

The number of gaols originally built in Adelaide – being a settler colony it was assumed none would be needed (this policy lasted for 5 years).

The Big Maths Theory

Fans of *The Big Bang Theory* will know that Leonard refers to 73 as the 'Chuck Norris of Numbers' after Sheldon points out that 73 is the 21st prime, and its mirror image 37 is the 12th prime. This enigma is the only known such combination.

S.e.v.e.n.t.y.t.h.r.e.e.

'Seventy-three' is the smallest whole number with 12 letters in its name.

73

*The **73rd** day of the year is March 14*

On this day in 1879 Albert Einstein was born

A fertile man produces around 1500 new sperm ...

... per heartbeat.

74

*The **74th** day of the year is **March 15***

A prime sum

22,796,996,699 is the 999,799,787th prime number.

'So what?' I hear you say. Well, note that in this case the sum of digits of this nth prime equals the sum of digits of n, that is:

2 + 2 + 7 + 9 + 6 + 9 + 9 + 6 + 6 + 9 + 9 = 9 + 9 + 9 + 7 + 9 + 9 + 7 + 8 + 7 = 74.

The number 74 is the largest known digit sum with this property (as of August 2004).

Your cerebral cortex rocks

The outer layer of grey matter inside your skull, though only 2–3 millimetres thick, is folded and deeply burrowed.

In humans, we think it is responsible for reasoning, perception, consciousness ... the very things that make us human.

The great scientist Carl Sagan loved the cerebral cortex and said, 'What distinguishes our species is thought. The cerebral cortex is in a way a liberation ... We are, each of us, largely responsible for what gets put into our brains, for what, as adults, we wind up caring for and knowing about. No longer at the mercy of the reptile brain, we can change ourselves. Think of the possibilities ...'

As with all things to do with the brain, we're a long way from fully understanding the cerebral cortex. One thing we do know is that compared to other mammals your cerebral cortex is massive!

Fair and square

The aliquot divisors of 75 are 1, 3, 5, 15 and 25. Their sum is a perfect square: 49. Their product is also a perfect square: $1 \times 3 \times 5 \times 15 \times 25 = 5625 = 75^2$.

Difference of 2 squares

Once you've mastered the piece of high school algebra $a^2 - b^2 = (a + b) \times (a - b)$ you can see the relationship between $75 = 15 \times 5$ and $75 = 10^2 - 5^2$.

Similarly, $75 = 25 \times 3$ points to $75 = 14^2 - 11^2$ and $75 = 75 \times 1$ helps us see why $75 = 38^2 - 37^2$.

Braaaaaaainsssssss

Here's a list of mammals by the number of neurons estimated to be in their cerebral cortices:

Mouse
4 million

Rat
21 million

Hedgehog
24 million

Dog
160 million

Cat
300 million

Domesticated pig
450 million

Horse
1.2 billion

Fin whale
1.5 billion

76

The 76th day of the year is March 17

On this day in 1948 Speculative fiction writer William Gibson was born

Automorphic

Seventy-six is an 'automorphic' number because the square of 76 ends in 76 (5 and 6 are automorphic because 5^2 ends in 5 and 6^2 ends in 6). Can you find the one other 2-digit automorphic number? Hint: It's in the 20s.

Alternative chess

If you're ever playing chess in a bizarre parallel universe where they use a 3 × 7 board and each side gets 3 queens, please drop the following into conversation, 'Hey, did you know there are 76 ways we could place 3 queens on this board so that none could capture each other?'

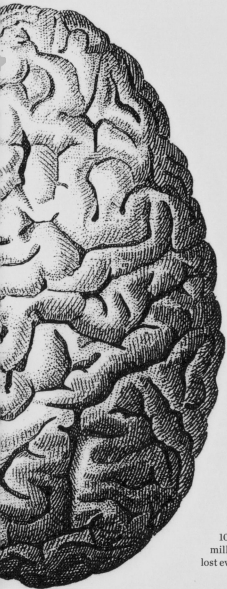

Gorilla
4.3 billion

Bottlenose dolphin
5.8 billion

Chimpanzee
6 billion

False killer whale
10.5 billion

African elephant
11 billion

Human being

Women have 19 billion. Men? 23 billion.
But before any guys start saying, 'See,
I told you men were smarter than women'
the difference is probably because men
are on average bigger, not necessarily
more intelligent.

And one thing you probably didn't know,
on average across your adult life you lose about
10% of these 'neocortical neurons'. That's about 31
million a year, or 85,000 a day or 1 neocortical neuron
lost every second ... ping ... there goes one right now.

More squares ...

Seventy-seven is equal to the
sum of 3 consecutive squares,
$4^2 + 5^2 + 6^2 = 77$ and also the
sum of the first 8 primes.

... and primes

77! + 1 is prime and as we saw
back on February 2 we call
primes of this form 'factorial
primes'. We say the same if
$n! - 1$ is prime.

The 2 largest factorial primes
we know are the 700,177-digit
brute 147885! – 1 and the even
larger 712,355-digit ogre
150209! + 1.

77

*The 77th day of the
year is March 18*

The eyes have it

Even though one of mine is a bit wonky and unkind people in the past have suggested I have at best one and a half, like most humans, I have 2 eyes.

And while most of the animals that immediately come to mind also have 2 eyes – a dog, a cat, a zebra (you weren't thinking of a zebra? you are now!) – it's by no means standard.

Most spiders have 8 eyes (others have 0, 2, 4 or 6) though to be honest, many can't really see that well with them. Some – like jumping spiders and wolf spiders – have at least 1 pair of large forward-facing eyes and quite good eyesight. Human eyesight is about 5 times sharper than jumping spiders'.

The animal with the most complex visual system is probably the mantis shrimp. While humans have 3 photoreceptors (red, green and blue), birds have 4 (including UV) and butterflies have 5, at the head of the pack, the mantis shrimp has 16 photoreceptors. They can see UV, visible and polarised light, they can perceive depth with just a single eye and they can move each eye independently. Being a mantis shrimp must be like having an IMAX screen in your head!

78

The 78th day of the year is March 19

Seventy-eight

is the smallest number that can be written as the sum of 4 distinct, positive squares in 3 ways. Can you find them?

... and 12 drummers

Seventy-eight is the 12th triangular number, so on the 12th day of Christmas, your true love gave you 78 gifts. Though by this stage you'd already received 11 partridges in a pear tree so the living room would be getting a teeny bit crowded.

Jumping spiders have 8 eyes and therefore almost 360-degree vision of their surroundings.

They're also great judges of distance and can leap up to 10 times their own body length to trap prey. That's like a human managing to jump on a pizza almost 20 m away.

Worded big

Letting A = 1, B = 2, C = 3 and adding up the sum of the letters that spell the whole numbers, you'll notice that 1 gives ONE = 15 + 14 + 5 = 34 and that 34 > 1. Similarly for TWO we get 20 + 23 + 15 = 58 which is greater than 2.

This keeps happening all the way up to SEVENTY-NINE, 19 + 5 + 22 + 5 + 14 + 20 + 25 + 14 + 9 + 14 + 5 = 152 > 79.

But for EIGHTY, 5 + 9 + 7 + 8 + 20 + 25 = 74 which is less than 80.

79

The **79th** day of the year is **March 20**

On this day in 1948 Dr Karl Kruszelnicki was born

On the topic of photoreceptors, a very small number of humans have been identified as 'tetrachromats'. This means they have a fourth receptor which gives them a greater ability to distinguish colours. But we're getting a bit off topic here.

Back to amazing animal eyes. Scorpions have anywhere from 2 to 12 eyes. Scallops have dozens and some species have over 100. They sit along the edges of the shell openings and in some cases are brilliantly blue in colour.

But this one I really love. Along with one of the most toxic venoms in the world, box jellyfish have 24 eyes located in 4 sets of 6 around the base of their bell. If you're thinking they'd need quite a brain to process all this information, I'm sorry to tell you that we don't fully understand how they do it. Rather than a complex verterbrate 'brain', they actually have 4 neural 'clusters'. Despite this, they do display a lot of quite complex behaviours using their 24 eyes that we usually do not associate with 'lower invertebrates'. If that's not awesome enough, their eyes actually face *inwards* so the jellyfish have 360-degree vision looking back through their own transparent bodies!

But when it comes down to numbers of eyes, it's hard to go past the largest of all the living bivalve molluscs. Of course I'm talking about *Tridacna Gigas*, the South Pacific giant clam. This extraordinary sea creature grows to more than a metre across, weighs over 200 kilograms, lives to 100 years of age and, in their largest cases, have thousands of eyes!

80

The 80th day of the year is March 21

Prime concatenations

There are 80 four-digit primes which are concatenations of 2-digit primes, for example, 3137. Can you find the smallest and largest such 4-digit primes?

For 'Adie'

When Green Day released the song '80' it had nothing to do with Billy Joe Armstrong's love of concatenated primes, but of his wife Adrienne whose nickname 'Adie' sounds like ...

It should be noted that when we say 'eyes' we are not talking eyes like ours that can detect subtle changes in colour and perceive moving objects at depth, and so on. The clam's eyes are simple photoreceptors which can tell the difference between light and dark. So a trip to the art gallery might be wasted on them. But some scallops' eyes are 'reflector eyes' and can detect moving objects.

Palaeontologists have discovered fossils of a sea creature called Anomalocaridid that was thought to rule the Cambrian seas half a billion years ago with anything up to 16,000 'eyes'! Here's looking at you, Anomalocaridid!

Our squares combined

$81 = 9^2$ and if you write the powers of 2^5 and 9^2 on the same line as the bases you get 2592 which is $2^5 \times 9^2$. It is believed that this is the only such example that doesn't get into the thorny old mathematical conundrum of whether $0^0 = 1$.

All except the 8

The reciprocal of 81, that is $1/81$, looks very cool. $1/81$ = 0.0123456790123456790 12345679... all the digits except for an 8 repeating infinitely.

81

The 81st day of the year is March 22

Speak up!

You probably know that we measure sound volume in decibels.

However, when comparing decibel (dB) levels on this list it's important to understand that it's what's known as a 'logarithmic', rather than 'linear' scale. What does that mean?

It means that every time you increase by 10 dB, you're actually *doubling* the volume. So 60 dB is twice as loud as 50 dB. And 120 dB is not double 60 dB ... it's 64 times the volume! Humans can detect a slight change in volume when sound increases by just 1 dB.

The weakest sound we can detect is 0 dB (depending on the type of the sound). Incredibly, when you hear something that is only 0 dB, your eardrum is moving back and forth a distance of the width of a hydrogen atom!

Not only that, the level at which you can damage your hearing is nowhere near the maximum volume on your iPhone. Many audiologists fear an avalanche of hearing problems and deafness coming our way. In fact, as my good friend and fellow sleek geek Dr Karl points out, 'hearing loss is the most common hidden [that is, not obvious] disability in Australia – and so avoidable.' Stay tuned. But turn the volume down a little, would you?

That wouldn't help you much if you're a Kansas City Chiefs NFL fan, though. In 2014, they set a (possibly dubious) record with a 142.2 dB stadium roar – the loudest recorded, and noisier than a 747 passenger jet taking off!

82

*The **82nd** day of the year is March 23*

On this day in 1882 Mathematician Emmy Noether was born

Pell-Lucas numbers

Eighty-two is the fifth Pell-Lucas number. They can be formed by taking:

$P_1 = 2$, $P_2 = 6$ and following the rule

$P_n = 2 \times P_{n-1} + P_{n-2}$.

This gives us 2, 2, 2 × 2 + 2 = 6, 2 × 6 + 2 = 14, 2 × 14 + 6 = 34, 2 × 34 + 14 = 82, and so on.

We call this rule a 'recurrence relation' and mathematics is full of such rules for generating sequences of numbers.

For example, the Fibonacci numbers which we've already encountered, namely 1, 1, 2, 3, 5, 8 ... are generated by the relation:

$F_1 = 1$, $F_2 = 1$ and $F_n = F_{n-1} + F_{n-2}$

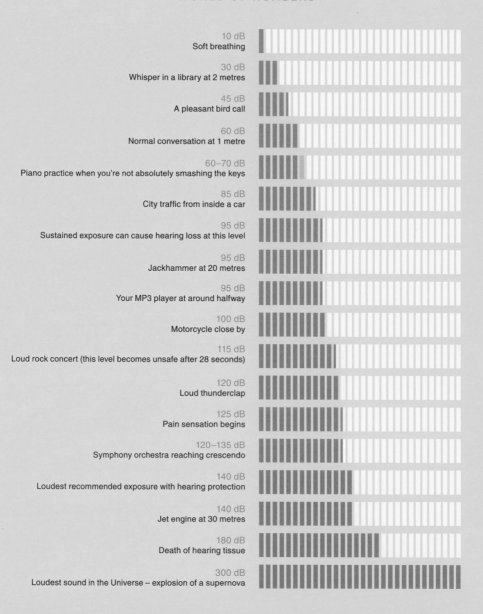

10 dB
Soft breathing

30 dB
Whisper in a library at 2 metres

45 dB
A pleasant bird call

60 dB
Normal conversation at 1 metre

60–70 dB
Piano practice when you're not absolutely smashing the keys

85 dB
City traffic from inside a car

95 dB
Sustained exposure can cause hearing loss at this level

95 dB
Jackhammer at 20 metres

95 dB
Your MP3 player at around halfway

100 dB
Motorcycle close by

115 dB
Loud rock concert (this level becomes unsafe after 28 seconds)

120 dB
Loud thunderclap

125 dB
Pain sensation begins

120–135 dB
Symphony orchestra reaching crescendo

140 dB
Loudest recommended exposure with hearing protection

140 dB
Jet engine at 30 metres

180 dB
Death of hearing tissue

300 dB
Loudest sound in the Universe – explosion of a supernova

Eighty-three

is the smallest prime number which is the sum of a prime number of consecutive prime numbers in a prime number of different ways!

That is, 23 + 29 + 31 = 11 + 13 + 17 + 19 + 23 = 83.

Twos aren't invited

If you kept doubling the number 2 you'd get 4, 8, 16, 32 ... and if you were really keen you'd eventually get to 2^{83} = 9671406556917033397649408. You might notice that this number doesn't contain a 2. Well, every higher prime power of 2 that we've ever tested does contain at least one 2.

83

*The **83rd** day of the year is March 24*

Who nose?

When you sniff, little particles in the air called 'odorants' are sucked into the top of your nose.

That's where you have about 40 million receptors – each attached to a neuron that links into a part of your brain called the 'olfactory bulb'. Your nose contains about 400 different types of receptors and they each respond to one or more odorants.

In 2014, a research paper in the journal *Science* suggested our noses can distinguish more than a million, and maybe even a trillion, different smells.

For example, a tomato gives off 400 different odorants but the smell of a tomato comes about from 16 of these odorants in a specific ratio.

It's not as simple as 'this odorant smells like blah blah'. The concentration or amount of the odorant can have a massive effect. For example, there is one odorant (4-mercapto-4-methylpentan-2-one if you have to know!) that when watered down smells like blackcurrant. But increase the concentration of it 30 times and ... *yuck* ... it smells like cat urine.

84

*The **84th** day of the year is **March 25***

84 triangles

With 9 points equally placed around a circle, there are 84 different triangles using 3 of these points as vertices.

This is just another way of saying there are 84 ways you can 'choose' 3 objects out of a set of 9 when the order in which you chose them does not matter.

Mathematicians would say this as '9 choose 3 equals 84'.

A glass of seawater ...

A glass of seawater contains at least 72 elements and could contain every one of Earth's naturally occurring elements.

A teaspoon of productive earth usually contains up to 1,000,000,000 bacteria. But they're tiny and represent about the same density of life per teaspoon as 4 cows standing on a football field. The bacteria are not alone: they're hanging out with thousands of single-celled organisms called protozoa, scores of nematodes or roundworms and metres of fungal filaments.

A glass of air is almost entirely made up of nitrogen (78.09%) and oxygen (20.95%). The remaining 1% is mostly argon (0.93%). But air does contain around 0.4% carbon dioxide. This very small percentage is rising as a result of burning fossil fuels.

A resting adult breathes in about 23,000 times a day. If you binge on exercise, or hot chillies, this can go up. Adults take between 6.3 and 8.4 million breaths per year so someone who lives into their 80s belts out well over half a billion breaths.

Neighbourhood primes

Eighty-five is the second smallest n such that $n, n + 1$ and $n + 2$ are products of 2 primes. That is:

$85 = 5 \times 17$, $86 = 2 \times 43$ and $87 = 3 \times 29$.

Way back on February 3 we met the first such triple, namely 33, 34 and 35.

Do I even need to ask? Go on, try and find the next smallest triple of 3 consecutive numbers with this property.

The **85th** *day of the year is* March 26

85

PERTH
by numbers

5000 years

5000 years ago, it was possible to travel from Perth to Rottnest Island ... on foot. (By the way, the word 'Rottnest' comes from the Dutch word for 'rats nest'!)

2697 km

The distance by road to Adelaide, making Perth the world's most remote capital city.

$1,000,000

The value of the largest gold coin in the world, weighing 1 tonne, and made by the Perth Mint in 2012.

4.6 km^2

The size of Kings Park – the world's largest inner city park – considerably bigger than New York's famous Central Park.

86

The 86th day of the year is March 27

Noughtless

Eighty-six is conjectured to be the largest number n such that 2^n (in decimal) doesn't contain a 0.

In case you're wondering,

$2^{86} = 77371252455336267181195264.$

3

The number of centuries in which the Perth Mint has been operating. The world's oldest functioning mint was opened in 1899, 2 years before Australia's Federation.

8 hours

Sorry Brisbane, that's the average hours of sunshine every day, making Perth Australia's sunniest capital.

1962

The year in which astronaut John Glenn orbited above Perth and named it the 'City of Light'.

$800

The cost of a bottle of the world's most expensive beer sold by Perth's Nail Brewing in 2010. Only 30 bottles were made.

Our primes combined

The sum of the squares of the first 4 prime numbers is $2^2 + 3^2 + 5^2 + 7^2 = 87$.

Four score and seven

$87 = 4 \times 20 + 7$ which doesn't look all that beautiful, but when Abraham Lincoln referred to the 87 years between the signing of the Declaration of Independence and the Battle of Gettysburg as 'Four score and seven years' he gave one of history's all-time greatest speeches.

87

The **87th** day of the year is **March 28**

Feral facts

Here's some grim reading for you.

75,000,000+ is the number of native animals killed by feral cats in Australia *every night*! Sad but true.

In fact, in Australia alone, cats have been implicated in the extinction of at least 20 mammal species and sub-species, including the lesser bilby and the desert bandicoot.

Feral cats help themselves to a phenomenal number of species in Australia – some 400 different vertebrates. This includes 123 bird species, 157 reptiles, 58 marsupials, 27 rodents, 21 frogs and 9 exotic medium- and large-sized mammals.

It's not exactly the sort of record you merrily submit to the folks at *Guinness,* but this is more than double the 179 species of animals that cats have been recorded eating on other islands worldwide.

While we're on bleak numbers, here's one more (in case you needed another reason to try to do your part to look after our planet): every day, about 74 more species become extinct.

88

*The **88th** day of the year is **March 29***

Strobogrammatic

Eighty-eight is 'strobogrammatic', a number that is the same when it is rotated 180° about its centre ... 69 is another example. If they make a different number when rotated, they are called 'invertible integers' (109 becomes 601, for example).

Birthday triplets

We mentioned on January 23 the surprising result that a group of 23 strangers is more likely than not to contain a common birthday. Well, in a group of 88 people, there's a slightly more than 50% chance that 3 people will share a birthday.

Un-average reign falls ...

On 9 September 2015, Queen Elizabeth II gathered the attention of the world as she reigned over England for her 63rd year and 108th day. In doing so, she passed the magical mark of 23,226 days set by her great-great-grandmother Queen Victoria.

But as impressive as that is, the Queen is still nowhere near the longest serving of the world's rulers.

That title goes to Sobhuza II of Swaziland, who took the throne on 10 December 1899 aged 4 months, ruling until his death on 21 August 1982, after an 82 year and 254 day reign. In fact, at 63 odd years, Queen Elizabeth II just makes it into the top 40 of longest reigning rulers. But there is quite a logjam and within a decade she could crack the top 10.

Surprisingly, in this age of improved medicine, diet, and so on, practically none of the top 50 longest-serving monarchs have reigned post-1900. Geez, those old fellas could hang around!

At the other extreme, the list of shortest reigns makes for some interesting and sometimes gruesome reading.

The shortest ever could be argued to be that of France's Prince Louis Antoine, Duke of Angoulême, 'King Louis XIX', who technically occupied the throne for all of 20 minutes on 2 August 1830.

All stops to 89

Apart from the trivial case of 0, if you write any integer and sum the square of the digits, and then continue to repeat this, eventually you will get either 1, or 89.

For example, starting with 16, you would get:

$1^2 + 6^2 = 37; 3^2 + 7^2 = 58;$
$5^2 + 8^2 = 89.$

If this sounds similar to the game we played back at number 58 you're right. It's exactly the same game because 58 and 89 are both in the 'loop' 4, 16, 37, 58, 89, 145, 42, 20, 4 ...

We call numbers that cycle down to 1 happy numbers and hence 16 is an unhappy number ;-(

89

*The **89th** day of the year is March 30*

You see, when his father, Charles X, abdicated the throne, he was succeeded by Louis Antoine who then abdicated himself in favour of his nephew, Henri V. As a result of the recent July Revolution, it had become a pretty unpopular gig! However, there were 20 minutes between abdications, giving Louis Antoine time to contemplate his abdication and arguably giving him a short 'reign'.

Not far behind Louis XIX is Emperor Modi, the final emperor of the Chinese Jin Dynasty. He was crowned on 9 February 1234 while under assault by Mongols at the Siege of Caizhou. He spent most of his brief tenure trying to reinforce the palace walls but was unsuccessful and was killed soon after, ending a reign that some estimate as being as short as 2 hours.

Sayyid Khalid bin Barghash was Sultan of Zanzibar for a grand total of 3 days being 25, 26 and 27 August 1896. He'd seized power following Sayyid Hamad bin Thuwaini Al-Busaid's death, resulting in the 38-minute Anglo-Zanzibar War. He was replaced following surrender.

Popes don't last anywhere near as long as other rulers because they tend to be a bit more senior before getting the gig. The most impressive reign the papacy can muster is that of the very first pope, St Peter, who ruled for either 34 or 37 years from the year 30AD, depending on who you ask.

Most people over the age of 50 will remember the short reign of Pope John Paul I who died a mere 33 days after taking over as the head of the Catholic Church (26 August–28 September 1978). But this barely makes the top 10 shortest papal reigns.

90

The **90th** day of the year is **March 31**

90, join the club

Calculate $(90^3 - 1)/(90 - 1)$. Convince yourself that this is a Mersenne prime (see also 31).

Picture semiperfect

The proper divisors of 90 are 1, 2, 3, 5, 6, 9, 10, 15, 18, 30 and 45.

And because we can write 90 as the sum of some of its proper divisors, for example,

$$90 = 45 + 30 + 10 + 5$$

we call 90 'semiperfect'.

Tying with JPI on 33 days is Benedict V who presided over the church for that same period of time way back in the year 964. But the rest of the top 10 tiny terms are:

- Leo XI (1 April 1–27 April 1605) = 27 days
- Pius III (22 September–18 October 1503) = 27 days
- Damasus II (17 July–9 August 1048) = 24 days
- Marcellus II (9 April–1 May 1555) = 22 days
- Sisinnius (15 January–4 February 708) = 21 days
- Theodore II (December 897) = 20 days
- Celestine IV (25 October–10 November 1241) = 17 days, died before consecration
- Boniface VI (April 896) = 16 days

Which brings us to the shortest serving Pope of all time: Urban VII who held office for just 13 days, from September 15–27 in 1590. Urban died of malaria before his papal coronation could take place. But in that short period of time he did achieve one thing, he was the first ruler known to have banned smoking anywhere in the world. Urban threatened to excommunicate anyone who 'took tobacco in the porchway of or inside a church, whether it be by chewing it, smoking it with a pipe or sniffing it in powdered form through the nose'.

An almost ton of fun

$6^3 - 5^3 = 4^3 + 3^3 = 91$

$91 = 1^2 + 2^2 + 3^2 + 4^2 + 5^2 + 6^2$

$91 = 1 + 2 + 3 + ... + 13$

$91^3 = 753,571$ and

$10^n + 91$ and $10^n + 93$ are twin primes, that is, a pair of prime numbers separated by 2, for $n = 1, 2, 3$ and 4.

All of these statements are true and not April fool's jokes.

But beware on April 1, every few years the old, 'Hey, they've worked out π isn't irrational after all' goes around. Hilarious for some ... offensive for others :-(

91

*The **91st** day of the year is April 1*

On this day in 1776 Mathematician Sophie Germain was born

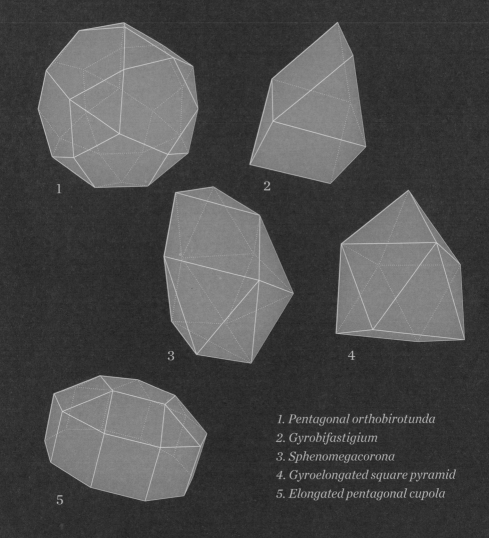

1. Pentagonal orthobirotunda
2. Gyrobifastigium
3. Sphenomegacorona
4. Gyroelongated square pyramid
5. Elongated pentagonal cupola

Johnson solids

92

We've already met the Platonic solids, where all the faces are the same regular shape meeting the same way at each vertex.

Likewise, we've also seen the Archimedean solids, which have two different regular faces instead of just one.

Well, once we don't care if the faces meet the same way at each vertex, we get to the Johnson solids. There are 92 of them, including such awesomely named figures as the elongated pentagonal cupola, gyrobifastigium, orthobirotunda and sphenomegacorona.

It is beautiful that if you let a group of 6-year-old kids loose with magnetic or plastic interlocking squares and triangles, they will naturally discover many of these shapes.

On this day in 1981
IBM released the IBM PC

Meet Frank Forde, the 15th Prime Minister of Australia

Forde has the honour of being the shortest-serving Prime Minister in Australia's history. He held the top job for a total of 8 days after John Curtin died, before losing the leadership to Ben Chifley.

Actually, for many years he held another record: longest-living Aussie PM (92 years, 194 days). However he was beaten in 2009 by Gough Whitlam, who lived to the grand old age of 98.

Give me 93 of 93!

93! = 115677250708164157475920516230624043621475322957641353518614228121324680712146731521520328951684484530383899628938707809075200000000000000000000000000 which is one massive number.

But interestingly, the first 93 digits of 93! (namely 115677250708164157475920516230624043621475322957641353518614228121324680712146731521520328951) is a prime number.

When I say 'interestingly'...

93

The 93rd day of the year is April 3

It takes a male flea...

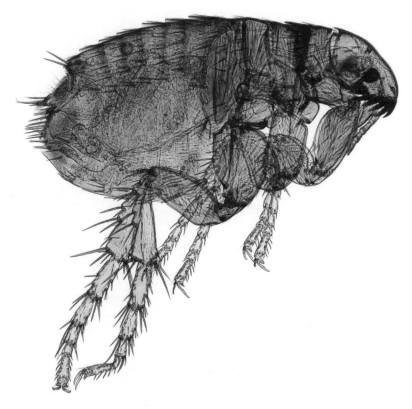

...around 8 hours to unfold all the different parts of its penis.

94

*The **94th** day of the year is April 4*

Factorial prime

94! − 1 = 10873661566567430802736528525678660100418680358018287230749737443404519986941792763022910921458341545856086565120238534053068799999999999999999999 and is prime.

This factorial prime looks pretty awesome the way it finishes with 21 consecutive 9s. But if you think about it long enough you can see why this has to be the case.

On this day in 1980 Pac-Man began chomping his way into arcades

How old are you ... altogether?

The cells in your body are constantly regenerating. So it makes sense that the lungs breathing inside you today might not be the same lungs you had 5 years ago.

Some people have twisted this fact of biology into mumbo jumbo claims like 'every 7 years your body is completely renewed at a cellular level, so it is possible to completely realign your spirit with ... blah blah blah'.

In fact, it turns out the cells that make up different parts of our body renew at different rates. By measuring the level of the fast-decaying version of carbon called carbon-14, scientists can accurately clock the speed of cell regeneration. The cells in your taste buds, for example, renew themselves every 10–14 days. You could therefore argue that while your age might be 12 or 24 or 86, your taste buds are really only 10 days old. Going by this logic, here's a map of how old your body *really* is.

An Anomaly

The fraction $19/95$ simplifies to $1/5$ but by coincidence you could just cross out the 9s and $19/95$ 'becomes' $1/5$.

Mathematically, you can't just cross out the 9s but when the maths does match up with 'just crossing them out' we call this an 'anomalous cancellation'.

There are only 3 cases of anomalous cancellations for 2-digit numbers on both the top (numerator) and bottom (denominator) of a proper fraction (a positive fraction that is less than 1). We also don't count just cancelling zeros on the end of both numbers. To find the next case check out April 8.

95

The 95th day of the year is April 5

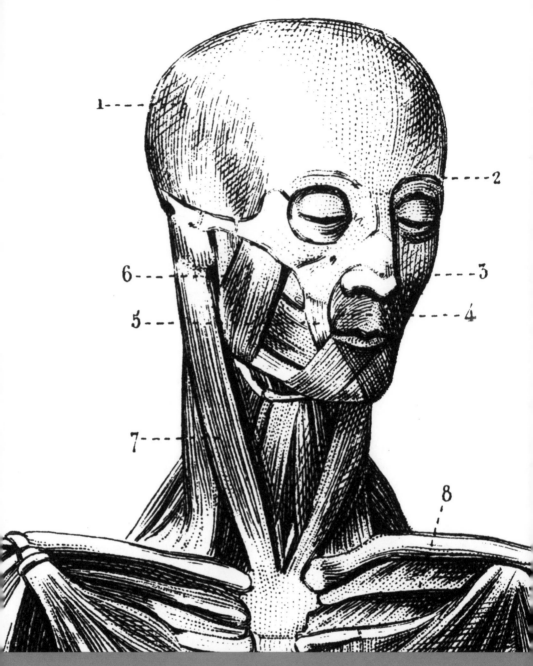

96

*The **96th** day of the year is April 6*

Ninety-six is the smallest number that can be written as the difference of 2 squares in 4 ways. One example is $10^2 - 2^2 = 100 - 4 = 96$.

Okay, I'm a reasonable guy, so here's another way: $11^2 - 5^2 = 121 - 25 = 96$.

Can you find the other 2 ways that 96 can be written as the difference of 2 squares?

Hair: 3–6 years

How old your hair is depends on the length of each strand, but for those of us who are lucky enough to have hair, it grows about 1 cm each and every month. A strand of female hair lasts up to 6 years while a strand of male hair lasts 3 years. Your eyelashes and eyebrows regrow every 6 to 8 weeks, but if you constantly pluck them you'll mess up their natural life cycle and they may stop growing. Go easy on the tweezers, all right?

Brain: same as your age

For better or worse, we are born with all the brain cells we'll ever have – around 100 billion. Unfortunately, most of the brain does not renew itself as it gets older. In fact, we actually *lose* brain cells, which is one of the reasons why people get dementia and why head injuries are so bad for you. All is not lost, though, because there are 2 areas of the brain that *do* regenerate: the olfactory bulb that looks after our sense of smell, and the hippocampus, which is responsible for learning.

Eyes: same as your age

Your eyes are one of the few body parts that don't really change throughout your life. The only part of your eye that is constantly being renewed is the cornea: the transparent top layer. If the cornea is damaged, it can repair itself in as little as 24 hours. The cornea has to have a smooth surface, so you can focus properly. That's why the cells renew themselves so quickly. Unfortunately, this isn't the case with the rest of the eye – as we grow older, the lens loses flexibility, which is why our eyesight deteriorates.

Taste buds: 10 days

Did you know your tongue is covered with around 9000 taste buds? These clever little marvels of biology help you to taste sweet, salty, bitter and sour flavours. The buds themselves are a collection of cells and they renew themselves every 10 days to 2 weeks. That said, if you're a smoker or prone to infection, your taste buds become damaged and won't renew as fast. They also lose sensitivity so you won't be able to taste things so well.

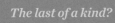

The last of a kind?

Ninety-seven is the largest prime that we can ever find that is less than the sum of the square of its digits $9^2 + 7^2 > 97$.

It is also conjectured, which means we don't know for sure but think it may well be the case, that $97 = 3^4 + 2^4$ is the largest prime of the form $3^n + 2^n$.

We do know that if there is another such prime out there it has to be bigger than $10^{16000000}$, which is pretty big, let's be honest.

97

Liver: 5 months

Your liver is truly a wonder. It has a rich blood supply and can repair itself and re-grow even while it goes about its business flushing the nasties from your system. Liver cells only live for about 150 days before regenerating, but that's no reason to go and abuse this very special organ. Would you believe doctors can remove up to 70% of a person's liver in an operation, and virtually all will grow back within 2 months? Well, it's true.

Heart: 20 years

Until recently, it was thought the human heart couldn't renew itself. However, a study conducted at the New York Medical College found the heart is actually dotted with stem cells that constantly rejuvenate it – at least 3 or 4 times over a lifetime.

Lungs: 2–3 weeks to a year

The cells in your lungs are constantly renewing themselves, but there are different types of cells that renew at different speeds. The cells that look after the exchange of oxygen and gases steadily regenerate over a period of around a year. But the cells on the lung's surface have to renew every 2 or 3 weeks.

15- -

Intestines: 2–3 days

Inside your stomach, your intestines are lined with tiny, finger-like branches that help the intestine to absorb nutrients. These branches are exposed to strong chemicals like stomach acid and so they renew themselves evey 2 to 3 days. The rest of the intestine is covered with a layer of mucous, but this can't protect it from stomach acid for long – so the cells have to regenerate every 3 to 5 days.

18- - - -

98

*The **98th** day of the year is April 8*

Another Anomaly

Back on April 5 we talked about 'anomalous cancellations' where the correct mathematical simplification of a fraction happens to match up with just crossing out a common number. I have to stress you can almost never just cross out a common digit and get the correct answer.

You can for $^{19}/_{95} = ^1/_5$. You can also do it for $^{16}/_{64} = ^1/_4$, $^{26}/_{65} = ^2/_5$ and for a fraction involving 98 as the denominator and a 2-digit numerator.

Some sticklers don't like this example because the fraction you get can simplify further, but can you find the anomalous cancellation that involves 98?

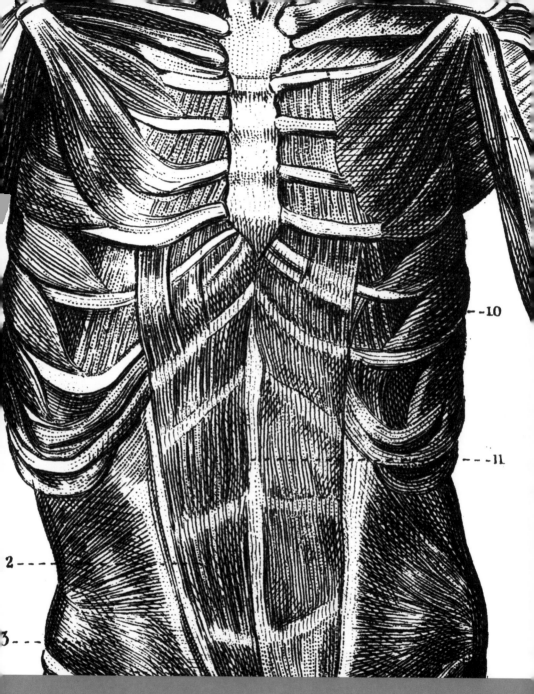

--10

--11

2 - - - -

3 - - -

Ninety-nine

is a Kaprekar number:

$99^2 = 9801$ and $98 + 01 = 99$.

Every which way

If 99 divides some 4-digit number ABCD, then 99 also divides BCDA, CDAB, and DABC. In fact, 99 will also divide DCBA, CBAD, BADC and ADCB.

99, you dividing funster you.

99

*The **99th** day of the year is April 9*

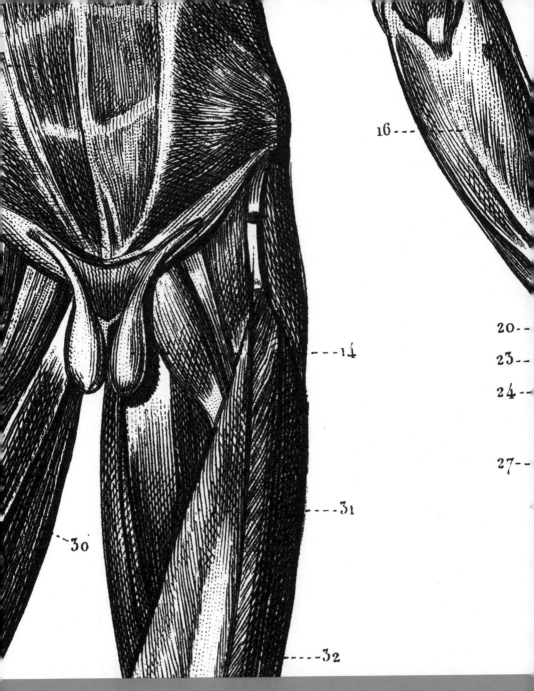

16 - - -

20 - -
23 - -
24 - -

27 - -

- - - 14

- - - - 31

- - 30

- - - - - 32

100

*The **100th** day of the year is April 10*

Another place, another prime

The first 3 primes add to 10 and the first $3^2 = 9$ primes add to $10^2 = 100$.

And just in case those little patterns above weren't enough for you, the $3^2 = 9$th prime is ... 23.

Also, 98, 99 and 100 is the smallest sequence of 3 consecutive numbers with at least 3 (not necessarily distinct) prime divisors.

Skin: 2–4 weeks

The surface layer of your skin (known as the epidermis) regenerates every 2 to 4 weeks. This happens because the epidermis is your outer defence against the elements: the sun, wind, rain and pollution. But no matter what some people say, constant regeneration does not make us younger! As we age our skin loses a substance called collagen: this is what gives it its supple softness. And there ain't nothin' we can do about it.

Bones: 10 years

Your bones are constantly renewing themselves. Pretty slowly, it has to be said: it takes around 10 years for your whole skeleton to regenerate. At any one time you have a mixture of old and new bone as the regeneration rates differ throughout the body. Unfortunately, when we hit middle age, this renewal process slows down, so our bones become brittle and thinner ... and this can lead to bone diseases.

Fingernails: 6–10 months

Your fingernails grow around 3.5 mm every month – over twice as fast as your toenails. It takes around 10 months for a full toenail to grow, but only 6 months for a fingernail. This may be because fingernails have a better blood supply and therefore better circulation.

And here's something you didn't know. Your nails are growing 25% faster than your grandparents did when they were your age. This 'growth spurt' is thought to be down to improved diets rich in protein.

Red blood cells: 4 months

Red blood cells carry oxygen to every living tissue in your body. They also carry toxins away. Given the amount of work they do, it's not surprising that they wear out every 4 months or so.

The path to perfection

We've spoken about perfect numbers on January 6 and 28. We don't know if there is an infinite number of perfect numbers and while all the perfect numbers we have so far discovered have been even, we don't know if there can be an odd one. We do know that if an odd perfect number exists, it must have at least 101 prime factors.

Countdown!

$101 = 5! - 4! + 3! - 2! + 1!$

101

The 101st day of the year is April 11

On this day in 1976 The Apple I, Apple's first computer, was released

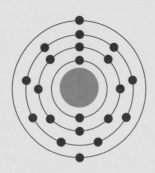

Scandium

Scandium has 21 protons in its nucleus and was discovered in 1879 after scientists analysed the minerals euxenite and gadolinite from Scandinavia (hence the name). These days, most deposits of scandium are found in Russia and China but production each year is low. Scandium alloys are used in fighter jet engine parts and some sporting goods, including bicycle frames and lacrosse sticks. But if you're thinking of packing a scandium cricket bat this summer, don't bother, they've already been banned!

12345678910111213141516171819202122232425262728293031323334353637383940414243444546474849505152 5455565758596061626364656667686970717273747576777879808182838485868788899091929394959697989991

102

The 102nd day of the year is April 12

Prime time

The sum of the cubes of the first 102 prime numbers is a prime number, and 102 itself can be written as the sum of 4 consecutive prime numbers. Can you find them?

A palindromic product

The product of 102 and its reverse is a palindrome. Huh? What I mean is:

$102 \times 201 = 20502$ where 20502 reads the same back to front as front to back.

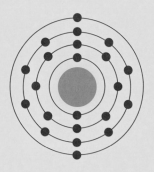

Titanium

At number 22 on the atomic hot list is the 'transition metal' known as titanium. It's silver in colour, has a low density and is very very strong. Like scandium, it's also used in the aerospace and motor racing industries. Boat builders love it too because it's super resistant to corrosion in seawater. Titanium is contained in meteorites as well as 'M-type' stars (red dwarfs, for example). M-type stars are some of the coolest stars in the galaxy – and by that I mean they have a surface temperature below 3500°C, not a fantastic record collection!

4567891011121314151617181920212223242526272829303132333435363738394041424344454647484950515253
5556575859606162636465666768697071727374757677787980818283848586878889909192939495969798991000

No bullseye

When playing darts, 103 is the lowest prime you cannot hit with 2 darts. The prime before it, 101, can be scored by a bullseye (50) and a triple 17. Similarly, every other lesser prime can be scored with just 2 darts.

Who's the squarest of them all?

The number 103 is the reverse of 301. Convince yourself that the squares of 103 and 301 are also each other's reverses.

103

The 103rd day of the year is April 13

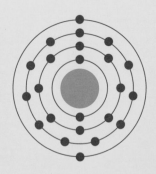

Vanadium

Vanadium is never found on its own in nature (it's needy and is always grouped with other elements), but once isolated, it's a highly toxic transition metal (like titanium) that is used in steel alloys for things like high speed tools. Vanadium also played a part in the history of cars. In 1905, Henry Ford encountered V-steel, a steel–vanadium alloy that reduced the weight of his Model-T by about half. Hank famously said, 'But for vanadium there would be no automobiles'!

104

*The **104th** day of the year is April 14*

What's this thing?

The number 104 is the smallest number of unit line segments that can exist in a 'regular graph' with 4 segments touching at every vertex but not crossing.

Next time you've got a couple of boxes of matches and a LOT of spare time ...

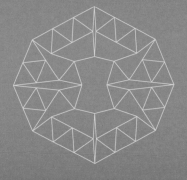

*On this day in 2003
The Human Genome Project
was declared complete*

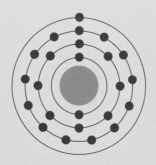

Chromium

The 24th element takes its name from the Greek word *chroma*, which means colour, because many compounds containing chromium are intensely coloured. In 1817, the French chemist, pharmacist and mineralogist, André Laugier, discovered chromium in the Pallas meteorite – a 680-kg stony-iron space rock that had been found near Krasnoyarsk in the Siberian mountains in 1749.

Chromium is essential for the body to process glucose and it is found most commonly in the placenta.

34567891011121314151617181920212223**24**2526272829303132333435363738394041424344454647484950515253
5556575859606162636465666768697071727374757677787980818283848586878889909192939495969798998100

105

*The **105th** day of the year is April 15*

Paul Erdös

was a famous Hungarian mathematician who conjectured that 105 is the largest number *n* such that the positive values of $n - 2^k$ are all prime (those primes are 103, 101, 97, 89, 73 and 41).

Erdös was one of the great enigmas of mathematics. Brilliant but eccentric – known to regularly arrive at a colleague's house saying only 'my brain is open', stay for a while, collaborate on work then leave – he also gave us this quote about the beauty of numbers: 'Why are numbers beautiful? It's like asking why is Beethoven's *Ninth Symphony* beautiful. If you don't see why, someone can't tell you. I know numbers are beautiful. If they aren't beautiful, nothing is.'

On this day in 1707 Leonhard Euler was born, 255 years after Leonardo da Vinci

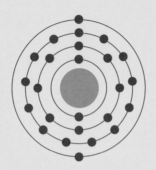

Manganese

There isn't much manganese in our bodies – only about 1 part per 5 million – but it's necessary for development, metabolism and the antioxidant system. Beetroot is absolutely packed with the stuff, which is great news because, in my humble opinion, beetroot rocks.

In 1974, the US government announced that they planned to mine the manganese-rich ocean floor. In fact, it turned out the story was a bluff and that they were instead looking for a sunken Soviet submarine!

1234567891011121314151617181920212223242526272829303132333435363738394041424344454647484950515253
5455565758596061626364656667686970717273747576777879808182838485868788899091929394959697989991

106

The 106th day of the year is April 16

10-point trees

A mathematical 'tree' is a connected joining of dots without any loops. There are 106 mathematical trees with 10 vertices. Here are several:

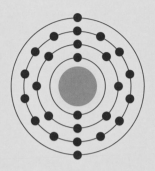

Iron Fe

Of all the nuclei of all the elements we've ever discovered, iron's nuclei are some of the most tightly bound together. This means that in the nuclear furnace of a star, no energy can be extracted from the fusion process. Instead, it starts to *cost* energy, which results in the core temperature dropping. As such, iron is the heaviest element that can be created in typical star furnaces.

Back around 160AD, the Greek physician Galen of Pergamon recommended iron filings as a laxative. If anything, they're likely to have the opposite effect! Not sure how popular Dr G might have been in some parts of Pergamon.

Interesting integer

There is no integer N such that $N!$ has exactly 107 zeros in it. The same is true if we replace 107 by the primes 3, 31 or 43.

Hexasyllabic

The number 'one hundred and seven' is the smallest whole number in English that requires 6 syllables to pronounce. Unless of course you like to run words together unintelligibly in which case it's just 'hhhunsen'.

107

The 107th day of the year is April 17

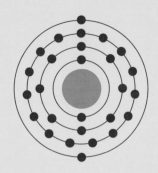

Cobalt

When miners in the 16th century tried to smelt a substance they were sure contained silver, they failed because, unknown to them, it was actually 'cobalt arsenide'. Thinking the substance must be cursed, they named it *kobald* – the German word for goblin – and from *kobald* we get the word cobalt.

Next time you see your craft-loving friend who's mad for making pottery, stained glass or porcelain tiles, tell them the rich Sevres Blue colour they use is probably cobalt silicate or cobalt blue.

Of the 25 elements considered 'essential for human life', cobalt occurs the least in our bodies, at a mere 20 parts per billion.

108

The 108th day of the year is April 18

Lost ... and found?

One hundred and eight minutes was the mysterious amount of time that the characters in *Lost* had between each time they entered the numbers 4 8 15 16 23 42. Spoiler alert, when someone finally decided not to do it and let the timer run down to zero, the results were pretty spectacular.

Of cubes and squares

The number 108 can be written as the sum of a positive cube and a positive square ($a^3 + b^2$) in 2 ways. Can you find them?

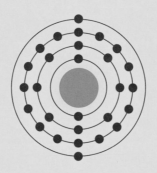

Nickel

'Nickel' comes from the German word *kupfernickel*, which means 'the devil's copper'. German copper miners gave this name to a particular reddish-brown ore that seemed to be of little use. Eventually, scientists realised *kupfernickel* contained not copper but an entirely new element ... nickel.

We all hate it when you go to play an old CD and it's dirty, or some goose has scratched it. A new CD called HD-Rosetta (named after the Rosetta stone) made of nickel can hold 1.5 million pages of info and lasts 1000 years even at temperatures of up to 800°C. My younger daughter Olivia can now rest easy knowing we can pass on the majesty of Katy Perry to future generations!

34667891011121314151617181920212223242526272829303132333435363738394041424344454647484950515253
5556657585960616263646566676869707172737475767778798081828384858687888990919293949596979899100

It's not about quantity

Convince yourself that 109 has more distinct digits than its square. It does and in fact it is the smallest number with this property.

109

The **109th** *day of the year is April 19*

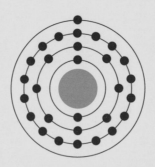

Copper Cu

Coming in at number 29 on the atomic hit list, copper is a ductile metal that conducts heat and electricity really really well. It was the mixing of 2 parts copper with 1 part tin that produced bronze and ushered many ancient civilisations out of the stone age and into ... you guessed it ... the bronze age. We all know that when you mix copper with zinc you get ... brass (though there has never been a brass age!?)!

The reason that octopuses have blue blood is that instead of the deep red haemoglobin that carries oxygen around your body and mine, our little 8-legged sea friends have a blue copper molecule called haemocyanin to do the job.

123456789101112131415161718192021222324252627282**9**3031323334353637383940414243444546474849505152
5455565758596061626364656667686970717273747576777879808182838485868788899091929394959697989 91

110

The 110th day of the year is April 20

Add 'em up

The sum of the first 110 primes has only 2 prime factors.

$2 + 3 + 5 + 7 + ... + 599 + 601$
$= 29,897 = 7 \times 4271$

$110 = 5^2 + 6^2 + 7^2$

Repunits

The number 111 being a string of 1s is called a 'repunit', specifically, it is R_3 because it uses three 1s.

$R_3 = 111 = 3 \times 37$ is not prime but we know that R_{1031} (pictured above) is prime and we strongly suspect that $R_{49,081}$, $R_{86,453}$, $R_{109,297}$ and $R_{270,343}$ are too.

Also, if you decided that you want to make 111 with eleven 1s, and I for one certainly wouldn't try to stop you, you could write:

$111 = (11 + 1) \times (11 - (1 + 1)) + (1 + 1 + 1) \times 1$

111

*The **111th** day of the year is April 21*

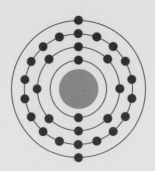

Zinc

Zinc and its compounds are widely used in deodorants, shampoos, as dietary supplements, and in some paints. Zinc is an essential element for humans, though too much can make you sick. *Viola guestphalica* is the scientific name of the flower Zinc Pansy which is grown in industrial areas of Germany where the soil contains high levels of zinc contamination.

When 2 atoms have the same number of protons in their nucleus but different numbers of neutrons, we say that they are different 'isotopes' of that element. Zinc has 30 protons in its nucleus but its isotopes can have anything from 24 to 53 neutrons.

123456789101112131415161718192021222324252627282930313233343536373839404142434445464748495051525354555657585960616263646566676869707172737475767778798081828384858687888990919293949596979899

112

The 112th day of the year is April 22

How practical!

The number 112 is a 'practical' number (aka a 'panarithmic' number), as any smaller number can be formed by adding distinct divisors of 112.

We can easily see that 12 is panarithmic because the divisors of 12 are 1, 2, 3, 4 and 6 and of the remaining numbers from 1 to 11 we have

$5 = 1 + 4$, $7 = 3 + 4$, $8 = 2 + 6$, $9 = 3 + 6$, $10 = 1 + 3 + 6$ and $11 = 2 + 3 + 6$.

It might take a bit long doing all numbers from 1 to 111, but pick a few at random and try and express them as the sum of distinct divisors of 112.

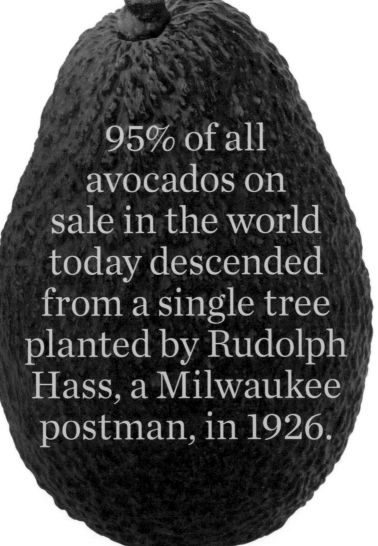

95% of all avocados on sale in the world today descended from a single tree planted by Rudolph Hass, a Milwaukee postman, in 1926.

Closer to pi

Most people can remember using the approximation of $\pi = {}^{22}/_{7}$ in high school mathematics. Well, ${}^{355}/_{113}$ is a better approximation, easily remembered by taking 11, 33, 55 and splitting it into 113 and 355.

On the topic of numbers joined together, I bet you never knew that 113 × 10925379566701 = 12345678910111213 is the first 13 counting numbers 'concatenated' or joined together.

113

*The **113th** day of the year is April 23*

On this day in 1858 Physicist Max Planck was born

Jack & Jill: political activists?

Stop me if you've heard this one before:

Jack and Jill went up the hill
To fetch a pail of water
Jack fell down
And broke his crown
And Jill came tumbling after.

Who knew that this innocent nursery rhyme we all sang as kids was actually a song of political activism bemoaning increased taxes and their effect on the working class!

Let's go back a step.

A 'gill' is a unit of volume which originated in the Middle Ages. To this day, it's still used to measure alcohol. In Ireland, for example, it's a standard measure. However, US and British gills were different.

A US gill equals half a cup, or 4 US fluid ounces, which equals 7.219 cubic inches, or 118.29 cubic cm. You get about 8 US gills to a litre. In the American Civil War surgeons prescribed a gill of whiskey to men to counter the ill effects of the previous day's battles.

114

*The **114th** day of the year is April 24*

On this day in 1990
The Hubble Space Telescope
was launched into space

Another quick primer

The sum of the first 114 digits of *e* is prime. This is the third consecutive day number with this property, but the 113th and 114th digits are both 0 so in some ways 114 is cheating and taking all of 112's hard work on this one!

On the topic of the decimal expansion of *e* and primes, the 114-digit number given by the first 114 digits after the decimal point of *e* is itself prime.

Note for this second prime we did not include the 2 before the decimal point – in generating the first prime we did include the 2.

In Great Britain a gill is slightly larger – it equals 5 British fluid ounces, or 8.669 cubic inches, one-fourth pint, or 142.07 cubic cm, or $1/7$th of a litre. The English gill was introduced in the 14th century to measure individual servings of whiskey or wine. It was also spelled jill. Soon after ascending to the English throne in 1625, King Charles I scaled down the standard serving of alcohol (a 'jack' or 'jackpot', sometimes known as a double jigger) in order to increase the sales taxes he took in. The jill was, by definition, twice the size of the jack, so as the jack fell down, the jill automatically 'came tumbling after'. I've said it before and I'll say it again: geek historical gold!

Charles I seen here with his head still attached to his body – which was not the case after he was charged with treason in January 1649.

Curious composites

Convince yourself that 115 (or 5! – 5) is the smallest composite number of the form $p! - p$, where p is prime. Obviously for p larger than 5 we can always factorise $p! - p = p \times (p-1) \times (p-2) \times ... \times 2 \times 1 - p = p[(p-1) \times (p-2) \times (p-3) \times ... \times 2 \times 1 - 1] = p[(p-1)! - 1]$ which will be composite for any prime p larger than 3.

It might seem a bit weird that this only kicks in for $p = 5$, but if you look back at the value of $(p-1)! - 1$ when $p = 2$ or 3 you can see why these cases 'go away'.

115

*The **115th** day of the year is April 25*

Livin' la vida longer

The oldest animal we've ever discovered is a quahog clam – an edible, hard-shell mollusc which, if cooked properly, makes for a damn fine chowder. Hey, I'm vegetarian. Don't complain to me!

We determine the age of these tough little critters by counting the growth rings on their shells. Back in 2007, researchers found one 80 metres underwater off the coast of Iceland but unfortunately while counting its growth rings they killed it. It was at least 405 years old but later estimates have claimed it was 507.

Sea animals are particularly long-living – there are various species of coral and sponges that live for thousands of years. I don't want to get into an emotional debate about whether these are 'animals' but, assuming they are not, after Ming the quahog clam our top 10 longest-living aquatic animals may well be filled out by these oldies:

Hanako the koi fish

When she died at the ripe old age of 226 on 7 July 1977 she was older than the USA.

Bowhead whales

There are reputable claims that some bowhead whales have lived over 200 years, making them the oldest mammals.

116

*The **116th** day of the year is **April 26***

The 10th in line

116! + 1 is prime. It is the 10th factorial prime of the form *n*! + 1 that we meet. The previous ones were for *n* = 1, 2, 3, 11, 27, 37, 41, 73 and 77. We'll meet another 3 of them this year when the year days are 154, 320 and 340.

Hundred Years' War
and sixteen

Unfortunately for the poor people fighting the Hundred Years' War, the fact that it had gotten to 100 years by 1437 wasn't enough to make everyone just lay down their swords and try to get along together. The war dragged on for another 16 years until 1453.

Freshwater pearl mussels

Freshwater pearl mussels live between 210 and 250 years.

Deep-sea hydrocarbon tubeworms

These guys have clocked up a quarter of a millennium. You can only imagine how these 2-metre-long, backbone-free, cold seep dwellers party when celebrating such a milestone.

Red sea urchins

Some red sea urchins live over 200 years with little sign of ageing, leading to them being branded 'virtually immortal'.

Orange roughy fish

The orange roughy, also known as deep sea perch, can live up to 149 years.

George the lobster

When PETA estimated George to be about 140, in 1999, the owner of the restaurant to which he had been sold described it as a 'no-brainer' to release him back into the wild.

Sturgeon

In 2012, a 100-kilogram specimen caught in Wolf River, Wisconsin, was estimated to be 125 years old.

Factorise!

The number 117 can be written as the difference of 2 prime squares and as the difference of 2 prime cubes. Can you find both of these ways of writing 117?

117 is a factor of 'one million minus one'. If you're up for a bit of fun why don't you factorise 999,999 into its prime factors, noting 117 is not itself prime.

117

The 117th day of the year is April 27

← ─────────────────────────────────── A tardigrade, to scale

But these little critters deserve a page all to themselves ...

Tardigrades (also known as water bears) are only 1 mm long but incredibly hardy. They have survived being heated at over 150°C for 15 minutes, frozen in liquid helium at –272°C, and even sent into space. They undergo a process called 'cryptobiosis' where all their metabolic processes shut down until the conditions return in which they can 'live again'. While they're only alive between 3 and 30 months, there are claims one has been revived after 120 years of its 'tun' state.

118

The 118th day of the year is April 28

On this day in 1906
Mathematician Kurt Gödel was born

Partition party

The number 118 can be partitioned into 3 parts that have the same product in 4 different ways: $14 + 50 + 54 = 15 + 40 + 63 = 18 + 30 + 70 = 21 + 25 + 72 = 118$ and $14 \times 50 \times 54 = 15 \times 40 \times 63 = 18 \times 30 \times 70 = 21 \times 25 \times 72 = 37,800$. It is the smallest number for which this is possible.

If this observation just trips your trigger, then you can have this for free: check out the number 130 which partitions this way ... 2 different ways!

Check the products of {[9, 56, 65], [10, 42, 78], [14, 26, 90], [15, 24, 91]} *and* the products of {[20, 54, 56], [21, 45, 64], [24, 36, 70], [28, 30, 72]}.

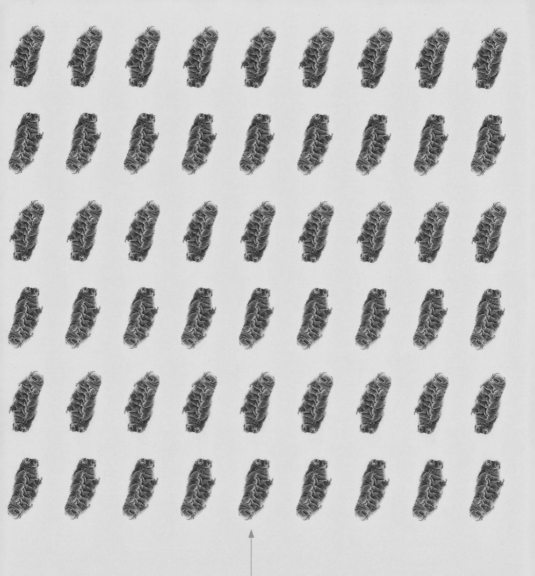

Tardigrades, magnified
approximately 15 ×

Crafty composite

Convince yourself that 119
is a composite number that is
1 less than a factorial.

It is and in fact is the smallest
example of such.

While you're at it ...

Can you write 119 as the sum
of 5 consecutive primes?

*The **119th** day of the
year is April 29*

Sadly, us landlubbers simply can't compete with those who like to splash around.

Tu'i Malila

Tu'i Malila was a radiated tortoise who died aged 188 in May 1965. At the time, Tu'i was the oldest verified vertebrate. However, the record is being hotly chased (or perhaps very slowly and calmly chased) by Jonathan, a Seychelles giant tortoise who lives on the island of Saint Helena. Jonathan is thought to be about 182 years old, and is probably the oldest currently-living terrestrial animal. Adwaita, an Aldabra giant tortoise, is estimated to have lived to 250 but that can't be verified. If true, Adwaita would have been the oldest terrestrial animal in the world.

Jeanne Calment

Jeanne lived her entire 122 years and 164 days in Arles, France, and holds the record for the longest confirmed human lifespan. She was quoted as saying, 'I've never had but one wrinkle, and I'm sitting on it!'

Henry

A tuatara (a type of lizard) at the Southland Museum in New Zealand is proudly claimed by Invercargill to be their oldest resident. Henry mated for the first time at the age of 111 years in 2008 with an 80-year-old female and fathered 11 baby tuatara. Good on you, Henry, for waiting till you found Ms Right.

120

The 120th day of the year is April 30

On this day in 1777 Mathematician Carl Friedrich Gauss was born

A prime suspect

All prime numbers (except the first couple we encounter, namely 2 and 3) are of the form $6n \pm 1$.

Start by looking at 6 and noticing that 5 and 7 are both prime. With $12 = 6 \times 2$, both 11 and 13 are prime, similarly, $18 = 6 \times 3$ and both 17 and 19 are prime.

However, when $n = 4$, we see that even though $6n + 1 = 25$ is not prime, $6n - 1 = 23$ is.

Keep investigating and convince yourself that $120 = 6 \times 20$ is the smallest multiple of 6 such that neither $6n + 1$ nor $6n - 1$ is prime.

Lin Wang

Lin Wang, an Asian elephant, died at the Tapei Zoo in February 2003 at the age of 86, surpassing the previous record of 84.

Muja

A still-alive American alligator was delivered to Belgrade Zoo in 1936, making him at least 80 years old.

Greater

When it comes to birds, a greater flamingo named – wait for it – Greater, died at Adelaide Zoo in January 2014 at the age of at least 83. However, Cookie the Australian-born Major Mitchell Cockatoo at Brookfield Zoo, Illinois, is almost 82 and closing in steadily.

Ol' Billy

The oldest living horse on record died in 1822 at the age of 62.

Debby

Debby the polar bear died in 2008 at the age of 42.

Creme Puff

A cat in Austin, Texas, lived to just beyond her 38th birthday.

Bluey

An Australian cattle dog lived to a happy, barky 29 years of age.

Square among squares

The number 121 is the only square of the form:

$$1 + n + n^2 + n^3 + n^4$$ where n is a positive whole number.

What is the value of n here?

Also, $121 = 11 \times 11$ and when we square 111 we get $111 \times 111 = 12{,}321$. Can you see the pattern? It leads to the gorgeous result that $111{,}111{,}111 \times 111{,}111{,}111 = 12{,}345{,}678{,}987{,}654{,}321$.

121

*The **121st** day of the year is **May 1***

The 27 Club myth

Fans of modern music would have heard of the '27 Club', the colloquial name given to influential musicians who died at the age of 27. The club has so many high profile members, some people think 27 is a cursed age for musos. Well, as with so many myths, a bit of good old-fashioned statistical analysis puts it in perspective.

Sure, Janis Joplin, Kurt Cobain, Amy Winehouse, Jimi Hendrix, Brian Jones and Jim Morrison all died at the age of 27, but if there was some crazy supernatural force at work here then what about poor old Otis Redding, Gram Parsons, Nick Drake, Bryan Osper, Jon Guthrie and a few others who left us at 26? Or Tim Buckley, Beverly Kenney, Bobby Bloom and those others who made it to 28 but went no further?

Professor of Psychology and Music at the University of Sydney, Dianna Kenny, created a database of over 11,000 dead musicians spanning from 1950–2010 and discovered 144 of them died at the age of 27. Now, 144 is a lot of dead musicians, but it's only 1.3% of the total sample and, looking a year either side, you see that almost as many (128 of them, or 1.2%) died at 26 and even more (153 or 1.4%) died at 28.

Perhaps the group who died at 27 contains a few more famous names and this captures people's attention, but from a statistical standpoint, we can once and for all reject the existence of the

122

The **122nd** *day of the year is May 2*

The art of partitioning

There are 122 different ways to partition the number 24 into distinct parts. A partition of 24 is a group of positive integers that add up to 24, for example, 4, 4, 16 or 3, 5, 6, 10.

But insisting upon distinct parts removes a partition like 4, 4, 16 because of the repetition of the 4. Insisting on no repetition reduces the 1575 partitions of 24 to a much smaller 122 distinct partitions.

27 Club. Of course, this is no great consolation for the legions of friends, family and fans of these or any of the dead stars, but it does bust the myth.

In fact, the age at which most of the 11,000+ musicians surveyed died was well past 27. A much larger 239 died at the age of 56, including Eddie Rabbitt, Tammy Wynette and Johnny Ramone.

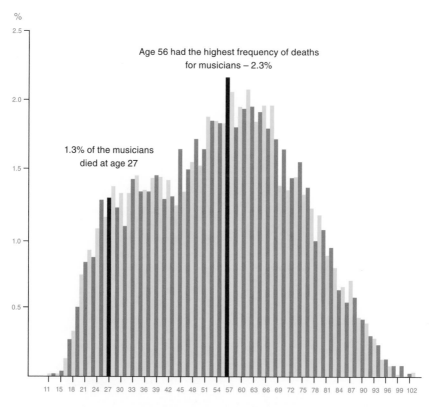

AGE AT DEATH OF MUSICIANS (1950–2010)

Ridiculous primes

The number $10^{123} + 3$ is prime. This means that the number 1000 ... 0003, with 122 zeros between the 1 and the 3 is a prime number.

If you think that's a big prime, the number formed by the concatenation of odd numbers from 123 down to 1 is prime.

That's right, someone actually bothered to work out that 12312111911171151131111091071 05103101999795939189878585 3817977757371696765636159 575553514947454341393735 33129272523211917151311975 31 is prime!

123

The 123rd day of the year is May 3

The number of countries in the world that have *not* been invaded by Britain? 22.

124

The 124th day of the year is May 4

On and on ...

$\pm 1 \pm 2 \pm 3 \pm 4 \pm 5 \pm 6 \pm 7 \pm 8 \pm 9 \pm 10 \pm 11 \pm 12 = 0$ has 124 solutions.

Can you write 124 as the sum of 8 consecutive primes?

On this day ...
May the fourth be with you ;-)

How long's a piece of string?

Depends on the piece of string, of course. Duh.

But in musical string instruments, that length determines the pitch of the note. We do know that if you had 2 strings of the same mass (equally taut and heavy), and one double the length of the other, the shorter string would vibrate with a pitch 1 octave higher than the long one. Of course, if you designed a piano based on this principle, you wouldn't be able to fit most of the bass notes. The solution? The bass strings on a piano are much thicker than the others, as heavy strings vibrate more slowly than lighter strings of identical tension and length ... producing a lower note. Neat, hey?

It's hip to be $^{2+1}$

125

It is obvious that 125 is a cube, namely $5^3 = 125$.

But 125 is also the sum of distinct positive squares and the smallest cube for which this is true. In fact, 125 can be written as the sum of distinct squares 2 ways. Can you find them both?

The 125th day of the year is May 5

Number of strings on (or in) musical instruments

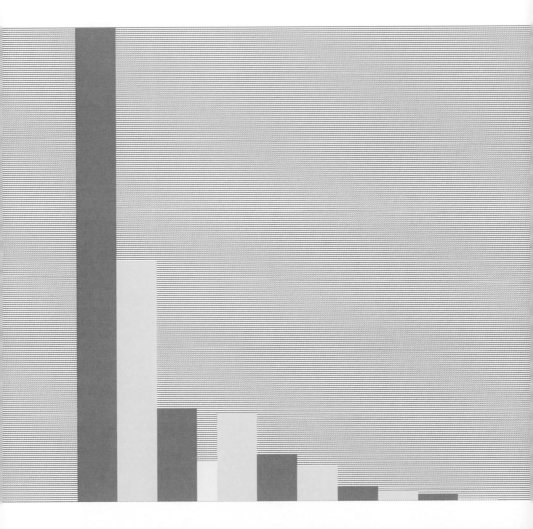

126

The 126th day of the year is May 6

Dot to dot to dot to dot

Nine points around a circle form the vertices of 126 unique quadrilaterals.

This is another way of saying that you can choose 4 things out of a group of 9 in 126 different ways.

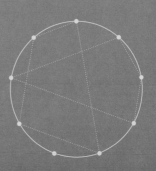

236 strings
Piano

120 strings
Harpsichord

47 strings
Harp

21–45 strings
European zither: 30–45 strings
Chinese zither: 21–25 strings

24 strings
Baroque lute

18 strings
Sitar

8 strings
Mandolin

6 strings
Standard guitar

4 strings
Cello
Violin
Viola
Double bass
Standard bass guitar
Ukulele
Banjo
Oud

2 strings
Erhu, sometimes known as a Chinese violin

Club Mersenne

The number 127 is another example of those beautiful things we call Mersenne primes. Because $127 = 2^7 - 1$ where 7 is a prime number, 127 is Mersenne. This happens for all primes up to 7, that is, $2^2 - 1$, $2^3 - 1$ and $2^5 - 1$ are also Mersenne primes. The next candidate is $2^{11} - 1$. Is this a Mersenne prime?

127

*The **127th** day of the year is **May 7***

DARWIN
by numbers

138,000

Darwin's population, making it the Northern Territory's largest city but the smallest and most northerly Australian capital.

$4.45 billion

The estimated damage cost of Cyclone Tracy that hit Darwin in 1974.

32°C

Darwin's average temperature.

1869

The year Darwin was established.

1942

The year in which, on 19 February, Japan mounted 2 air raids on Darwin, killing up to 252 people.

128

*The **128th** day of the year is **May 8***

None bigger

The number 128 is the largest known even number that can be expressed as the sum of 2 primes in exactly 3 ways. Find them!

It's pretty amazing to think that this can happen for 128, but no matter how far we have gone on looking, we just haven't been able to find a bigger even number that can be expressed as the sum of 2 primes in exactly 3 ways.

30,000

The number of beer cans used in the construction of Mick Keeley's boat *Extravacanz* that entered Darwin's annual Beer Can Regatta at Mindil Beach in 2013.

3

The number of streets you drive on to get from Adelaide to Darwin (including 3004 km on National Highway 1), making it further than driving from London to Moscow!

5000

The number of lightning strikes recorded within 60 km of Darwin in *1* storm on 31 January 2002 – about 3 times the amount Perth experiences *per year*.

Square dance!

The number 129 is the smallest number with 4 representations as a sum of 3 positive (but not necessarily distinct) squares. Can you find the 4 ways to write 129 as the sum of 3 positive squares?

129

The 129th day of the year is May 9

Loooooooooooooooooooongest words in the English language

I can still remember reading as a kid about 'the longest word in the English language'.

It was in a little book called *Oddities* that my mum and dad bought for me. The book contained, well, a series of oddities ... in language, mathematics, art, and so on, that really excited my young mind. I read, reread and eventually committed to memory the longest English word. It was this 29-letter beast:

Floccinaucinihilipilification

Which you pronounce *floxee-nawsee-nee-hilly-pilly-fick-ashun*.

Floccinaucinihilipilification means 'the act of estimating something as worthless'. So, for example, if my younger daughter Olivia were to ask her big sister, 'What do you think of the music of One Direction?' and she was to say, 'It completely and absolutely sucks' she would be entitled to reply, 'Ellie, I can't stand your floccinaucinihilipilification of my favourite band'.

The word was entered into English Hansard, the written record of the daily proceedings of parliament, in February 2012. Conservative MP Jacob Rees-Mogg asked for permission to

130

The **130th** *day of the year is* May 10

Divide and conquer

Did you know that 130 is the only number equal to the sum of the squares of its first 4 divisors? What does that mean? Well, the divisors of 130 are 1, 2, 5, 10, 13, 26, 65 and $130 = 1^2 + 2^2 + 5^2 + 10^2$.

indulge in the floccinaucinihilipilification of judges of the European Union, labelling them unjust in one of their decisions. Since that day, floccinaucinihilipilification has been the longest such word entered into Hansard.

But it turns out that floccinaucinihilipilification is not *strictly* the longest word in the English language, though it beats these 3 bad boys:

Antidisestablishmentarianism (28): This means a doctrine of opposition to disestablishment, that is, the removal of an organisation/entity's official status. It's a very old-fashioned term rarely used and it isn't included in the Merriam-Webster dictionaries because of this. It's generally only used as an example of a long word. It is what's known as an 'agglutinative construction', that is, a legitimate extension of an existing word through the addition of bits at the front and end called prefixes (such as 'anti' and 'dis') and suffixes (for example, 'arian' and 'ism').

Electroencephalographically (27): This mega medical term simply means the detecting and recording of brain waves using an electroencephalograph. Medical and scientific terms tend to dominate lists of long words because they often involve joining together lots of smaller words or bits of words to describe a complicated procedure or condition.

Honorificabilitudinitatibus (27): The longest English word with alternating consonants and vowels refers to the state of being

I'm absolutely prime

Any ordering of the digits of 131 is still prime. This is called an 'absolute' prime. Obviously, 131 being an absolute prime means that 113 and 311 are also absolute primes.

Repeat offender

The reciprocal of 131 repeats with a period of 130 digits.

$1/131 = 0.00763358778625954$
$1984732824427480916030534$
$3511450381679389312977099$
$2366412213740458015267175$
$5725190839694656488549618$
$3206106870229...$ with this string of 130 digits repeating endlessly!

131

The 131st day of the year is May 11

able to achieve honours. It appears just once in William Shake-speare's *Love's Labour's Lost* and, as such, is what's known as a *hapax legomenon* in the Shakespeare canon. The word is spoken by the comic rustic Costard in Act V, Scene 1 after an absurdly pretentious dialogue between the pedantic schoolmaster Holofernes and his friend Sir Nathaniel. The two really faff on in a mixture of Latin and florid English. When Moth, a witty young servant, enters, Costard says of the two pedants, '*O, they have lived long on the alms-basket of words. I marvel thy master hath not eaten thee for a word; for thou art not so long by the head as honorificabilitudinitatibus: thou art easier swallowed than a flap-dragon*'.

Flap-dragon was a game which involved trying to eat hot raisins from a bowl of burning brandy!

There are in fact words with more than 29 letters in the English language, but most of these are so odd and obscure I'll leave it to you to look them up if the mood takes you. The longest non-medical word in the *Oxford English Dictionary* is the 34-lettered supercalifragilisticexpialidocious meaning extraordinarily good and coming from the song of the same name in the movie *Mary Poppins*. Now, if you really wanted, we could spend hours debating which is the cooler of these 2 words. But I'd judge the merits of such a discussion with floccinaucinihilipilification and form your own opinion.

132

The **132nd** day of the year is **May 12**

The sum of its parts

Prove that if you take all of the 2-digit numbers you can make from the digits of 132 and add them up, you get 132. Once you've done that sit back and reflect on the fact that 132 is the smallest number with this property.

A blue whale's daily intake of krill weighs the equivalent of 40,000 cheeseburgers.

Don't worry, be happy

The number 133 is what's known as a 'happy number'. If you sum the squares of the digits and then repeat the process the sum will eventually come to 1 (133 becomes $1^2 + 3^2 + 3^2 = 19$ becomes $1^2 + 9^2 = 82$ becomes $8^2 + 2^2 = 68$ becomes $6^2 + 8^2$ = 100 becomes $1^2 + 0^2 + 0^2 = 1$).

But other numbers, 'unhappy ones', never reach 1. By trying this process on other numbers, can you work out what happens to the 'unhappy' ones?

133

*The **133rd** day of the year is **May 13***

Pure poetry!

I am certainly no expert, but for me, there is a beautiful numerical structure that underpins many types of poem.

Depending on your variety of verse, the rhyming structure might follow a 'formula', for example, the lines might rhyme *abab cdcd*, but also the number of lines in the poem and even the number of syllables in each line might all obey a numerical structure.

In giving a few examples, I really don't want to rile any poets out there by suggesting they're all frustrated mathematicians just playing around with numbers. But as you read, pay close attention to the underlying 'framework' ... and reach your own conclusion ...

134

The 134th day of the year is May 14

The hottest 134

On 10 July 1913 the temperature reached 134 degrees Fahrenheit (56.7°C) in Death Valley, California. The residents of nearby Baker commemorated this by building a 134-foot-high thermometer, proudly trumpeted as the world's tallest.

Con-tastrophe!

$134^2 - 67^2 = 13,467$, which is the base numbers concatenated.

Cinquain

The cinquain is a comparatively recent poetic form and is credited to American poet Adelaide Crapsey who published 28 of these 5-line poems in 1915.

Adelaide is said to have taken her inspiration from Japanese haiku and tanka which also have strict rules regarding the number of lines and syllables they can contain.

There are many different forms of cinquains, some with catchy names such as 'mirror', 'garland' and 'butterfly', but for the most part, they have 5 lines (*cinq* being French for 5), a 1-word opening line and lines getting longer until the fifth which is again short containing only 1 or 2 words. Here's Adelaide Crapsey's *November Night*.

Listen ...
With faint dry sound,
Like steps of passing ghosts,
The leaves, frost-crisp'd, break from the trees
And fall.

Change for a dollar?

In Australian currency (5c, 10c, 20c, 50c), the most amount of money in silver coins you can have without having the right amount of change for a dollar is 135 cents. How?

By the way, the humble Aussie 50c piece is one the few dodecagons you'll regularly come across.

135

*On this day in 1859
Physicist/chemist Pierre Curie was born*

Shakespearean sonnet

A Shakespearean sonnet has 14 lines consisting of 3 quatrains of 'abab', 'cdcd', 'efef', followed by a couplet 'gg'.

Often the beginning of the third quatrain, the first *e* is the 'volta' or turn, where the sonnet changes pace or resolves a problem established in the earlier lines. Shakespeare released *The Sonnets* in 1609 and almost all 154 of them follow this pattern. Here's one of his greatest hits, the famous *Sonnet 18*.

Shall I compare thee to a summer's day? (a)
Thou art more lovely and more temperate: (b)
Rough winds do shake the darling buds of May, (a)
And summer's lease hath all too short a date: (b)
Sometimes too hot the eye of heaven shines, (c)
And often is his gold complexion dimm'd; (d)
And every fair from fair sometime declines, (c)
By chance or nature's changing course untrimm'd; (d)
But thy eternal summer shall not fade (e)
Nor lose possession of that fair thou owest; (f)
Nor shall Death brag thou wander'st in his shade, (e)
When in eternal lines to time thou growest: (f)
So long as men can breathe or eyes can see, (g)
So long lives this and this gives life to thee. (g)

136

The **136th** *day of the* year is **May 16**

Did you get that?

Convince yourself that 136 is the sum of the cubes of the digits of the sum of the cubes of its digits. First step, get your breath back and read that sentence again ... slowly.

On this day in 1718 Mathematician Maria Gaetana Agnesi was born

April 23
The date of Will's birth. And death, some 52 years later.

3000
The number of words, nearly, that he introduced to the English language.

80
There are at least 80 variations on the spelling of his name.

37
The number of plays he wrote, part of a grand total of 154 works (unless you believe the conspiracy theorists who say most were written by Francis Bacon, Christopher Marlowe or J. K. Rowling).

884,429
The total number of words in his plays.

2
of his plays are written entirely in verse. It's also the number of his plays have been translated into ... Klingon.

1380
Number of characters he created.

8
The number of children he had.

You guessed it – these are but a few of the astonishing numbers about William Shakespeare. Or was it Shaksper? Or Shakespere. Or Willm Shakespere. Or ...

Trenchant truncating

The number 137 is the third term in a sequence of primes that can be created by starting with 7 and creating a new term by adding a single digit to the front of the previous term: 7, 37, 137 ...

It is possible to create a sequence of 24 prime numbers in this way ending in the longest such 'left-truncatable' prime: 357686312646216567629137.

137
*The **137th** day of the year is May 17*

Haiku

Traditional Japanese haikus contain 3 lines of 'kana', distributed 5, 7 and 5.

Unfortunately, kana don't translate directly into English, so English haiku tends to be 3 lines of 5-7-5 syllables.

For example, Basho Matsuo (who lived from 1644–94 and is known as the first great poet of haiku) wrote this beauty:

An old silent pond ...
A frog jumps into the pond,
splash! Silence again

Not bad, Basho. But here's one I wrote myself (in my capacity as an uncelebrated and never-to-be-celebrated haiku poet):

A haiku is made
Of seventeen syllables
That shine like the sun

138

*The **138th** day of the year is May 18*

The most anomalous time of year

$138/184$ gives a great anomalous cancellation. If you just cross out the common 1s and 8s you get $138/184$ becoming $3/4$ and $138/184 = 3/4$. Note this is a coincidence and *not* the way you simplify fractions in general.

We'll see anomalous cancellations a few more times in this book and from now on we'll only worry about when the numerator and denominator only have 3 digits each. If you're feeling adventurous, you can look for more anomalous cancellations by ignoring this last condition. But you won't see these in the answers.

Limerick

A limerick is a short, often vulgar, funny poem.

Actually, most limericks aren't rude; indeed, the earliest known limerick is a Latin prayer by Thomas Aquinas from the 13th century that most definitely does not begin 'There once was a man from ...'.

A limerick consists of 5 lines and can be broken into lines 1, 2 and 5 in one group and lines 3 and 4 in the other. Lines 1, 2 and 5 almost always have the same number of syllables (7 to 10), all rhyme and have the same verbal rhythm.

Similarly, lines 3 and 4 are shorter (5 to 7 syllables), but also rhyme and have the same rhythm. Here's a (slightly rude) example.

There once was an artist named Saint,
Who swallowed some samples of paint.
All shades of the spectrum
Flowed out of his rectum
With a colourful lack of restraint.

Find a prime

The numbers 139 and 149 are the first consecutive primes differing by 10. The next pair isn't that far away. Can you find them?

Anomalous cancellations

As we mentioned yesterday, $138/184 = 3/4$ is an anomalous cancellation. Can you find the anomalous cancellation involving 139? It's a tough question this one – good luck.

139

The **139th** day of the year is **May 19**

Petrarchan or Italian sonnet

A Petrarchan or Italian sonnet is a 14-line poem consisting of 8 rhyming lines (the octave) 'abbaabba' followed by 6 closing lines (the sestet) which might be 'cdcdcd' or 'cdecde' or similar.

Often the opening octave would establish a situation or problem and the sestet would resolve it. In the following example, William Wordsworth's *London, 1802*, the first 8 lines address the decline and failing of the English race. Hey Bill, heavy stuff already! The last 6 lines, beginning with line 9 (the volta or 'turn'), explain why Milton was so great.

Milton! thou shouldst be living at this hour: (a)
England hath need of thee: she is a fen (b)
Of stagnant waters: altar, sword, and pen, (b)
Fireside, the heroic wealth of hall and bower, (a)
Have forfeited their ancient English dower (a)
Of inward happiness. We are selfish men; (b)
Oh! raise us up, return to us again; (b)
And give us manners, virtue, freedom, power. (a)
Thy soul was like a Star, and dwelt apart; (c)
Thou hadst a voice whose sound was like the sea: (d)
Pure as the naked heavens, majestic, free, (d)
So didst thou travel on life's common way, (e)
In cheerful godliness; and yet thy heart (c)
The lowliest duties on herself did lay. (e)

140

*The **140th** day of the year is May 20*

*On this day in 1990
The Hubble Space Telescope
took and sent its first photo*

What's in a number?

The number 140 is the sum of the squares of the first 7 positive integers: $1^2 + 2^2 + 3^2 + 4^2 + 5^2 + 6^2 + 7^2 = 140$.

$140 = 160 - 20$, which isn't groundbreaking in itself, but explains why tweets are capped at 140 characters.

Twitter names

Because the worldwide standard for SMS was 160 characters, the founders of Twitter decided to allow 20 spaces for the Twitter username back in the day when mobile phones were the main way of accessing those communications.

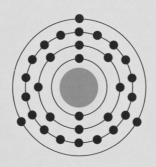

Ga**llium**

Gallium is thought by many to be the second element (after francium) to be named after France. But a theory advanced by John Emsley in his superb Periodic Table bible *Nature's Building Blocks* is that the French chemist Boisbaudran may have named the element after his middle name 'Lecoq' which is French for 'the rooster' which in Latin is *gallus*. If that's true it makes the big B a bit of a cheeky bugger, but then again he did help discover gallium, samarium and dysprosium, so maybe he was due.

Gallium can be used in the treatment of not 1 but 2 murderous maladies that begin with the letter M – malaria and melanoma.

345678910111213141516171819202122232425262728293031323334353637383940414243444546474849505152 53
5556575859606162636465666768697071727374757677787980818283848586878889909192939495969798 99100

Pi chart

Good old 141 is the first non-trivial palindrome appearing in the decimal expansion of π. It comes immediately after the decimal point, 3.14159...

46264

In case you're wondering, the first 5-digit palindrome, 46,264, begins at the 19th decimal place before we've met our first 4-digit palindrome 3993 which starts at the 43rd decimal place.

141

*The **141st** day of the year is **May 21***

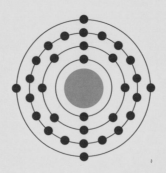

Germanium

Alongside francium, americium, polonium, scandium, copper (Cyprus), ruthenium (Russia) and thulium (Norway), germanium is another element named after a country.

A massive germanium-led health craze in the late 1980s – off the back of the bestselling book *Germanium: the health and life enhancer* – was quickly snuffed out by the UK government. Germanium supplements, oils, blood pressure and heart disease treatments and even salt bath detoxes are still around, though not to be trusted, according to medical authorities.

1 2 3 4 5 6 7 8 9 10 11 12 13 14 15 16 17 18 19 20 21 22 23 24 25 26 27 28 29 30 31 **32** 33 34 35 36 37 38 39 40 41 42 43 44 45 46 47 48 49 50 51 52

54 55 56 57 58 59 60 61 62 63 64 65 66 67 68 69 70 71 72 73 74 75 76 77 78 79 80 81 82 83 84 85 86 87 88 89 90 91 92 93 94 95 96 97 98 99 1

142

*The **142nd** day of the year is May 22*

Plane and simple

There are 142 possible planar graphs with 6 vertices. A planar graph is a graph that can be drawn in the 2-dimensional plane without any of its edges crossing each other no matter where we slide the points. The graph on top is planar, the one on the bottom is non-planar because its edges cross over.

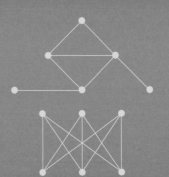

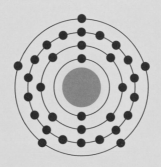

Arsenic

Arsenic was the poison of choice among villains in the 19th and early 20th centuries. It could be extracted from everything from fertilisers to flypaper and, if taken in small doses over a few weeks, the symptoms looked a lot like general wasting diseases or other nondescript sicknesses.

Of course, arsenic has been around for a lot longer than that and has been found in the hair of a 5000-year-old 'iceman' whose remains were preserved in the Italian Alps. It's suspected that he was a coppersmith because copper is smelted from metals that often contain high levels of arsenic.

345678910111213141516171819202122232425262728293031323334353637383940414243444546474849505152535
555657585960616263646566676869707172737475767778798081828384858687888990919293949596979899100

3-digit trio

$1^3 + 5^3 + 3^3 = 153$. There are only 3 other 3-digit numbers which are the sum of the cubes of their digits. Go forth and seek them. I'll give you a couple of hints – 2 are very close together in the 370s and 1 is just past 400.

also ...

$153 = 1! + 2! + 3! + 4! + 5!$

143

*The **153rd** day of the year is June 2*

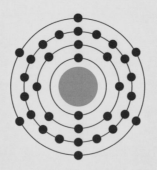

Selenium

With 34 protons packed into its nucleus and hence that atomic number, selenium is used in glassmaking, pigments and electronics. It's also an essential micronutrient for animals. The parts of your body containing the most selenium are your hair, your kidneys and, if you have them, your testicles. In fact, every cell in your body contains over 1,000,000 atoms of selenium. But go easy on the stuff because if you get too much you risk selenium poisoning, which causes, among other things, putrid breath and body odour.

144

*The **144th** day of the year is May 24*

erauqS

144 is the smallest square number which is also a different square when its digits are reversed, that is, $144 = 12^2$ while $441 = 21^2$.

Now strictly you could suggest 100 which is 001 backwards, but no offence, 100, you're not invited to this party.

Fibonacci piazze

144 is a perfect square. As is 1 + 4 + 4 and 1 × 4 × 4. 144 is also the largest square Fibonacci number.

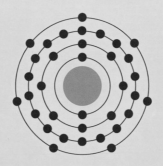

Bromine

Along with mercury, bromine is the only other element that is liquid at room temperature.

If you're fighting a fire in an enclosed space where it's too risky to use water because of nearby computers, artworks or engines (I know, we've all been there), you may want to reach for a Halon fire extinguisher which uses organobromine compounds. At the same time, these halons aren't great for the ozone layer, so don't overdo it, okay?

Factorions away!

$145 = 1! + 4! + 5!$ There are only 4 such numbers with this property. 1, 2 and 145 are 3 of them and in case you're wondering, the fourth is 40,585. Feel free to check it out and if $0! = 1$ worries you, don't let it.

Such numbers are called 'factorions', a term created by Cliff Pickover in 1995.

Anomamay

May 25, the 145th day of the year, brings us to another anomalous cancellation. Can you find a denominator for 145 where the fraction simplifies to the same answer you get by just crossing out common numbers? Hint: The denominator is in the 400s.

145

The 145th day of the year is May 25

On this day in 1977 The first Star Wars film was released

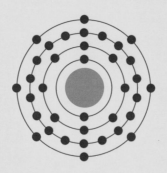

Krypton

Krypton is a tasteless and odourless gas that should never be confused with 'kryptonite', the dangerous and highly radioactive ore found on Superman's home planet. I'm glad we've got that sorted.

In 1960, the standard metre bar of platinum and iridium was replaced as the official international measurement of a metre. From 1960 until 1980, a metre was defined as 1,650,763.73 times the wavelength of the bright orange line in the spectrum of krypton-86.

146

*The **146th** day of the year is May 26*

Base jumping

146 is 222 in base 8. This means that $146 = 2 \times 8^2 + 2 \times 8 + 2$.

And talking of 222, when we add the divisors of 146 we get $1 + 2 + 73 + 146$ which also equals 222.

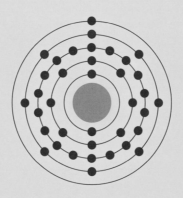

Rubidium

Rubidium comes from the Latin word *rubidus* after the 2 ruby-red lines that this element's atomic spectrum emits.

In 1995, American physicists Eric Cornell and Carl Wieman cooled a gas of rubidium atoms to only a few billionths of a degree above absolute zero (more fancily we say 'to about 170 nanokelvin (nK)'). In doing so they created the first ever Bose-Einstein condensate. What's that you ask? A Bose-Einstein condensate occurs when a large fraction of particles occupy the lowest possible quantum state and start doing amazing quantum stuff on a large scale. It's hard to get your head around, but suffice to say the lads won the 2001 Nobel Prize in Physics for their stellar work.

Three's company

147 is divisible by 3. Here is something pretty cool you can do with any number divisible by 3. Keep summing the cubes of the digits of the number and eventually you will get to 153 which then repeats.

So in this case 147 gives:

$1^3 + 4^3 + 7^3 = 408$;
$4^3 + 0^3 + 8^3 = 576$;
$5^3 + 7^3 + 6^3 = 684$;
$6^3 + 8^3 + 4^3 = 792$;
$7^3 + 9^3 + 2^3 = 1080$;
$1^3 + 0^3 + 8^3 + 0^3 = 513$;
$5^3 + 1^3 + 3^3 = 153$ ...

147

*The **147th** day of the year is May 27*

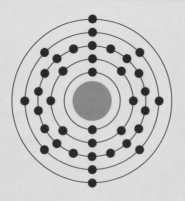

Strontium

Coming in at number 38 is strontium, a highly reactive silver-white metallic element that turns yellow when exposed to air. Strontium prevents the emission of X-rays so was used a lot in the glass of old-fashioned cathode ray tube TVs and computers. Strontium titanate crystals are more sparkly than diamonds, but unlike that very tough gemstone, they scratch easily. So while strontium certainly ranks high on the bling ladder, if you're thinking of impressing that special someone by 'saying it with strontium' you might want to think again.

148

*The **148th** day of the year is May 28*

Vampire numbers

A 'vampire' number is a number whose digits can be regrouped into 2 smaller numbers of equal length (called 'fangs') that multiply to make the original; for example, $1260 = 21 \times 60$. We also don't let both fangs end in 0.

There are 148 vampire numbers with 6 digits. For example, $108,135 = 135 \times 801$.

Can you show that the following 6-digit numbers are vampire numbers: 125,433, 378,450 and 567,648?

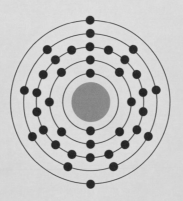

Yttrium

Yttrium is number 39 on the atomic hottest 100 and is used in the treatment of cancer and, not quite as critically, in the manufacture of jewellery. The highly toxic silvery-metallic transition metal was the first of 4 elements all to be named after the otherwise undistinguished Swedish town of Ytterby where a sample was found in 1787. Ytterby also gives us erbium, terbium and of course, ytterbium. But you knew that, didn't you? Not a bad effort for a single village 150 km from Stockholm!

345678910111213141516171819202122232425262728293031323334353637383940414243444546474849505152535
5556575859606162636465666768697071727374757677787980818283848586878889909192939495969798991100

Three squares to heaven

Can you express 149 as the sum of 3 consecutive squares? Really, can you? C'mon, show me right now.

Once you've seen how 149 can be expressed as the sum of 3 squares you might find it cute that the sum of digits of 149 can also be expressed as the sum of 3 consecutive squares: $1 + 4 + 9 = 14 = 1^2 + 2^2 + 3^2$.

149

*The **149th** day of the year is May 29*

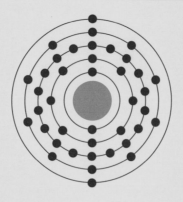

Zirconium

Zirconium is a lustrous, strong, grey-white transition metal that is highly prized for several reasons, in particular for its ability to handle heat, and also for its undeniable bling factor! What am I talking about? Well, while diamonds are formed naturally within the Earth by the compression and heating of carbon over time, the natural form of diamond's competitor – cubic zirconia (zirconium dioxide) – is so rare almost all of it used in jewellery has been created by humans.

150

The 150th day of the year is May 30

Rubik's Cube

The 5 × 5 × 5 Rubik's Cube is sometimes called the Professor's Cube and is covered with 6 × 5 × 5 = 150 coloured stickers.

The Professor is a wily beast and can be arranged in 28287 09422777418565361803331 0715032829312773198567213 47215360000000000000000 different ways.

The world record for solving a Professor's Cube is an incredible 48.42 seconds by the Australian maestro Feliks Zemdegs. This plucky Aussie backed up his 2013 World Championship in the traditional cube with a consecutive victory in 2015. Well done you dextrously digited demon.

In 1979, Esperance Shire Council in Western Australia hit NASA with a $400 fine.

The fine – for littering – came when *Skylab* burnt up re-entering the Earth's atmosphere. Tough NASA never paid, but US DJ Scott Barley, based in Barstow, California, raised the money from listeners and presented the cheque at the 30th annual Esperance-*Skylab* Day on 12 July 2009. Barstow and Esperance are now twin cities.

Prime & proper

151 is the smallest prime that begins a 3-run of primes that are sums of 5 consecutive primes: 151 + 157 + 163 + 167 + 173 = 811; and starting at 811, summing the run of the next 5 consecutive primes gives us 811 + 821 + 823 + 827 + 829 = 4111; and guess what, summing the 5 primes from 4111 gives 4111 + 4127 + 4129 + 4133 + 4139 = 20,639 which is also prime.

It ends here because starting at 20,639 the sum of the next 5 primes is 20,639 + 20,641 + 20,663 + 20,681 + 20,693 = 103,317 = 3 × 34,439.

151

*The **151st** day of the year is **May 31***

One for all the abecedarians out there …

I love language and always have. As you may have guessed I also love mathematics. And in the same way that numbers are at the heart of mathematics, letters and the alphabets in which they exist are at the heart of language.

English speakers might be tricked into thinking that alphabets are pretty simple things. You have a set number of letters and you put them in an order, make your words and off you go. But it's nowhere near as simple as that.

For a start, there isn't just one alphabet. There are *heaps*.

About 2.6 billion people around the world (that's approximately 36% of the total population) use the Latin (or Roman) alphabet. Nice going. About 1.3 billion people (18%) use the Chinese script. About 1.2 billion people (16%) use the Devanagari alphabet (India). About 1 billion people (14%) use the Arabic alphabet and about 300 million people (4%) use the Cyrillic alphabet.

In other languages, letters can change shape depending on where they occur in a word; not just as in capitals to start sentences like we do in English.

152

The 152nd day of the year is June 1

Still got prime

The number 152 is the largest known even number that can be expressed as the sum of 2 prime numbers in exactly 4 ways. Can you celebrate the 'pinch and a punch' for the first day of the month by finding these 4 ways?

Of course, anyone who has learnt English knows that it has 26 characters (many of the other alphabets seem to settle on around the same number) but whoa whoa whoa, don't go thinking that applies to *all* other alphabets.

The language thought to contain the *least* number of characters is the East Papuan language Rotokas, which uses a mere 12 characters and is spoken by around 4000 people on the island of Bougainville.

Hawaii's national language was created by missionaries in 1826 to codify what had until then been a purely oral form of communication. These missionaries were nothing if not efficient, because they managed to summarise Hawaiian in a mere 13 characters, A E I O U H K L M N P W and the 'okina' or glottal stop.

Cyrillic is an absolute cracker of an alphabet. Named after St Cyril, who may or may not have invented it (hey, it was around the year 860 and we didn't have cameras on phones back then so it's a little sketchy), it is based on the Greek alphabet with a dozen or so *extra* letters thrown in to supply the Slavic sounds that are not found in Greek. In capitals, the 33 letters look like this:

А	Б	В	Г	Д	Е	Ё	Ж	З
И	Й	К	Л	М	Н	О	П	Р
С	Т	У	Ф	Х	Ц	Ч	Ш	Щ
Ъ	Ы	Ь	Э	Ю	Я			

153

3-digit trio

$1^3 + 5^3 + 3^3 = 153$. There are only 3 other 3-digit numbers which are the sum of the cubes of their digits. Go forth and seek them. I'll give you a couple of hints – 2 are very close together in the 370s and 1 is just past 400.

also …

$153 = 1! + 2! + 3! + 4! + 5!$

The 153rd day of the year is June 2

You've probably seen a few of these letters around the traps.

Also fascinating are *abjads*. Put simply, an abjad is a writing system where most or all of the characters are consonants and it is up to the reader to supply the appropriate vowel. Talk about free speech!

An *abugida*, on the other hand, is a syllabic 'alphabet' in which consonants and vowels are joined together and written as a unit. Among the most longstanding and important of the abugidas are the Brahmi scripts of South and South East Asia in which some of the most famous texts of the ancient world were written.

Brahmi alphabets range from Tibet's 30 characters through Thailand's 44, and Khmer's 50, to the Sri Lankan Sinhalese whose 61 characters contain almost no straight lines. This was thought to be because Sinhala used to be written on dried-out palm leaves which would split along their veins if the author used straight lines!

No discussion of Brahmi scripts would be complete without mentioning 2 other amazing 'alphabets'. With 50 characters, Bengali is an abugida used by around 300 million people worldwide, mostly in Bangladesh and India. This makes it the seventh most spoken language on Earth. The other abugida used across much of India is called Devanagari and it dwarfs Bengali. Devanagari is used in Sanskrit, Hindi, Nepali, Marathi, Pali, Konkani, Bodo, Sindhi and Maithili among others, and is used by over 1 billion people worldwide.

154

*The **154th** day of the year is June 3*

Equation nation

154 generates the cute equation:

$$1 + 5^6 + 4^2 = 15,642.$$

Anomaly

$154/253 = 14/23$ is an example of an anomalous cancellation where you remove only 1 digit from numerator and denominator.

Arabic, also used by about 1 billion people worldwide, is written from *right to left* and contains the following 28 characters:

خ	ح	ج	ث	ت	ب	ا	ص
ش	س	ز	ر	ذ	د	ق	ف
غ	ع	ظ	ط	ض	ي	و	ه
ن	م	ل	ك				

The word *abjad* comes from pronouncing the first letters of Arabic in order.

Chinese is part of the Sino-Tibetan family and the dialects form the 'languages'. The Chinese writing system is semanto-phonetic and represents both sound and meaning. Because each character has its own meaning, Chinese is written using a collection of characters (hanzi) known as logograms (or ideograms). Some of the larger Chinese dictionaries contain over 50,000 logograms that can be categorised into beautiful sounding collections such as pictograms, ideograms and radical-phonetic compounds. To read a Chinese newspaper you need to understand a mere 3000 of them. (How hard could that be! 有多难算得上是!)

There's prime for more

155 is the sum of the primes between its smallest and largest prime factor. That means we can write 155 = 5 × 31 and at the same time 5 + 7 + 11 + 13 + 17 + 19 + 23 + 29 + 31 = 155.

155

The 155th day of the year is June 4

In Chinese culture, the art of writing characters well – known as calligraphy – is greatly respected and considered by many people to be a high art form. Fair enough, too. Check out this beauty – 'Biang', a type of noodle popular in the Shaanxi Province – which requires an astonishing 57(!) brush strokes to write:

Finally, Japanese consists of not one but *three* alphabets – Hiragana, Katakana and Kanji. Hiragana and Katakana each contain 46 basic characters which represent sounds, with Katakana being reserved exclusively for foreign words. Kanji is logographic and while similar to Chinese, there is no precise count of the number of characters. Of the potential 80,000+ characters, it is thought that around 2000–3000 are in common use in Japan. Word!

156

The 156th day of the year is June 5

Join the dots

156 is the number of graphs with 6 vertices.

Here are some cuter ones:

10 metres

That's the longest length straw a human can possibly suck water through. (Don't believe me? You'll struggle with even 2 metres ... give it a go!)

Consecutive squares

$157^2 = 24,649$ and $158^2 = 24,964$. These consecutive squares use exactly the same digits just in a different order.

157

The **157th** *day of the year is* June 6

On this day in 1984
Alexey Pajitnov released Tetris

283

The average number of days of sunshine per year in Brisbane.

BRISBANE
by numbers

48%

This is how much of Queensland's economy Brisbane accounts for.

26,000,000

This many people visit the Queen Street Mall every year – quite possibly Australia's most successful mall!

75,000

The number of international students.

400,000

The number of attendees at the Ekka each year – showbags, rides and massive vegetables abound at the annual show.

158

The 158th day of the year is June 7

Non-palindromic prime

158 is the smallest number such that the sum of the number plus its reverse is a non-palindromic prime: 158 + 851 = 1009 and 1009 is a non-palindromic prime.

On the subject of primes, $158^6 + 158^5 + 158^4 + 158^3 + 158^2 + 158 + 1$ is prime, as is $158^2 + 159^2 + 160^2 + 161^2 + 162^2 + 163^2$.

83

The number of hours (and 38 minutes) Sir Charles Kingsford Smith took to fly across the Pacific from Oakland, California to ... you guessed it, Brisbane. Bet he destroyed the lamingtons and XXXX when he arrived!

100,000+

The minimum number of people who cross the Sir Leo Hielscher Bridge every single day.

92 m

The height of the City Hall Clock Tower which, when built, was the second largest ever Australian construction project after the Sydney Harbour Bridge.

1877

The year in which XXXX beer, one of Queensland's best-known products, was created.

35

The average age of a Brisbanite.

1

The number of lamingtons French Chef Armand Galland created when he recycled a day-old vanilla sponge cake to entertain surprise guests Lord and Lady Lamington in 1900 at Government House.

Time for prime

Can you show that 159 is the sum of 3 consecutive prime numbers? Hint: They must all be around about 1/3 of 159 which would be 53. Why don't you start looking there?

Woodall numbers

A Woodall number W_n is defined as any whole number of the form $W_n = n \times 2^n - 1$.

Work out the first few Woodall numbers and confirm in your mind that 159 is indeed one.

159

The 159th day of the year is June 8

On this day in 1935 Architect Richard Padovan was born

160

*The **160th** day of the year is June 9*

Polyiamonds are forever

Back on March 7, we met the 8-polyiamonds. Well, there are 160 9-polyiamonds and one of them is particularly cool because it has a hole in the middle of it!

The games we play

From fast food to footy, we're a pretty competitive mob ...

Distinctly prime

Every number greater than 161 is the sum of distinct primes of the form $6n - 1$. For example, $162 = 5 + 17 + 23 + 29 + 41 + 47$; $163 = 11 + 17 + 23 + 29 + 83$; $164 = 11 + 41 + 53 + 59$; and so on. Note that in each example, every odd number is prime of the form $6n - 1$.

You can try if you'd like, but you will not be able to write 161 as the sum of distinct primes of the form $6n - 1$.

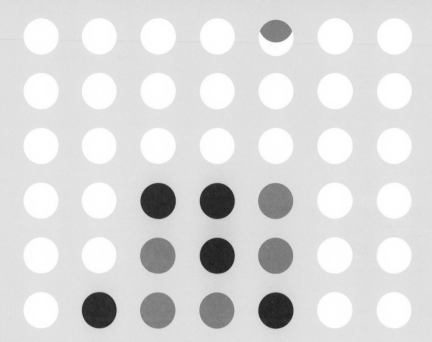

Connect Four!

Connect Four is a game with 'perfect information'!

On a standard Connect Four board (7 columns, 6 rows) there are 4,531,985,219,092 possible positions. When played as well as possible by 2 players, Connect Four will result in a first player win. With perfect play, by starting in the middle column, the first player can always force a win on or before the 41st move. If the first player starts in the columns either side of the centre, perfect play by both players will lead to a draw. But if the first player starts in the outside columns and both then play perfectly, the first player will lose after 40 moves (columns 1 and 7) or 42 moves (columns 2 and 6).

162

The 162nd day of the year is June 11

Still hip to be²

162 is the smallest number that can be written as the sum of 4 positive squares in 9 ways. Apart from $162 = 12^2 + 4^2 + 1^2 + 1^2$ can you find the other 8 ways?

Fastballs

The rules are simple.

Rank the following sporting skills in terms of the fastest ever recorded. On the off-chance it helps you: many of these fastest efforts were _not_ performed in competition but in special record-setting attempts or demonstration events.

- Badminton smash
- Baseball pitch
- Cricket ball bowled
- Football (soccer) shot
- Golf drive
- Ice hockey shot
- Jai-alai shot
- Lacrosse shot
- Squash smash
- Tennis serve (men's)
- Tennis serve (women's)

How'd you go? Turn the page to see if you were right. I reckon you might be surprised ...

Ramanujan's constant

The number $e^{\pi\sqrt{163}}$ is either beautiful or freakishly scary depending on your point of view. But it is not just a random jumble of numbers and mathematical terms. Rather, it is called Ramanujan's constant after the great mathematician Srinivasa Ramanujan. It's famous because despite its being composed of 3 irrational terms (numbers which can't be written as a fraction) it is awfully close to a whole number:

$$e^{\pi\sqrt{163}} = 262537412640768743.99999999999925...$$

163

The **163rd** day of the year is June 12

1. Badminton smash

The fastest badminton smash was belted by Tan Boon Heong and hit an incredible 493 km/h. Lest you disapprove of the fact that this figure was reached during an unofficial demonstration event, the fastest in competition still reached 332 km/h, courtesy of Fu Haifeng and his racquet.

Who'd have thought? A shuttlecock is the fastest travelling object in an interactive sport!

2. Golf drive

Coming in at number 2, and only marginally faster than the fastest competition badminton smash, is Ryan Winther's 349.38 km/h whopping golf drive.

3. Jai-alai (pelota or zesta-punta) shot

Jai-alai is sometimes known as the 'fastest sport in the world' because of the ball speed (and, sure, leaving those demons with their badminton racquets to one side, it's close). It involves bouncing a ball off a walled space using a device called a 'cesta'. Doesn't sound that exciting? Did I mention it's fast? Really fast. José Ramón Areitio holds the record – hitting a blistering 302 km/h shot.

164

*The **164th** day of the year is **June 13***

For argument's sake

Convince yourself that starting with the number 164, if you remove any digit and add or subtract 3 to the remaining 2-digit number, you always get a prime.

Scrabble

In the most gorgeously geeky of word games, Scrabble, of the 225 squares on the board, 164 are blank with no double or triple letter or word scores. If just the mention of Scrabble got you all breathy, turn to the Scrabble chapter in this book!

4. Squash smash

That'd be 281.6 km/h – courtesy of big-hitting Australian squash sensation Cameron Pilley. I can only imagine some of Cam's closest buddies would have bruises that will last a lifetime!

5. Tennis serve

At an ATP Tour event in Busan, South Korea, Aussie Samuel Groth served 263 km/h to Uladzimir Ignatik. Down a triple match point, Samuel unleashed the fastest serve ever recorded. Sadly, he still lost the match 6-4, 6-3.

The fastest female serve to date blasted off the racquet of Sabine Lisicki – a mighty 210.8 km/h at the 2014 Stanford Classic. Like Groth, she also lost her match!

6. Lacrosse shot

Zack Dorn broke the world record at the 2014 Major League All Star weekend by throwing a 186.7 km/h thunderbolt. But here's the best bit: he wasn't an all-star player, he was 'merely' a fan!

7. Ice hockey shot

The fastest someone has ever hit an ice hockey puck came at one of two demonstration events – you're either in the camp of Denis Kulyash (177.5 km/h) or Alex Riazantsev (183.46 km/h). Having seen what ice hockey players do to each other when they have a disagreement, I'm leaving this one well alone!

Triangular tennis

165 is the sum of the first 9 triangular numbers. Think of each triangular number (1, 3, 6, 10, 15 ...) as being represented by a grid of tennis balls. If we placed each triangular layer on top of each other with the biggest at the bottom, you can see why we also call 165 the ninth 'tetrahedral number'.

Vampire hunting

165 is a 'fang' of a 6-digit vampire number (see May 28). If I told you that its partner 'fang' was the number 951, can you work out the 6-digit vampire number that is their product?

165

The 165th day of the year is June 14

8. Baseball pitch

Fastest pitch? That'd be the 169.14 km/h scorcher that Aroldis 'The Cuban Flame Thrower' Chapman threw, playing for the Cincinnati Reds, against San Diego Padres.

9. Cricket ball bowled

There's a string of bowlers who have been credited with deliveries above 160 km/h including Australians Brett Lee, Shaun Tait and Jeff Thomson. That said, their bowling was measured with fairly primitive machinery and could well have been faster. The fastest recorded ball bowled acknowledged by *Guinness* is Shoaib Akhtar's 161.3 km/h blinder.

10. Football (soccer) shot

When it comes to shot speed, football is very hard to judge. Compared to the other balls, pucks, and so on that travel in pretty much straight lines or are hit from stationary positions, football shots come from out of nowhere, bend and swerve and aren't usually timed as a part of the sport's coverage. So while *Guinness* acknowledge 183 km/h (David Hirst, 1996, Sheffield Wednesday vs Arsenal) as the fastest shot in an English top division, some people claim that Ronny 'Homem-Bomba' (human bomb) Heberson struck a – get this – 212.2 km/h cracker for Sporting Lisbon against Naval in 2006 ...

166

*The **166th** day of the year is **June 15***

I wanna be prime

The reverse of 166 (661) is prime. If you rotate it 180° (991) it is also prime. The same is true if you put zeros between each digit; i.e. starting with 10,606, 60,601 and 90,901 are both prime numbers.

Anomalous

166 is the numerator of an anomalous cancellation. Can you work out the 3-digit denominator needed to make it so?

Since 1940, 157 people

have fallen from planes without parachutes and survived.

One hundred and sixty-seven

167 is the only prime number that can be expressed as the sum of exactly 8 but no fewer positive cubes. In fact, it can be done 2 different ways. C'mon, that's pretty special.

Surely you can find it within yourself to try and express 167 as the sum of these 8 cubes.

What if I gave you a hint and told you that one of the ways involves a term that occurs 5 times?

167

*The **167th** day of the year is June 16*

On this day in 1963 Valentina Tereshkova became the first woman in space

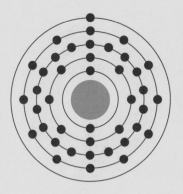

Niobium

Niobium was named after Niobe who, in Greek mythology, was the daughter of Tantalus. Niobium was originally identified in 1801 and was to be called columbium. But people weren't sure if it was a new element or actually just another form of tantalum (which we haven't met yet; see element 73). When you mix niobium with tin or titanium you get a substance that is a superconductor at very low temperatures (–250°C brrrrrr!). Because of this, these niobium alloys are important in magnetic resonance imaging (MRI) and full body imaging.

168

The 168th day of the year is June 17

No room at the inn

2^{168} = 37414441915671114706 014331717536845303191873 1 001856 which is a big number but doesn't look all that special – no offence, 2^{168}.

If you look closer you'll notice this 51-digit beast lacks the digit 2. Well, as far as we know, no larger 2^n exists that misses any of the digits 0 to 9 up to $2^n = 10^{399}$.

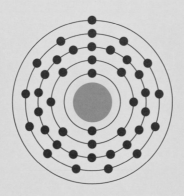

Molybdenum

Molybdenum is another silver-grey transition metal and has an atomic number of 42. It has been used by humans for a very long time and has been found in 14th-century samurai swords. Strong and resistant to corrosion, these must have been awesome weapons at the time. However, for various reasons, the use of molybdenum didn't become widespread until World War I, when the British Army successfully replaced manganese shields on their tanks with much lighter and stronger molybdenum plating.

Mirrored roots

169 is the reverse of 961. The same is true of their square roots ... $\sqrt{169} = 13$ and $\sqrt{961} = 31$.

Once a square ...

$169 = 13^2$ so in base 13 we write it as 100. But interestingly, in base 11 it is 144 ($11^2 + 4 \times 11 + 4 = 169$) and in base 12 it is 121 ($12^2 + 2 \times 12 + 1 = 169$), making it look like a square in all 4 bases.

169

*The **169th** day of the year is June 18*

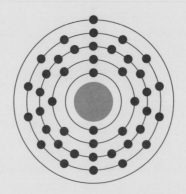

Technetium

The interesting thing about technetium is that it is the first element we meet on the Periodic Table that is radioactive in every form of its isotopes (remember, 2 isotopes of an element contain equal numbers of protons but different numbers of neutrons in their nuclei). Technetium's properties were predicted by the famous Russian chemist Dmitri Mendeleev before it was even discovered. He noticed a gap in his Periodic Table and knew something fishy was going on! Technetium was also the first artificially produced element, created in 1937 by bombarding molybdenum atoms with pairs of protons and neutrons which we call deuterons.

1 2 3 4 5 6 7 8 9 10 11 12 13 14 15 16 17 18 19 20 21 22 23 24 25 26 27 28 29 30 31 32 33 34 35 36 37 38 39 40 41 42 **43** 44 45 46 47 48 49 50 51 52 53 54 55 56 57 58 59 60 61 62 63 64 65 66 67 68 69 70 71 72 73 74 75 76 77 78 79 80 81 82 83 84 85 86 87 88 89 90 91 92 93 94 95 96 97 98 99 1

170

The 170th day of the year is June 19

One hundred and seventy

is the smallest number that can be written as the sum of the squares of 2 distinct primes, where each of these primes is the square of a prime added to another prime $(170 = (2^2 + 3)^2 + (3^2 + 2)^2)$.

Try saying that fast 3 times in a row when you're a bit sleepy.

In fact, the very astute of you may have noticed that 170 can actually be written in this form in 2 separate ways. That's right, you could also go for:

$$170 = (2^2 + 3)^2 + (2^2 + 7)^2.$$

Now there's no excuse for staying awake!

On this day in 1623 Mathematician Blaise Pascal was born

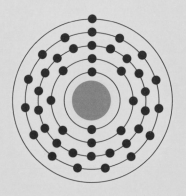

Ruthenium

Position 44 on this catalogue of chemical coolness belongs to ruthenium, a really rare metal that's a member of the platinum group. Ruthenium is mostly used for super-tough electrical contacts as well as in the production of thick-film resistors, though it has had an unintended foodie application, too. The traditional Welsh dish laverbread is made from the sea algae porphyra which, courtesy of the nearby nuclear reprocessing plant at Sellafield in the UK, contains lashings of ruthenium!

It's a long way to the top

The number 12 is not prime. Nor is 123 or 1234 or 12,345 or 123,456; in fact, if you wanted to keep cycling through 1, 2 ... 9, 0 you'd have to write out 171 digits before getting to 123456789012345678901234567890 ... 78901 which is the first prime number in this series. To me that seems an amazingly long time to have to wait!

171

The *171st day of the year* is *June 20*

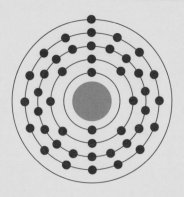

Rhodium

The word rhodium comes from *rhodon*, the Greek word for rose-coloured which refers to the vibrant rose-red crystals of rhodium chloride from which rhodium was first extracted by the English chemist and physicist William Hyde Wollaston in 1803.

Other elements named after colours include caesium 'sky blue', chlorine 'greenish-yellow', indium 'indigo', iodine 'violet' and rubidium 'ruby red'.

172

The 172nd day of the year is June 21

Sweet 17 (and 2)

Splitting 172 into 17 and 2 we have the quaint little fact that seventeen 2s followed by two 17s, 22222222222222222221717, is prime.

The power of ... 7

$7^2 = 49$, $7^3 = 343$, $7^4 = 2401$ and if you kept going through the powers of 7 looking for the first number that contained 5 consecutive identical digits, you'd have to wait until you got to the 146-digit 7^{172}.

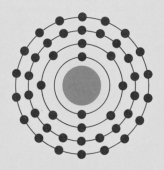

Palladium

You'll soon meet cerium, which was named after the asteroid Ceres which was discovered around the same time. Well, for a while the discoverers of palladium toyed with naming it ceresium, also after the asteroid Ceres. This must have been one pretty cool asteroid! They instead named it palladium after the Pallas asteroid.

You're quite possibly carrying some palladium on you right now. In your pocket; in your phone; in the form of tiny ceramic capacitors that are layers of palladium sandwiched between layers of ceramic for insulation.

Fancy-pants maths

Did you know that 173 is the only prime number for whom the sum of its cubed digits equals its reversal? Don't worry, neither did I! This is just a fancy way of saying that $1^3 + 7^3 + 3^3 = 371$.

173

The 173th day of the year is June 22

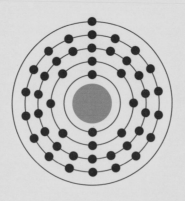

Silver Ag

The soft, white, lustrous – and let's not forget *precious* – transition metal silver conducts heat and electricity better than any other. It's highly prized and is used all over the place: in industry, as currency, for jewellery, in solar panels, in cutlery and other tableware ... I could go on and on but I won't. While plenty of elements are named after countries – like francium or americium – silver is the only element that has given its name to a country: Argentina comes from the word *argentum*, the Latin word for silver.

174

The 174th day of the year is June 23

Twin primes

Twin primes are pairs of primes separated by only 2, for example (3, 5), (5, 7), (11, 13) ... We know a bit about twin primes, but nowhere near as much as we'd like. For example, we don't know if there is an infinite amount of twin primes, but we have found some as large as $3756801695685 \times 2^{666669} \pm 1$.

We do know that there are exactly 174 twin prime pairs among the first 1000 primes.

On this day in 1912
Mathematician Alan Turing was born

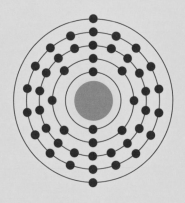

Cadmium

A group of English workers building the Severn Road Bridge in 1966 used an oxyacetylene torch to melt some bolts. They didn't know the bolts were covered in cadmium and by oxidising them they inhaled poisonous fumes. One of the workers died and so cadmium is on the UN's list of top 10 environmental pollutants.

Small amounts of cadmium sneak into your body by being confused with zinc. Luckily your gut keeps most of it out but an atom of cadmium that gets absorbed will hang around in your body for approximately 30 years.

One seventy-five

is the smallest number n such that $n^6 \pm 6$ are both prime.

$175 = 1^1 + 7^2 + 5^3$

175

The **175th** day of the year is June 24

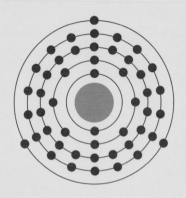

Indium

The soft and malleable metal called indium has 49 protons in its nucleus and hence an atomic number of 49. It gets its name from the Latin word *indicum* which means indigo or violet. The next element alphabetically, iodine, is named after *iodes*, the Greek word for, you guessed it, violet.

You've probably heard the sound a sheet of tin gives as you bend it. Before breaking, it will emit what is called a 'tin cry'. Less well known is that indium also gives off a high-pitched shrieking sound when bent. Talk about over-sensitive!

176

The 176th day of the year is June 25

Eleven which way

176 is divisible by 11 (176 = 11 × 16). So number theorists immediately know that its reversal 671 is also divisible by 11. You can try this for other numbers that are divisible by 11 if you like.

$176^2 = 30,976$; $176^3 = 5,451,776$; $176^4 = 959,512,576$. In fact, 176^n ends in 76 for any whole positive number n.

This happens when we take the powers of any number that ends in 76.

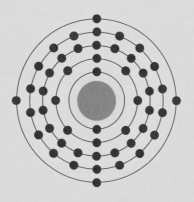

Tin Sn

Coming in at number 50 on our atomic hot list, tin is an incredibly versatile metal and humankind has been working with it for aeons. The mixing of copper with small amounts of tin over 5000 years ago created bronze, ushering in the bronze age and changing the world profoundly. Since then, tin has been used in making pewter (for cutlery and tableware) and in solders. But probably its most well-known use is for plating other metals, for example cans. Tin totally rocks because it's not particularly toxic and is very resistant to corrosion.

3456789101112131415161718192021222324252627282930313233343536373839404142434445464748495051525355565758596061626364656667686970717273747576777879808182838485868788899091929394959697989910

Lucky number 7

There are 177 graphs with 7 edges and no unused vertices.

Interestingly, the objects below are different versions of the same graph.

177

The 177th day of the year is June 26

Bolt by the numbers

By running 100 metres in 9.58 seconds, Jamaican sprinter Usain Bolt is the fastest human ever. But how fast is he really?

A basic calculation suggests that if he ran 100 m in 9.58 seconds, in 1 second he would run $100/9.58$ = 10.438 m. Now, 10.438 m per second is 10.438 × 3600 m in 3600 seconds or 37.58 km/h. That's pretty swift. It's faster than the traffic speed Google Maps assumes for New York, Boston and San Francisco!

But Bolt's much faster than that. Don't forget he starts from a crouching stationary position so it takes him a bit of time to reach his 'top speed'. We can measure this by observing him running on high-speed film, frame by frame, measured at 10 m intervals and translate the time he takes to run 10 m into his speed for that 10 m section of track. We get data like this:

How far he has run	Seconds / decametre (10 metres)	Kilometres / hour
0–10 m	1.89	19.048
10–20 m	0.99	36.364
20–30 m	0.90	40.000
30–40 m	0.86	41.860
40–50 m	0.83	43.373
50–60 m	0.82	43.902
60–70 m	0.81	44.444
70–80 m	0.82	43.902
80–90 m	0.83	43.373
90–100 m	0.83	43.373

178

The 178th day of the year is June 27

178^5

begins with a 178. Now, for a small percentage of you, the true calculation geeks, my real brothers and sisters, this statement is like a red rag to a bull.

Go on, grab that pen and paper and convince yourself – calculator schmalculator – you know you can do it!

... and a graph like this, for his world record run at the 2009 World Championships in Berlin.

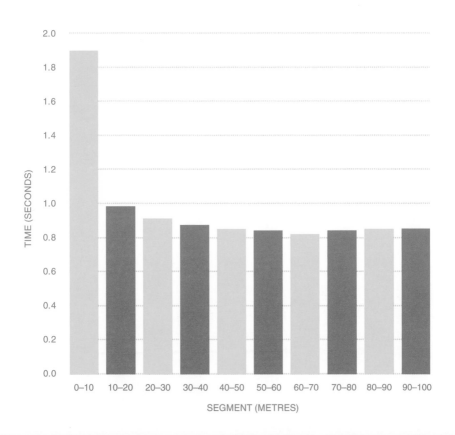

Different technologies can give different results and some people claim Usain has even bolted at 44.72 km/h at his very fastest.

Certainly, at a top speed of 44.44 km/h, Usain is moving a lot faster than his average speed of 37.58 km/h.

But to bring him back a peg, and let's be honest not many people have managed to do this, if the animal kingdom had a 100 m race, it's estimated Usain would barely scrape into the fastest top 30. He'd probably tip out an elephant but he wouldn't get close to the fastest land-based bird, the ostrich, which can maintain its 50 km/h average speed for 30 minutes at a time. An ostrich could, in fact, run a marathon in about half the time of the fastest human being.

Gold in this festival of freakishly fast fauna would go to the cheetah who can attain short bursts of speed well over 100 km/h (62 mph). The cheetah can also run 100 m in under 6 seconds. Nice work. Silver would quite possibly go to the prong-horned antelope, a greyhound, or even the Mongolian wild ass, all very speedy critters.

However, these fast-footed fiends are nothing compared to the creatures of the air. The peregrine falcon – the fastest animal of them all – flies at up to 240 km/h.

Of course in a race, Usain Bolt would be more likely to stay in his lane and if the other 27 competitors were disqualified, he'd certainly give the best victor's speech!

180

*The **180th** day of the year is June 29*

Plural primes

$180 + 1$ is prime, $180^2 + 1$ is prime, $180^4 + 1$ is prime and $180^6 + 180^5 + 180^4 + 180^3 + 180^2 + 180 + 1$ is ... you guessed it ... prime.

Due to his immense height (he's 6 foot 5 inches – 195.5 cm) Usain covers 100 metres in 41 strides. His opponents need more like 47.

His feet are size 13, he weighs 94 kg but says he 'only' bench presses 140 kg!

Photo: J. Brichto – taken at the London Anniversary Games

Rollicking repeater

The number $1/7 =$ 0.142857142857142857... with the 6-digit string 142857 repeating endlessly after the decimal point. Well, $1/181$ is similar, except that the repeating string is 180 digits long!

You really want to see the decimal expansion of $1/181$? Are you sure? Okay, here it is:

0.00552486187845303867403314917127071823204419889 50276243093922651933701657458563535911602209944751 38121546961325966850828729281767955801104972375690 60773480662983425414364 6408839779... (repeating)

181

The 181st day of the year is June 30

That litre of milk you just bought from the shops?

It might very well contain milk from over 1000 different cows!

182

*The **182nd** day of the year is **July 1***

Believe me ...

$(1!)^2 + (2!)^2 + (3!)^2 + ... + (181!)^2 + (182!)^2$ is prime. I think it's best you just take my word for this!

Anoma-you, Anoma-me

182 is the numerator of an anomalous cancellation – can you work out the 3-digit denominator and therefore the fraction from which the cancellation derives?

Grandmother flash

Harriette Thompson became the oldest woman to complete a full 26.2-mile marathon on 31 May 2015 in San Diego, finishing the Rock 'n' Roll Marathon with a time of 7:24:36. Sure, 7 and a half hours is more a 'slow groove' than rock 'n' roll pace for a marathon, but hey, she was 92!

Her effort is astonishing but even she pales in comparison to centenarian athletic freak Fauja Singh, who took up running at the age of 89 to cope with family tragedies.

As a 100-year-old, Singh set the record for oldest person to complete a marathon at the Toronto Waterfront Marathon. He was the final contestant to finish – in 8 hours 25 minutes and 17 seconds – but the achievement earned him a place in *Guinness World Records*.

Get this. A mere 3 days before the Waterfront Marathon, they held the Ontario Masters Association Fauja Singh Invitational Meet also in Toronto. Now some people might feel a bit of pressure having a whole athletics meet named after them ... not Fauja Singh. On the one day, 13 October 2011, he set not 1, not 2, but 8 world records: the 100-year-old men's 100 m (23.40 seconds), 200 m (52.23), 400 m (2:13.48), 800 m (5:32.18), 1500 m (11:27.81), mile (11:53.45) and 3000 m (22:52.47). He covered the 5000 m in a comfortable 49 minutes 57.39 seconds. He set 5 of these world records in a 94-minute period. Played, Fauja.

Tagalong squares

If you write the consecutive numbers 183 and 184 next to each other as one big number you get 183,184.

We also know that the number $183,184 = 428^2$.

The fancy way of saying this is 'the concatenation of 183 and 184 is a perfect square'.

There are no smaller numbers for which the concatenation of 2 consecutive numbers in order is square. If you're really keen you might want to try and find the next such pair of numbers. I'll give you a hint, they'll occur as 'year days' in late November.

183

*The **183rd** day of the year is July 2*

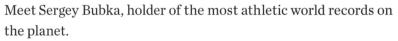

What's a Bubka?

Actually, it's not so much 'what' as 'who'.

Meet Sergey Bubka, holder of the most athletic world records on the planet.

Over his career, the incredible Sergey set an astonishing 35 world records – the most ever held by one person. He set 17 outdoor and 18 indoor world records in pole vault. In the decade between 1984 and 1995, he raised the outdoor record, often 1 cm at a time, from 5.85 m to 6.14 m, and the indoor from 5.81 m to 6.15 m.

Between 1984 and 1988 alone he raised the bar, literally, by *21 cm* and cleared the magical 6 m mark 45 times. The rest of humanity has done it on only 100 other occasions.

He certainly didn't rest on his laurels after retiring from sport, either – he has since been heavily invloved with a variety of sports associations, including becoming vice president of the International Association of Athletics Federations (IAAF). About that role, Bubka says, 'I have been working at the IAAF for a long time and my work is not limited to one area. The good of athletics is something deep in my heart.' What a high-flying dude.

Perhaps a Bubka should be a unit of measurement for athleticism, or at least tenacity. 'We'll never climb over that. It would have to be at least 8 Bubkas!'

184

*The **184th** day of the year is July 3*

Cousins ...

We've spoken about twin primes, which are primes separated by 2, such as the pair (3, 5) or (41, 43) and so on.

Well, primes that differ by 4, for example, (37, 41) are not quite as close as twin primes so we call them 'cousin primes'.

... and sexy primes

When 2 primes differ by 6 we call them 'sexy primes' which is based on the Latin word for six. I'm telling you this because $184^5 \pm 3$ are sexy primes.

It ain't whether you win or lose ...

If you're upset your netball team lost by 1 goal in the semi-final last Wednesday, don't be.

In the final of the 2015 Trans Tasman netball championships, my beloved NSW Swifts lost to the awesome Queensland Firebirds despite having led for all but the last 30 seconds of the game. It was heartbreaking. But for every nail-biting finish in sport, there's another game that's an absolute blow-out.

In the fifth Test of the 1938 Ashes, England beat Australia by an innings and 579 runs. England won the toss and chose to bat first, but they declared after scoring 903 for the loss of just 7 wickets. In the end, Australia were bowled out for 201 in their first innings and 123 in their second. Ouch.

More recently, on the soccer pitch, Australia thumped American Samoa 31-0 in a 2001 World Cup qualifier. The striker Archie Thompson scored 13 of the goals, which was an international record. This achievement came just 2 days after Australia thrashed Tonga 22-0. Clearly we were on a roll.

And although it doesn't stack up against the actual number of goals scored, who will ever forget the crushing 7-1 defeat of host nation Brazil by Germany in the 2014 World Cup? It's been cited as the most humiliating, shameful and downright embarrassing

Distinct expressions

Can you express 185 as the sum of 2 distinct squares in 2 different ways? Let me rephrase that, you can ... now go do it ;-)

Independence Day

American readers will think of the 4th of July as both Independence Day and as 7/4. On the topic of 7s and 4s:

$7 = 2 + 4 + 0 + 1$ and
$7^4 = (2 + 4 + 0 + 1)^4 = 2401.$

185

*The **185th** day of the year is **July 4***

*On this day in 2012
The Higgs boson was found at the LHC,
16 years after Hotmail.com was launched*

defeat in Brazilian football history. Apparently you can still hear grown men crying in the streets in Rio today. Talking of Germany, at the 2007 FIFA Women's World Cup in Shanghai, they dispatched Argentina 11-0. Achtung!

Of course, humiliating losses aren't confined to the round ball game. At the 2003 Rugby Union World Cup, the Wallabies defeated Namibia by a whopping 142-0. Would you believe in the same year, at the cricket World Cup, Australia posted 6/301 from 50 overs before bowling Namibia out for 45 to win by 256 runs.

On the tennis court, at the 1988 French Open, the supremely speedy Steffi Graf successfully defended her title by defeating Natash Zvereva 6-0, 6-0 in just 32 minutes. Poor ol' Tash won only 13 points the entire match.

But the final word must fall, once again, to the 'beautiful game'. There are blow-outs, and then there's Madagascar's premier football league, in which AS Adema demolished Stade Olympique l'Emyrne by a record-breaking margin back in 2002. What made it worse was the fact that SOE did not concede the avalanche of goals; they scored them as *own* goals. The opposition stood around looking confused, and spectators rioted, demanding a refund as SOE carried out a bizarre protest against refereeing decisions in previous games.

The fallout from this annihilation was so extreme the Olympique head coach Zaka Be was banned from soccer for 3 years.

And the final score? ...

186

The **186th** *day of the* year is *July 5*

Know your product

Convince yourself that 186 is the product of the first 4 primes less the product of the first 4 positive integers.

186 are odd

While 186 is not itself an odd number, there are 186 dates in a non-leap year for which the number of the day *is* an odd number.

AS ADEMA **STADE OLYMPIQUE L'EMYRNE**

 v

The big anomaly

187 is the numerator of not 1, not 2 but 7 anomalous cancellations with 3-digit denominators (see April 5, May 19 and so on if you missed this concept). What are the 7 such cancellations? Warning, this is a brute of a question. Bring it on!

A big birthday party

With 187 people in a room, there's a slightly greater than 50% chance that 4 will share the same birthday.

187

*The **187th** day of the year is July 6*

The numbers of Wimbledon

54,250
The number of tennis balls used per tournament.

665 minutes
The longest match ever when American John Isner defeated Frenchman Nicolas Mahut 6-4, 3-6, 6-7 (7-9), 7-6 (7-3), 70-68 in 2010.

8 mm
The height of the rye grass used on the courts.

212
The number of aces served by Goran Ivanisevic in winning the tournament in 2001.

238 km/h
The fastest serve ever (Taylor Dent, 2010); Aussie Sam Groth put one past Roger Federer in 2015 at a lazy 236 km/h.

201 km/h
The fastest serve by a woman (Lucia Hradecka, 2015).

28,000 kg
The amount of strawberries are eaten each year, washed down by 7000 l of cream.

102 kPa
The air pressure inside a tennis ball.

9
The number of singles titles won by Martina Navratilova.

13
The number of known Wombles, all told.

188

*The **188th** day of the year is July 7*

An even expression

188 is the largest known even number that can be expressed as the sum of 2 primes in exactly 5 ways. Can you find them?

86 is the number of world records set at North Sydney Olympic Pool.

This number itself is a world record! One has a unique distinction: it was set at a *school* competition on 3 April 1971 by Graham Windeatt, who swam the 800 m freestyle in 8.28.6 – the fastest *ever* at the time.

Prime quadruplets

A prime quadruplet (also called a prime quadruple) is a set of 4 primes of the form $\{p, p + 2, p + 6, p + 8\}$.

Now that you know that, I can reliably inform you that the product of the primes in a prime quadruplet always ends in 189, except for the very first one: $5 \times 7 \times 11 \times 13 = 5005$.

Can you find the next smallest prime quadruplets and check it has this property?

189

*The **189th** day of the year is July 8*

$S_1 C_3 R_1 A_1 B_3 B_3 L_1 E_1$

I used to love Scrabble. One hundred tiles, 225 (15 × 15) squares, strategy, the beauty and idiosyncrasies of the English language, and a huge dollop of mathematics thrown in for good measure. Nerd smorgasbord!

However, when I say 'used to love', I do feel the modern-day explosion of digital Scrabble apps and games have changed things – and not necessarily for the better. I haven't had much experience in 'tech Scrabble' so I apologise if I'm wrong or offending any hardcore iPhone Scrabble enthusiasts, but some of the digital incarnations seem to be dominated by guesswork and 'cheating' where the players use totally obsure words neither of them could ever define ...

But enough CHUNTER (verb meaning 'monotonous' grumbling; 36 points if played on a triple word score) from me – in my humble opinion, old-school Scrabble rocks!

For those unfamiliar with the phenomenon, Scrabble is a word game where 2 to 4 players score points by placing tiles, each bearing a single letter, onto a gameboard which is divided into a 15 × 15 grid of squares. The tiles must form words which, in crossword fashion, flow left to right in rows or downwards in columns. To start the game, each player takes 7 tiles from the pile and arranges them on their rack. You have to spell accepted

190

The 190th day of the year is July 9

CXC

Roman numeral freaks will be thrilled to be able to use today's date as an excuse to explain to people that 190 is the largest number with only distinct prime Roman numeral palindrome factors that is itself a Roman numeral palindrome. By that I mean $190 = CXC = II × V × XIX$.

English words (no proper nouns) and you score points based on the value of the tiles you play. Apart from the opening move, each new word must involve a tile or tiles already on the board. You score points for all the words you form if your tiles create more than one word.

QUANTITY

POINT VALUES	×1	×2	×3	×4	×6	×8	×9	×12
0		(BLANK)						
1				L S U	N R T	O	A I	E
2			G	D				
3		B C M P						
4		F H V W Y						
5	K							
8	J X							
10	Q Z							

As you can see, letters that appear in lots of words like, S, E, T ... are worth 1 point, up to Q and Z which are worth 10 points each.

Sophie Germain

191 is prime and when you double 191 and add 1 you get another prime. This makes 191 a Sophie Germain prime, named after one of the greatest mathematicians of all time.

We think there is an infinite number of these primes but we haven't yet proved it.

Along with 131, our friend 191 is the only other 3-digit palindromic Sophie Germain prime.

191

The 191st day of the year is July 10

On this day in 1856 Inventor Nikola Tesla was born

Your score can increase by placing your tiles on squares that double or triple the value of that tile or even the entire word. The most coveted squares on the board are the 'triple word squares' and if you place all 7 tiles down in a word (called a 'bingo' by enthusiasts even though that only has 5 letters) you score a bonus 50 points.

The secret to winning at Scrabble isn't actually knowing incredible 7-letter words, but having a massive vocabulary of 2- and 3-letter words to get you out of trouble regardless of your tiles. So bone up on terms like AA (a type of lava), XU (1/100th of a Vietnamese dong) and QAT (an Arabian shrub). Trust me, they're worth their weight in ZUZ (a Jewish silver coin)!

At the elite level there have been some pretty awesome high-scoring words and games played in competitions over the years. Some people would dispute if all of these are records because different countries use different dictionaries, but let's not get bogged down in that; here is a sample of some pretty amazing Scrabble-playing feats ...

192

The 192nd day of the year is July 11

Small but mighty

192 is the smallest number that together with its double and triple contain every digit from 1 to 9 exactly once.

There are 3 other values of n so that n, $2n$, and $3n$ contain each non-zero digit exactly once. Can you find them?

Highest scoring game

TOH WEIBIN set a record score of 850 (with a winning margin of 591) at the Northern Ireland Championships on 21 January 2012.

Highest combined score

1320 (830–490) by Michael Cresta and Wayne Yorra in a Massachusetts, US, club game in 2006. Also in that game, Michael played QUIXOTRY for 365 points. An excellent score, though there has been one greater scoring move played in the history of this noble game ...

As an Aussie I should give an honourable mention to the highest Australian combined score – 1210 (721–489) by Edward Okulicz and Michael McKenna at the 2013 Jamboree in NSW.

Highest losing score

552 BY AMERICAN STEFAN RAU to American Keith Smith's 582 in round 12 of the 2008 Dallas Open in the US. Bad luck, Stef, you caught Keith on a hot day.

Highest tied game

532–532 BY THAI COMPETITORS Sinatarn Pattanasuwanna and Tawan Paepolsiri at the 2012 World Youth Scrabble Championships.

Highest opening move score

MUZJIKS (WITH A BLANK FOR THE U) 126 by Jesse Inman at the 2008 National Scrabble Championships in Florida in the US. This is very close to the highest possible legal score on a first turn – MUZJIKS 128 – which uses an actual U rather than a blank.

(Note: The odds of potentially opening with MUZJIKS without a blank is about 1 in 55,581,808.)

Longest game ever

IN AUGUST 1984, Brits Peter Finan and Neil Smith played Scrabble for 153 hours at St Anselm's College in Merseyside in the UK setting a new duration record. A longer record was never recorded by *Guinness World Records*, as the publishers decided that records of this nature were becoming too dangerous and stopped accepting them. I just love the idea of someone playing Scrabble and pushing it too far!

e on the prize

Before I started researching this book, I didn't know that $193/71$ is a good approximation of the wonderful and important mathematical constant e, which you meet in calculus, exponential growth and decay and a whole bevy of places. $e = 2.71828...$ and $193/71 = 2.71830...$ accurate to within 1 in 10,000.

193

The **193rd** day of the year is July 12

Scrabble was invented in 1938

IT WAS ORIGINALLY CALLED Lexiko, but was rebadged in 1944 as Scrabble with the multiple point squares.

The points values of tiles

WERE BASED ON the inventor, Alfred Mosher Butts', analysis of editions of *The New York Times* to work out that the letters E, T, A, O, I, N, S, H, R, D, L, U account for 80% of the letters used in English.

Sales of Scrabble

WERE MODEST UNTIL the boss of Macy's department store played it on his summer holidays in 1953. In 1954 over 4 million games were sold!

Over 150,000,000 Scrabble sets

HAVE BEEN SOLD in 29 languages since 1948.

An estimated 30,000 games

OF SCRABBLE start every single hour.

When the word *QI*

(PRONOUNCED CHEE), a Chinese word for 'life force', was added to the list of acceptable words, Scrabble was transformed. Now the Q is the best letter to have because you don't just have the 4 U's in the bag but also 9 I's that can complement it. QI has gone on to become the most commonly played word in tournament Scrabble.

The shortest possible game

OF SCRABBLE would involve a mere 14 moves.

The greatest move ever

WAS SURELY IN APRIL 1982, when Dr Karl Khoshnaw had up his sleeve a totally obscure word which means a type of Latin American political leader or chieftain and also a species of bird.

Karl leant forward and made Scrabble history when he added his 7 letters to a letter already there, spelling CAZIQUES across not 1, but 2 triple word scores. In the process, he racked up an incredible 392 points in a single move!

194

*The **194th** day of the year is July 13*

One ninety-four

is the smallest number that can be written as the sum of 3 positive squares (not all unique) in 5 ways. Go on, you know you want to find those too.

A quickie

194 can be written as the sum of 2 squares. Can you find them?

On this day in 1944
Inventor Ernö Rubik was born

C₃ A₁ Z₁₀ I₁ Q₁₀ U₁ E₁ S₁

Triple word score

Double letter score

Triple word score

Here's the arithmetic behind this incredible wordplay.

CAZIQUES with Q on a double letter score scores

$$3 + 1 + 10 + 1 + 2 \times 10 + 1 + 1 + 1 = 38$$

This on 2 triple word scores, jackpots to $38 \times 3 \times 3 = 342$

And with the bonus 50 points for using all 7 tiles (bingo):

$$342 + 50 = 392$$

Dr Khoshnaw, I'll just bring the stretch Hummer around the back for you now.

We lucky few

Take the numbers 1, 2, 3, 4, 5, 6, 7 ... and remove every second number (all the evens) getting 1, 3, 5, 7, 9, 11, 13 ... The next surviving term is 3 so remove every third term on this new list getting 1, 3, 7, 9, 13, 15, 19, 21 ... Now remove every seventh number, and so on. The remaining numbers are the lucky numbers. 195 is a lucky number.

195

*The **195th** day of the year is **July 14***

On this day in 1983 Mario Bros was released

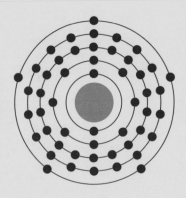

Antimony Sb

If you drink a glass of wine that has had antimony dissolved in it ... you'll spew your guts out. Why on Earth would we do that, Adam? You probably wouldn't these days, but from the 1500s on it was seen as a way to expel bad 'humours' from the body. I know, it's a pretty weird definition of humour!

Antimony may well have been a component of the Byzantine weapon 'Greek fire'. Greek fire was an absolute bugger to deal with because it continued to burn even in water. It's thought it contained stibnite (antimony sulfite) but we'll never know because revealing the secret ingredients was punishable by death.

196

The 196th day of the year is July 15

A Lychrel number

A Lychrel number is a natural number which cannot form a palindromic number through the iterative process of repeatedly reversing its digits and adding the resulting numbers. Say what?

Well, take yesterday's number, 195, for example. If we do the process I just mentioned we get: 195 + 591 = 786. And, repeating:

786 + 687 = 1473, 1473 + 3741 = 5214, 5214 + 4125 = 9339.

So we arrive at a palindromic number, in this case 9339. If we don't get a palindrome the number is called a Lychrel number. That said, it's hard to prove: 196 isn't necessarily a Lychrel number, but it's the lowest *conjectured* one.

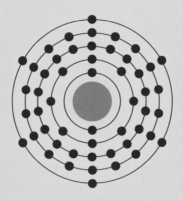

Tellurium

Tellurium gets its name from the Latin word for earth, *tellus*. It's mostly used in making alloys and helps make other metals more malleable. It is quite toxic, though, and it's nearly impossible to get rid of it. The naturally occurring isotope tellurium-128 is radioactive and decays with a half-life of 2.2 septillion years (that's 2,200,000,000,000,000,000,000,000 years!), the longest such half-life of any radioactive isotope we've ever discovered.

3 4 5 6 7 8 9 10 11 12 13 14 15 16 17 18 19 20 21 22 23 24 25 26 27 28 29 30 31 32 33 34 35 36 37 38 39 40 41 42 43 44 45 46 47 48 49 50 51 52 53 54 55 56 57 58 59 60 61 62 63 64 65 66 67 68 69 70 71 72 73 74 75 76 77 78 79 80 81 82 83 84 85 86 87 88 89 90 91 92 93 94 95 96 97 98 99 100

Prime specimen

Our friend here, 197, has some great properties to do with adding primes. Check it out:

197 is the sum of all the digits of all the 2-digit prime numbers: (11, 13, 17, 19, 23, 29, 31, 37, 41, 43, 47, 53, 59, 61, 67, 71, 73, 79, 83, 89, 97).

It's the sum of the first 12 prime numbers:

$197 = 2 + 3 + 5 + 7 + 11 + 13 + 17 + 19 + 23 + 29 + 31 + 37$

And it's also the smallest prime number that is the sum of 7 consecutive primes.

Can you find this string of 7 consecutive primes that add up to 197?

197

The 197th day of the year is July 16

On this day in 1945 Code name Trinity, the first nuclear detonation, occurred

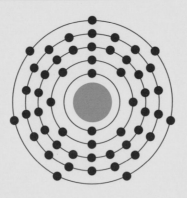

Iodine

With 53 protons clustered in its nucleus, iodine is very important in the first 3 months of pregnancy as a baby's nervous system develops, while iodine vapour was a crucial ingredient in the mid-1800s photographic technique of the daguerreotype.

It's also used in cloud seeding – the process of depositing chemicals in clouds to encourage water vapour to form and fall as rain. There's a bit of argy-bargy as to whether cloud seeding actually works, but the organisers of the 2008 Beijing Olympics claim they seeded clouds near the stadium to encourage rain before it could affect the opening and closing ceremonies.

198

*The **198th** day of the year is July 17*

On this day in 1975 Terence Tao was born. Happy birthday Terry!

Harshad

198 is a Harshad number because it's divisible by the sum of its digits. That is, 1 + 9 + 8 = 18 and 198 = 18 × 11.

Harshad numbers were defined by D. R. Kaprekar, an Indian mathematician. Why aren't they called Kaprekar numbers? That's because he had already invented those (see February 14).

The word 'Harshad' comes from the Sanskrit *harṣa* (joy) + *da* (give), meaning joy-giver.

If for some unfathomable reason the word Harshad doesn't give you joy, Harshad numbers are sometimes called Niven numbers after Ivan M. Niven who delivered a cracking paper at a conference on number theory in 1977.

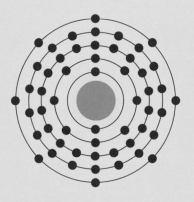

Xenon

Xenon is a colourless and odourless noble gas that is used a lot in illumination. By that I don't mean it makes you wise or enlightened, but rather you'll find xenon in flash lamps, lasers and in some top-end car headlights. It usually gives off a characteristic blueish tinge to white light. Xenon is the most easily ionised of the noble gases (that means it loses an electron and becomes positively charged) and is comparatively heavy. It is the perfect fuel for the xenon-ion thruster engines that power many satellites and spacecraft.

3456789101112131415161718192021222324252627282930313233343536373839404142434445464748495051525354
5556575859606162636465666768697071727374757677787980818283848586878889909192939495969798991100

The sum of us

The prime number 199 is the sum of 3 consecutive primes and of 5 consecutive primes. Can you find them?

A199

199 is the numerator involved in an anomalous cancellation. Given that the 9 is repeated it is a lot easier to find the 3-digit denominator. Off you go!

199

The 199th day of the year is July 18

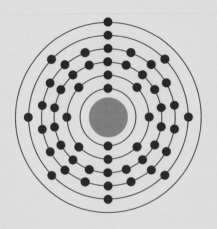

Caesium

Caesium is a soft alkali metal with an atomic number of 55. An atom of one type of caesium, caesium-133, is used in atomic clocks. The atoms alternate between 2 energy states precisely 9,192,631,770 times per second and that is now the official definition of a second. Caesium clocks are so accurate they would have lost only 2 seconds since the extinction of the dinosaurs 66 million years ago (if one had been invented back then). If you're wearing a caesium clock, there's really no excuse being late for that meeting.

200

The 200th day of the year is July 19

Unprimeable!

200 is the smallest 'unprimeable' number – that means it cannot be turned into a prime number by changing just 1 of its digits to any other digit (including changing it to a 0). What would be the next one? And what is the smallest odd unprimeable number?

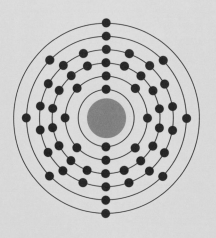

Ba**rium**

Surprisingly for a heavy element, barium is more abundant in the Earth's crust than the common elements carbon, sulphur and zinc.

While we don't need barium in our diet, large, green, single-celled algae called 'desmids' just love the stuff. They suck barium out of the water of boggy marshes and other not-particularly-glamorous locations. We think the barium functions as a gravity sensor for the desmid to orientate themselves. But if you're speaking with a desmid, make sure to ask them.

456789101112131415161718192021222324252627282930313233343536373839404142434445464748495051525 3
556575859606162636465666768697071727374757677787980818283848586878889909192939495969798 99100

Giving me joy

201 is a Harshad number as was yesterday's number 200. If you can't remember Harshad numbers, have a quick look at July 17. You don't have to look too far ahead to meet the next pair of consecutive Harshad numbers. What are they?

A thirst for blood

201 is a 'fang' of 4 different 6-digit vampire numbers. 201 × 510 = 102,510; 201 × 600 = 120,600; 201 × 627 = 126,027; 201 × 897 = 180,297.

Being involved with that many vampire numbers you'd half expect 201 to be called 'bloodthirsty' but as far as I know it isn't. You read it here first, people.

201

The 201st day of the year is July 20

On this day in 1976 Viking 1 landed on Mars

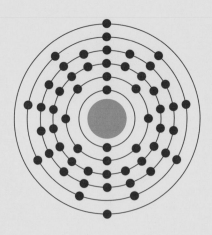

Lanthanum

Lanthanum is a soft, silvery-white metal and the first of 15 elements referred to as the 'rare Earth' elements. Just to confuse matters, most 'rare Earth' elements aren't that rare at all. But they tend to be blended with other substances and don't often occur in isolation in large amounts. Lanthanum compounds are used in glass, carbon lighting, ignition elements and in the batteries of hybrid cars. The word lanthanum comes from the Greek *lanthanō*, which means 'to be hidden'. It certainly hid from scientists for quite a while – it was only discovered in 1839 by the inquisitive Swedish chemist Carl Gustav Mosander.

123456789101112131415161718192021222324252627282930313233343536373839404142434445464748495051525354555657585960616263646566676869707172737475767778798081828384858687888990919293949596979899

202

The *202nd* day of the year is *July 21*

Role reversal

202^{293} begins with the digits 293 and 293^{202} begins with the digits 202.

$10^{202} + 9$, that's the number 1000 ... 0009 with 201 zeros in the middle, is a prime number.

On this day in 1969 Neil Armstrong took the first step on the Moon

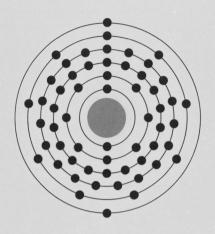

Cerium

With an atomic number of 58, cerium is a soft, silvery and ductile metal and the most abundant of the so-called 'rare Earth' metals (which you'll recall from reading about lanthanum). Cerium was used as the basis for discovering the element californium (98) but it's so intensely radioactive that it took 3 years to collect the few millionths of a gram needed to conduct the experiment.

Cerium was discovered in 1803 and is named after the dwarf planet, Ceres, the largest object in the asteroid belt between Mars and Jupiter which had been discovered 2 years earlier.

Pi day

In Australian date notation, July 22 is written 22/7 and hence today is π day. π is so awesome we also celebrate it on March 14, written as 3.14 as an American date.

Here are some cute ways we can express π:

$$\pi = 4 \times \left(\frac{1}{1} - \frac{1}{3} + \frac{1}{5} - \frac{1}{7} + ... \right)$$

$$\pi \approx \sqrt{7 + \sqrt{6 + \sqrt{5}}}$$

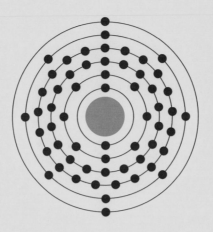

Praseodymium

The name praseodymium comes from the Greek words *prasios didymos,* meaning 'green twin'. Green refers to the bright green colour of praseodymium's principal compounds. The word twin belies the great mystery that surrounded praseodymium's discovery. In 1841, Swedish chemist Carl Gustav 'the Mozz' Mosander claimed that he had separated 2 other elements from some cerium salts. He named these elements lanthanum and didymium. It was a great effort but he was in fact only half-right. Forty years later it was confirmed that didymium was actually two different elements – which we named 'neo' and 'praseo' 'dymium'.

204

The 204th day of the year is July 23

An extra set of fangs

We discussed vampire numbers earlier, see May 28. Well, 125,460 is a vampire number because 125,460 = 204 × 615. But it has another vampire decomposition. It is the only 6-digit number that can be written 2 different ways as the product of two 3-digit numbers taken from its digits. Can you find it?

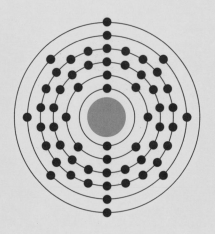

Neodymium

Magnets of neodymium, iron and boron are so strong they can slam together and splinter. They've even been used by people to attach metal studs to the outside of their cheeks by putting a magnet inside their mouths. This certainly avoids a painful piercing, but often needs an equally painful surgical removal of the metal from the magnet!

Neodymium comes from the Greek and means 'new twin' reflecting that it and praseodymium (green twin) were once thought to be the same element. I know it sounds about as complicated as a plot from *The Bold and the Beautiful*, but it's actually a fascinating story from 19th-century chemistry.

Too low for zero

The number 205^7 = 15215177646953125 is 17 digits long and does not contain a zero.

You think that's impressive? Well, if you're reading this book there is a pretty good chance you do think that's impressive, so how about something else to chew on:

205^{13} = 1,129,276,247,943,131, 871,729,736,328,125 is a 31-digit brute that also does not contain a 0.

Returning to the world where mere mortals like you and I can check things by hand, why don't you bust out that:

$205 = 4^4 - 4^3 + 4^2 - 4^1 + 4^0$

205

The 205th day of the year is July 24

The Final Chowdown

Sometimes a champion announces themselves by arriving on the scene with a truly extraordinary performance. Well, in the sport of competitive eating, the undisputed Greatest of All Time did just that. At the 2001 Nathan's Coney Island Hot Dog Eating Contest, Takeru 'The Tsunami' Kobayashi monstered 50 hot doggies in 12 minutes, doubling the previous record of 25.

The organisers were so surprised by his extraordinary efforts they actually ran out of printed signs trying to keep up with his consumption, and had to start writing them by hand!

Aside from obliterating his own record years later, Kobayashi has gone on to establish himself as the Bradman of buffalo wings, the LeBron of the lamb hotpot, the Liz Ellis of lobster rolls. All told, he's set world records in at least 15 different food categories.

Kobayashi at the Johnsonville World Bratwurst Eating Championship in 2006.
Source: www.flickr.com/photos/51035630117@N01/207657996/

206

The 206th day of the year is July 25

Two hundred and six

is the lowest positive integer (when written in English) to employ all of the vowels once only. This requires the use of the word 'and', that is 'two hundred AND six'.

What's the first such word you can find that uses all vowels if we don't get the 'a' from the word 'and'? Hint: You're better off thinking about it than trying to write them all out until you get there.

58 kilograms, 173 centimetres tall and *very* hungry.

Here are a few of the things Takeru Kobayashi has eaten ... in record time.

41 lobster rolls in 10 minutes

57 cow brains (8.03 kg) in 15 minutes

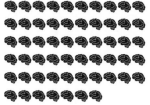

62 slices of pizza in 12 minutes

93 hamburgers in 8 minutes

150 rice balls (9.07 kg) in 30 minutes

110 hot dogs in 10 minutes

Not to mention:

- 60 bunless hot dogs in 2½ minutes
- 13 grilled cheese sandwiches in 1 minute
- 337 buffalo wings in 30 minutes
- 130 tacos in 10 minutes
- 55 lamb hotpots in 24 minutes
- 1 cheesesteak in 24.3 seconds
- 9.66 kg of soba noodles in 12 minutes
- 100 roast pork buns in 12 minutes

Prime management

207 is the smallest possible sum of primes which are formed using each of the digits 1 through 9.

For example, you can write $89 + 61 + 43 + 7 + 5 + 2 = 207$.

There are 2 other ways you can write 207 as the sum of primes using each digit 1 to 9 only once. Can you find them?

207

The 207th day of the year is July 26

There are over 360,000 registered netball players in Australia

... including the awesome Susan Pettitt who regularly shoots bombs for my favourite netball team in the world, the NSW Swifts.

The action at the 2015 ANZ Championship Grand Final. Source: SMP Images

208

The 208th day of the year is July 27

Cube up, cube down

Convince yourself that 208 is the sum of the squares of the first 5 primes.

Now convince yourself that $7^3 - 6^3 + 5^3 - 4^3 + 3^3 - 2^3 + 1^3 = 208$.

Checkmate!

One of the things I love about chess – and trust me there are lots of things I love about chess – is how the simple use of numbers and letters can summarise any game that has ever been played.

Chess is considered an 'open problem' in mathematics. Compared to noughts and crosses, for example, where if both players play well the game will always be drawn; or Connect Four (see page 162), where there's a guaranteed winning strategy, chess is so complex that we have not been able to yet calculate if there is a 'perfect' strategy, a way of playing the white pieces that is guaranteed to win.

White can chose from 20 opening moves – any pawn going out 1 or 2 squares, or either knight making 1 of 2 moves. So after Black's first move there are 20 × 20 = 400 possible positions the board could be in. Now, some of these are more likely and more sensible than others, but all 400 are theoretically possible. After 6 moves, this escalates rapidly and around 10 million positions can occur!

There's anything up to 10^{120} possible games that can be played (much more than fundamental particles in the Universe) and many millions of these games are of reasonable quality and would satisfy 2 good players trying their hardest. The really beautiful thing is that you can recreate any of these games – even if played by players far beyond your ability.

Find a number

$209 = 1^6 + 2^5 + 3^4 + 4^3 + 5^2 + 6^1$.
Pretty nifty. Similarly, on March 6 I'm sure you noted that $65 = 1^5 + 2^4 + 3^3 + 4^2 + 5^1$. Will the next number in this series, which uses 1, 2, 3, 4, 5, 6 and 7, give us a date for this year?

209

The 209th day of the year is July 28

What do I mean? Well, say you and I love tennis – really love it. No matter how deep our passion, we just can't walk onto a court and re-enact Sam Stosur beating Serena Williams to win the 2011 US Open 6-2, 6-3 (great work, Sam). Much as we would like to, we can't serve like they did, and can't control our shots to replay the match faithfully, point by point, game by game.

But with the wonder of chess notation you can do exactly that!

A chessboard has 64 squares labelled from a1 to h8. We call a, b, c ... h the 'files' and 1, 2, 3, 4 ... 8 the 'ranks'.

So the Black queen in this diagram is moving from e7 to b4.

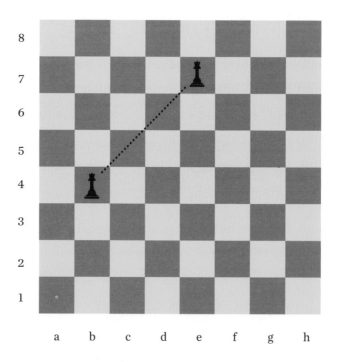

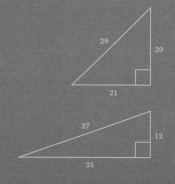

210

*The **210th** day of the year is **July 29***

Primitive triangles

These 2 right-angled triangles both have an area of 210 and are both 'primitive' which means they are not a smaller triangle with each side doubled or tripled or similar. They have integer size lengths and are the smallest such right-angled triangles with different hypotenuses (longest side) but the same area.

We also label the pieces K for king, Q (queen), R (rook), B (bishop), and N (knight – the king grabbed K already). Pawns are so commonplace we often don't bother writing P at all.

So the move opposite would be notated Qb4.

To recreate any of the great chess games in history, there are only 3 other things you need to know. First, if I move a pawn to any square, say e4, instead of writing Pe4 we just write e4 to speed things up. Second, the notation 0-0 refers to 'castling' where the White king moves from e1 to g1 and the White rook at h1 jumps the king and moves to f1. Similarly, when Black plays 0-0, the king and rook end up on g8 and f8 respectively. Finally, the x means 'captures that piece'.

Now you're ready to go. Grab a board and re-enact this absolute cracker of a game between Boris Spassky and David Bronstein in 1960. Spassky, of course, came to international fame when he lost his world championship crown to Bobby Fischer in 1972.

Here's a hint – and possibly a bit of a spoiler – you might want to be White (Spassky) and convince your friend to play Black (Bronstein).

Boris Spassky vs David Bronstein, 1960

Armchair sport doesn't get much more exciting than this!

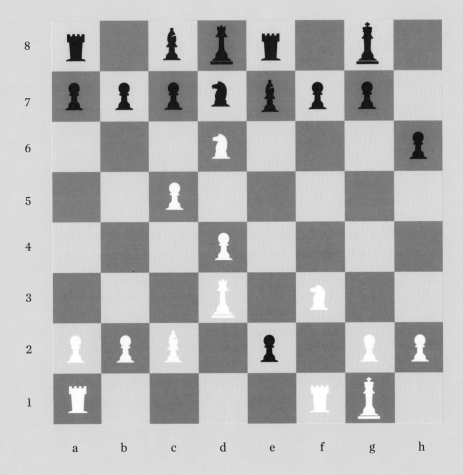

This is the position after White's 15th move.

212

The 212th day of the year is July 31

Boil, baby, boil

212° Fahrenheit is the boiling point of water at sea level.

Also, 212, 213, 214, 215, 216, 217, 218 and 219 all have exactly 2 distinct prime divisors.

Here we go!

1. e4 e5
2. f4 ... this opening is called the king's gambit ... exf4
3. Nf3 d5
4. exd5 Bd6
5. Nc3 Ne7
6. d4 0-0
7. Bd3 Nd7
8. 0-0 h6
9. Ne4 ... White offers the pawn at d5 in order to get his more powerful pieces moving ... Nxd5
10. c4 Ne3
11. BxN fxe3
12. c5 Be7
13. Bc2! ... the exclamation mark indicates that this is a strong move by Spassky. He earns this applause by focusing his attack on Black's kingside defences. His queen can now go to d3 and both it and the bishop are aimed along the diagonal to h7. If you think getting a ! is cool, just wait and see what the Russian gets soon ... Re8
14. Qd3 e2
15. Nd6!! ... this is a famously good move by Spassky. The diagram shows the current position. What is amazing here is that in chess if your opponent can get a pawn to the far end of the board

they can promote it to become a queen. Bronstein can use the pawn on e2 to both capture Spassky's rook on f1 and turn that pawn into a queen, but old Boris has calculated he is willing to give up both those things to press his advantage ... Nf8

16. Nxf7!! exf1=Q+ ... the pawn takes the rook, the pawn becomes a queen so Black now has 2 queens on the board! And the + sign means that White's king is now being attacked so White is in check
17. Rxf1 Bf5
18. QxB Qd7
19. Qf4 Bf6
20. N3e5 ... here either of the White knights could have moved to e5 so the 3 indicates that Spassky moved the knight that was on f3 to e5 ... Qe7
21. Bb3 BxN
22. NxB+ Kh7
23. Qe4+ and Bronstein resigns. Both players are good enough to realise that Bronstein can't escape checkmate. One of the ways he could go down from here is ... Kh8
24. RxN+ QxR 25. Ng6+ Kh7
26. NxQ+ Kh8 27. Qh7#

Bye bye, Bronny!

Young and squarefree

213 = 3 × 71 and so is called a 'squarefree number' as it has no repeated prime factors. In fact, 213 is the beginning of a triple of consecutive integers, 213, 214 = 2 × 107 and 215 = 5 × 43 which are all the products of 2 distinct prime factors.

213

The 213th day of the year is August 1

CANBERRA *by* numbers

2005
The year when security guards at Canberra's Parliament House were banned from calling people 'mate'.

1 day
The length of that ban on calling people 'mate' at Parliament House.

195.2 m
The height of Telstra Tower (aka Black Mountain Tower, née Telecom Tower) at the summit of Black Mountain.

386,000
Canberra's 2015 population, making it Australia's largest inland city.

664 ha
The size of Canberra's famous manmade Lake Burley Griffin.

214
*The **214th** day of the year is August 2*

Purring perfection

We explained perfect numbers back on January 6 and 28. Well, the perfect numbers keep going, 6, 28, 496, 8128 … We don't know if there is an infinite number of perfect numbers or if they eventually stop.

We do know that the 11th perfect number $2^{106} \times (2^{107} - 1)$ = 1316403645856964833723975346045872291022347231838369431177837281 28 (all 65 digits long of it) has 214 divisors.

660 km

The distance from Canberra to Melbourne. Canberra was chosen in 1908 as the compromise capital city over both suitors.

280 km

The distance from Canberra to Sydney.

61.7

Per 100,000 people: the number of festivals in Canberra (the most in Australia).

21,000 years

The time the Ngunnawal people have lived in what we now call Canberra – Canberra means 'meeting place'.

1913

The year in which construction of Canberra began, following Walter Burley and Marion Mahony Burley's international contest-winning plan.

20,000

The approximate number of public servants currently working in Canberra.

Interesting integers

There are 215 sequences of 4 (not necessarily distinct) integers, counting permutations of order as distinct, such that the sum of their reciprocals is 1.

Huh? Ow, Adam, that hurts to read, let alone think about.

Well, $1/4 + 1/4 + 1/4 + 1/4 = 1$ so (4,4,4,4) is one of these sequences.

Also, $1/8 + 1/8 + 1/4 + 1/2 = 1$, giving the sequence (8, 8, 4, 2) but we can also write $1/8 + 1/8 + 1/2 + 1/4 = 1$ giving (8, 8, 2, 4) and similarly, (8, 2, 4, 8) and so on.

Can you find any other ways of writing 1 as the sum of 4 reciprocals?

215

*The **215th** day of the year is August 3*

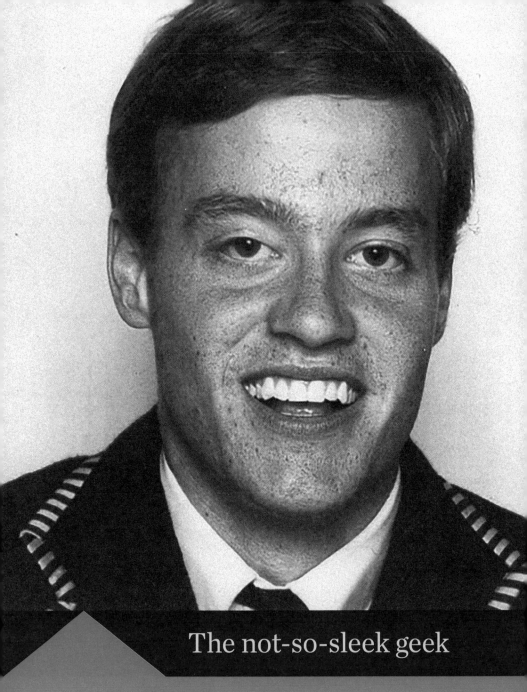

The not-so-sleek geek

216

We know from Pythagoras and right-angled triangles that $3^2 + 4^2 = 5^2$. Well, I can still clearly remember the day I stumbled upon something that just about every amateur mathematician stumbles upon at some point:

$$216 = 3^3 + 4^3 + 5^3 = 6^3.$$

I had that same sense of excitement that thousands had before me and thousands more will in the future – 'OMG ... I've discovered an amazing pattern in mathematics. They'll call this the Spencer series and I'll be world famous!'

Here's a bit of a more abstruse quiz question for you: what did I think I had discovered? Convince yourself that I hadn't actually discovered anything.

Pick a shuffle. Any shuffle.

What do you reckon the chances are that you've ever shuffled a pack of cards in the same way as anyone else in the history of the world? Pretty good?

Actually, no. The chances are *infinitesimally* small, statistically speaking. How many ways can a deck be shuffled? Well, for any shuffling there are 52 possible cards that can come out on top, 51 cards that could be second in the pile, 50 possible third cards, and so on, all the way down to the bottom of the pile. So the number of possible shuffles of 52 cards is what we call 52! (52 factorial) which is: $52 \times 51 \times 50 \times 49 \times 48 \times 47 \times 46 \times 45 \times 44$ ... you get the drift, all the way down to 1.

I'm sure you've already crunched the numbers but, if not, that's 80,658,175,170,943,878,571,660,636,856,403,766,975,289, 505,440,883,277,824,000,000,000,000 different possible deals.

Now, just in case any of you croupiers out there are wondering how long it might take for you to 'get' every possible permutation of card shuffle in your life, well, I have some bad news.

Say you had a lot of friends. Specifically, a trillion trillion of them. And these friends had a trillion trillion decks of cards. Each. And say they managed to make 1000 unique shuffles. *Per second.* Did I mention they'd been doing it since the Big Bang?

Well, the good news is that they'd have seen all possible shuffles right about now (and stopped, I guess).

Executive consecutive

217 is both the sum of 2 positive cubes and the difference of 2 positive consecutive cubes. Can you find each of them?

Semiprime-time

217 is also semiprime because $217 = 7 \times 31$ with 7 and 31 both prime. But because 7 and 31 are both of the form $4t + 3$ ($7 = 4 \times 1 + 3$, $31 = 4 \times 7 + 3$) we call 217 a Blum integer after Venezuelan computer scientist Manuel Blum. Find the next Blum integer.

217

*The **217th** day of the year is August 5*

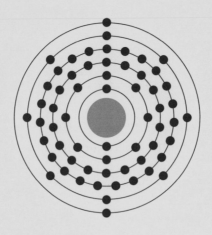

Promethium

As I've already mentioned, 'rare Earth' elements aren't necessarily at all rare. Well, this one certainly is. In fact, there is virtually no promethium on Earth. There may have been plenty when the Earth was formed, but in the intervening 4.5 billion years, all of its atoms have decayed. While there is no promethium on Earth or in our solar system, the star HR465 Andromeda pumps the stuff out at a rapid rate. The fact that we can look across the galaxy and detect this rare element being emitted by a star 520 light years away is truly wonderful.

218

*The **218th** day of the year is August 6*

Colour me edgy

Take a cube and 2 different coloured textas. Colour the 12 edges of the cube in whatever combination of colours you'd like. If picking the cube up and spinning it around doesn't change the colouring, there are 218 different ways you can colour that cube.

Anomaly's the norm

$218/981 = 2/9$ but again it's only a coincidence and you can't usually just cross out common numbers on the top and bottom of fractions.

On this day in 1991
The World Wide Web first
became available to the public

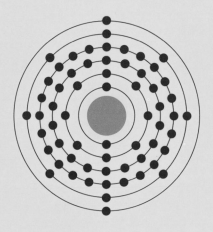

Samarium

Coming in at number 62 on the atomic rich list is samarium, a moderately hard metal that oxidises quickly when exposed to the air. Magnets containing samarium are incredibly powerful – 10,000 times more so than regular iron magnets. They've got so much grunt, in fact, that they resist demagnetisation better than any other known material. Without samarium, we would not have had personal stereos. Just as importantly, countless rock stars of the world would have to make do with inferior pick-ups on their basses and guitars.

A prime result

2^{219} = 8424983333484574935 83344221469363458551160763204392890034487820288

219^2 = 47,961

$2^{219} - 219^2$ = 8424983333484574935833442214693634585511607632043928900344877 72327 is prime.

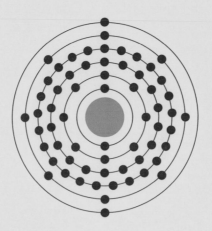

Europium

The bright red colour old cathode ray television tubes produce comes from the red emissions given by europium phosphors. Even in the swish-bang fancy-pants new LCD and plasma televisions, europium is used in the display to provide colour.

Europium (III) oxide is used in euro banknotes to help prevent counterfeiting. The notes give off a red glow when placed under a certain light wavelength thanks to europium. Speaking of euros, europium was discovered in 1901 and named after ... you guessed it: Europe!

220

The 220th day of the year is August 8

Getting married

Proper divisors are all the factors of a number apart from the number itself. Convince yourself that the sum of the proper divisors of 220 is 284 and that the sum of the proper divisors of 284 is 220. We say that 220 and 284 are 'amicable' or 'betrothed' numbers. 220 is the smallest such number.

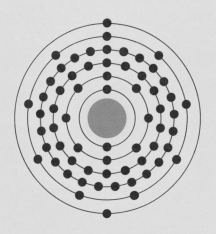

Gadolinium

With 64 protons in its nucleus, and hence next on our list, is the 'rare Earth' metal gadolinium. But don't get me started on actually how 'rare' this might make it. What we do know is that gadolinium is magnetic and can be introduced to, and then followed through, the human body. For this reason it's used in various medical experiments, including about 30% of MRI (magnetic resonance imaging) where it functions as a 'contrasting agent'. This just means it gives greater contrast and clarity when doctors are examining a patient's internals. It's an icky job, but some chemical has got to do it. Good on you, gadolinium!

Think on this ...

Write 221 as the sum of consecutive prime numbers in 2 different ways.

And this ...

221 can also be written as the sum of 2 squares in 2 different ways. Feeling lucky? Go on!

221

The 221st day of the year is August 9

On this day in 1776 Mathematician Amedeo Avogadro was born

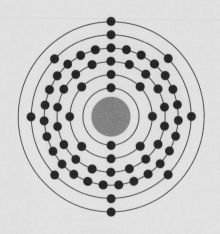

Terbium

Discovered in 1843 by the legendary Swedish chemist Carl Gustav 'The Mozz'* Mosander, terbium is another of those 'shy' metals that is never found alone in nature – only in the company of other minerals. But don't hold that against it. In the late 1970s, a US patent was filed for ceramic false teeth made of terbium because they were thought to glow the same way as real teeth. Unfortunately, the idea lacked sufficient bite to make it to market. Get it? Bite ... false teeth ...? Tough crowd.

*Note: there is no recorded instance of Carl Gustav being called 'The Mozz'.

222

The 222nd day of the year is August 10

We're getting there

Before you started reading this book you might have found the following statement nauseating, but now you can convince yourself that $222 = (3!)^3 + (2!)^2 + (1!)^1 + (0!)^0$.

So $(3!)^3 + (2!)^2 + (1!)^1 + (0!)^0 = 6^3 + 2^2 + 1^1 + 1^0 = 216 + 4 + 1 + 1 = 222$.

Okay, you might have to trust me on the $0! = 1$ bit ;-)

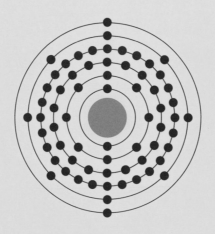

Dysprosium

Sounding like a medical condition as much as anything else, dysprosium comes from the Greek word *dysprositos* meaning 'difficult to obtain'. It was named in honour of Paul-Emile Lecoq de Boisbaudran who had to complete 58 precipitations on the marble slab of the fireplace in his house to isolate this particularly *dysprositos* element. Now that's an episode of *Renovation Rumble* I'd like to watch!

Dysprosium and its neighbour on the Periodic Table, holmium, (which you'll meet in just a minute) have the highest magnetic strengths of any elements, especially at low temperatures.

456789101112131415161718192021222324252627282930313233343536373839404142434445464748495051525354555657585960616263646566676869707172737475767778798081828384858687888990919293949596979899100

Two twenty-three

is prime. Show that it is also the sum of 3 consecutive primes and the sum of 7 consecutive primes.

$7^2 = 49$ and $27^2 = 729$.

Well, when you bang them together you get 49,729 = 223^2.

223

The 223rd day of the year is August 11

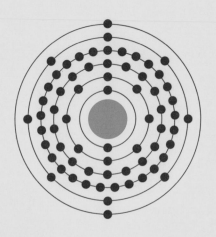

Holmium

The rare Earth element holmium was discovered by another Swedish gun scientist, Per Teodor Cleve, back in 1878. The 'holm' in holmium comes from *Holmia*, the Latin word for Stockholm.

Holmium lasers are used for certain medical procedures including kidney stone removal and prostate surgery. While we're on the topic of prostates, if you're reading this book and you're a man over 50, get your prostate checked out please. Not right now ... you can finish reading this page. But seriously, do.

224

*The **224th** day of the year is August 12*

All lined up

A couple of cool looking things about 224:

$224 = 23 + 45 + 67 + 89$ and it also equals $2^3 + 3^3 + 4^3 + 5^3$.

Sexy primes

$224^3 \pm 3$ are both prime making them sexy primes. Non-mathematicians get very excited when they hear about this family of prime numbers but the word 'sexy' here unfortunately has no erotic connotations. It simply derives from the Latin word for 'six'.

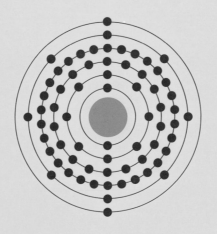

Erbium

Coming in at number 68 on the atomic hot list, erbium is a silvery solid metal that was discovered by, yep, you guessed it, Carl Gustav Mosander back in 1843. Er:YAG lasers, which use erbium, yttrium, aluminium and garnet can be used for laser resurfacing of human skin, cutting bone and soft tissue, implant dentistry and the removal of warts. Erbium doesn't serve a strict biological purpose, but on average we consume about 1 mg of the stuff each year. The highest concentration of erbium is in our bones, but it can also be found in our kidneys and liver.

No coincidence

$225 = 1^3 + 2^3 + 3^3 + 4^3 + 5^3 = 15^2$. But this is no coincidence. In general:

$$1^3 + 2^3 + \dots + n^3 = (1 + 2 + \dots + n)^2$$

and 225 is just the case where $n = 5$.

Convince yourself this equality holds when we go one term further up to $n = 6$.

225

The **225th** day of the year is **August 13**

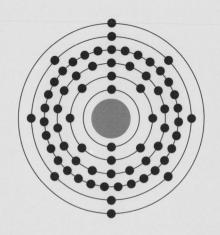

Thulium

Element 69 is thulium, which, along with holmium, was also discovered by the ace Swedish chemist, Per Teodor Cleve, back in 1879. Poor old thulium might need a bit of a hug, though. Of all the 15 so-called 'rare Earth' elements (elements 57 to 71) it is the only one about which we don't know something surprising or unique.

That said, the blue fluorescence given off by a euro banknote under UV light is due to thulium. In your face, counterfeiters!

226

The 226th day of the year is August 14

Don't be daunted

Convince yourself that $226 = (3!)^3 + (2!)^3 + (1!)^3 + (0!)^3$.

You might find the concept of $0!$ a bit daunting, but $0!$ is defined as equalling 1. I know it doesn't make sense to think about multiplying 0 by whole numbers less than it down to 1 in the same way that $4! = 4 \times 3 \times 2 \times 1$, but defining $0! = 1$ makes sense when we consider other places in which $0!$ arises in mathematics. Is that enough of a reason for you?

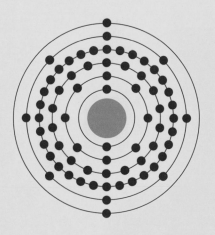

Ytterbium

Along with yttrium, terbium and erbium, ytterbium (discovered by the Swiss chemist Jean Charles Galissard de Marignac in 1878) is the fourth element to be named after the Swedish village of Ytterby. I don't know about you, but the next opportunity I get I'm taking the family to Ytterby for a nerdfest holiday!

When under very high physical stress, ytterbium's electrical resistance increases significantly. As such, it's perfect to use in devices that monitor the size of ground deformations caused by earthquakes and nuclear shockwaves.

4567891011121314151617181920212223242526272829303132333435363738394041424344454647484950515253
5556575859606162636465666768697071727374757677787980818283848586878889909192939495969798991OO

Sum 227

227 is prime, but it can also be written as the sum of the first 4 primes and their product: $(2 + 3 + 5 + 7) + (2 \times 3 \times 5 \times 7) = 227$.

In a similar way, it can also be written as the sum of 2 primes with their product, in a similar fashion as $(2 + 3) + (2 \times 3) = 11$. Can you express 227 as the sum of the sum of 2 primes and the product of those same 2 primes? They are not consecutive, just so you know.

227

The **227th** day of the year is **August 15**

On this day in 1957
Maths/science author
Clifford Pickover was born

NEW YORK CITY *by* numbers

$289,000
The cost of a 1-year hot dog stand permit in Central Park.

25 m
The depth below ground of the Federal Reserve Bank's Wall Street vaults, home to ¼ of the world's gold bullion. *Ocean's 14* anyone?

2
The number of Albert Einstein's eyeballs that are stored in a safe deposit box in New York City. After his death they were gifted to Einstein's eye doctor, Henry Adams.

130 km
The distance you can see from the top of the Empire State Building on a clear day.

228
The 228th day of the year is August 16

Dissecting a hen

228 is the number of ways, up to rotation and reflection, of dissecting a regular hendeca-gon into 9 triangles.

If you're feeling in any way inadequate because you'd never heard of a 'hendecagon' please don't; they are pretty obscure little blighters.

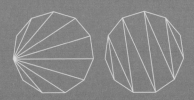

2

The days a year when the sunset is directly aligned with the east-west street grid, giving rise to what some call 'Manhattanhenge' – currently around 28 May and 12 July.

60,000

Roughly the number of hot dogs' worth of junk food scraps eaten by ants and other insects on some of New York's busiest streets. This plays a significant part in the city's waste management.

0

The number of people shot or stabbed on 28 November 2012, the first such day in living memory for the NYPD.

830 km

The length of coastline in NYC – longer than Miami, LA, San Francisco and Boston combined.

220 tonnes

The mass of Cleopatra's Needle, a 3000-year-old Egyptian artefact given to the city by the Khedive (Turkish ruler) of Egypt in 1879. It stands in Central Park.

High yield prime

229 is the smallest prime that, when added up to the reversal of its digits, yields another prime, 229 + 922 = 1151.

We had to wait all the way until 229, the 50th prime to find one with this quality, but the next such prime is much closer. Can you snoop around and find it?

229

The 229th day of the year is August 17

On this day in 1601 Mathematician Pierre de Fermat was born

230

*The **230th** day of the year is August 18*

A sphenic view

We call a number 'sphenic' if it is the product of 3 distinct primes. So $30 = 2 \times 3 \times 5$ is sphenic but $28 = 2 \times 2 \times 7$ is not because the 2 is repeated.

Can you show that both 230 and 231 are sphenic? In fact, 230 is the first number such that it and the next number are both sphenic.

The geeks ~~will~~ *have* inherit*ed* the Earth

A Stetson gallon

There are 231 cubic inches in a US gallon (admit it, you did *not* know that). At the same time, while Stetsons are waterproof and ads did show cowboys slaking their horses' thirst from them, even the largest famous cowboy '10-gallon hat' would only hold about ¾ of a gallon. The name '10 gallon' might well come from '10 *galón*', meaning '10 braids'

in Spanish referring to the number of hat braids worn on some more ornate Mexican versions of the hat. Or it could be a corruption of the Spanish phrase *tan galán* which translates as 'very handsome'.

231 is the sum of the squares of 4 distinct primes. Can you write 231 this way?

231

*The **231st** day of the year is August 19*

It is an exciting time to be a geek. The ever-evolving digital world, the explosion of big data and the creation of more and more powerful, cheaper, smaller devices will be a defining characteristic of this age.

But as much as geeks like nourishing their minds with mathematics, science and all matter of trivia, they also love nourishing their bodies. While it's not the *entire* geek diet, it's hard to imagine we'd live in the world we do if we'd never invented takeaway pizza, energy drinks and chocolate. And I can tell you, as a fully-inducted, card-carrying geek, what's even better than just eating it? Knowing some of the numbers behind it, of course!

Peak chocolate

Named after its inventor, the Swiss chocolate maker, Theodor Tobler, Toblerone is a mix of nougat, almonds and honey in a unique triangular ridge formation.

The number of triangles depends on the size of the Toblerone.

SIZE	TINY	MINI	35 G	50 G	75 G	100 G	200 G	400 G	750 G	4.5 KG
PEAKS	3	3	8	11	11	12	15	15	17	12

232

The 232nd day of the year is August 20

Abundant numbers

If you add up all the proper divisors of a number, *n*, they can be less than *n* ('deficient', for example 10 gives us 1 + 2 + 5 = 8 which is less than 10), equal to *n* ('perfect', like 6 or 28) or greater than *n* which we call 'abundant'. Twelve is the smallest abundant number (1 + 2 + 3 + 4 + 6 = 16 >12).

Nicomachus wrote only of even numbers because he thought all odd numbers were deficient, but he was wrong. The 232nd abundant number is 945, the first abundant odd number. Go on, get one up on old Nico and prove that 945 is abundant.

Of course these pyramids of particular pleasure are dwarfed by the creation at the annual Toblerone *Schoggifest*, where each year a special oversized bar is made to celebrate Toblerone's anniversary. The bar's weight represents the years of Toblerone, so the initial 2008 centenary bar weighed in at 100 kg.

Big, prime bikkies

Australia's biggest biscuit producer, Arnott's, began life as a small family affair in 1865 in Newcastle, NSW.

It remained in the family's hands until 1977 when it was taken over by the American Campbell's Soup Company. A descendant of the founder William Arnott, Ross Arnott was the man who christened a delectable little chocolate biscuit 'Tim Tam' in honour of the winner of the 1958 Kentucky Derby horse race. Tim Tams Original variety are notorious for coming in packs of 11 (a prime number) which for a long time people suggested was part of a mathematically savvy conspiracy so a group of 3, 4 or 5 people can't share them evenly and have to open a second packet. Personally, I find that hard to buy. And anyway, Tim Tam Double Coat, Tim Tam Chewy Caramel, White and Classic Dark all come 9 to a pack. Trust me on that! Chomping through an estimated 400 million Tim Tams per year, Australia's obsession makes them quite possibly the world's most popular chocolate biscuit per capita.

Prime Fibonacci

233 is the only 3-digit prime that is also a Fibonacci number. Can you work out the Fibonacci numbers up to 233, starting 1, 1, 2, 3, 5, 8 and adding the most recent 2 terms to get the next one until you reach 233? What term of the Fibonacci sequence is 233?

233

*The **233rd** day of the year is August 21*

Consumption of chocolate (per capita, in kilograms) in 2012

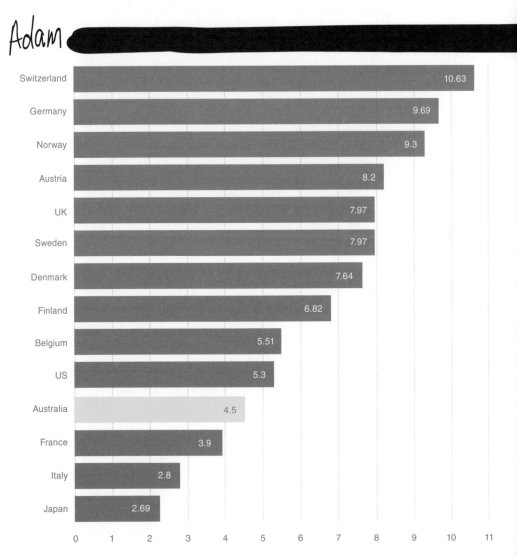

Adam

Country	Consumption
Switzerland	10.63
Germany	9.69
Norway	9.3
Austria	8.2
UK	7.97
Sweden	7.97
Denmark	7.64
Finland	6.82
Belgium	5.51
US	5.3
Australia	4.5
France	3.9
Italy	2.8
Japan	2.69

234

The 234th day of the year is August 22

Get out your coin purse

234 is the number of ways you can stack 12 coins in a line so that each coin lies on the table or on 2 coins.

Prove it

'Both the sum of 234 and the sum of its digits and the difference between 234 and the sum of its digits are perfect powers. One is a square and one a fifth power.'

Sure, not the sort of thing you would drop into conversation at a party, but can you prove that it is correct?

Chocolate consumption per country changes from source to source and it's almost impossible to find 2 charts that agree, but few dispute Switzerland is top of the pops.

Mars & Murrie's

Legend has it that the American candy baron Forrest Mars Snr witnessed soldiers in the Spanish Civil War eating hard-shelled lollies that didn't melt in their bags.

Back in the US, in partnership with Bruce Murrie from the Hershey's confectionery company, Mars set about recreating these lollies and in the early 1940s the US military was one of the company's biggest customers. This was the birth of M&Ms and the rest, as they say, is history. The 'M' and 'M' in M&Ms refer to Mars and Murrie's surnames. The colours were chosen by conducting consumer preference tests but in recent years Mars have stopped providing a precise rundown of the mix of colours.

However, as of 2008, the ratios were ...

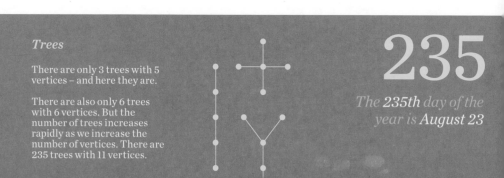

Trees

There are only 3 trees with 5 vertices – and here they are.

There are also only 6 trees with 6 vertices. But the number of trees increases rapidly as we increase the number of vertices. There are 235 trees with 11 vertices.

235

The 235th day of the year is August 23

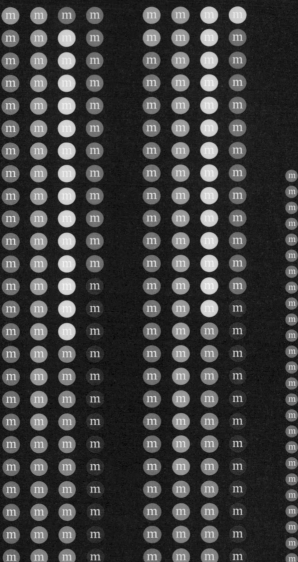

236

*The **236th** day of the year is August 24*

The oddest prime

236 is the sum of the first 12 consecutive odd primes, 3 + 5 + 7 + 11 + 13 + 17 + 19 + 23 + 29 + 31 + 37 + 41.

Double trouble

The numbers $236^2 + 236 \pm 1$ = 55,931 and 55,933 are both prime. Because they differ by just 2 we call them 'twin primes'.

M&Ms Milk Chocolate

24% cyan blue
20% orange
16% green
14% bright yellow
13% red
13% brown

M&Ms Peanut

23% cyan blue
23% orange
15% green
15% bright yellow
12% red
12% brown

M&Ms Kids Minis

25% cyan blue
25% orange
12% green
13% bright yellow
12% red
13% brown

M&Ms Dark

17% cyan blue
16% orange
16% green
17% bright yellow
17% red
17% brown

M&Ms Peanut Butter & Almond

20% cyan blue
20% orange
20% green
20% bright yellow
10% red
10% brown

Here's Johnny!

The room number in the film *The Shining* was switched from 217 (in the novel) to 237. The Timberline Lodge had a room 217 but no room 237, so the hotel management asked Stanley Kubrick to change the room number because they were afraid their guests might not want to stay in room 217 after seeing the film.

The Aronson sequence

Take the infinitely long sentence '*T* is *t*he first, four*t*h, eleven*t*h, six*t*een*t*h, ... letter in this sequence' and you'll notice you can keep adding numbers defined by where the previous letter Ts have fallen. The sequence of spaces occupied by these Ts is Aronson's sequence; 1, 4, 11, 16, 24, 29 ... and contains 237 as its 48th entry.

237

The 237th day of the year is August 25

Tasty oblate spheroids

The distant cousin of the M&M, the Smartie, was created by the Rowntree's company in the UK.

Originally called 'chocolate beans', they were rebranded as Smarties in 1937. Today they are produced by the Swiss giant Nestlé, the biggest food and beverage company in the world. There are 8 Smarties colours to choose from: red, orange, blue, green, yellow, pink, violet and brown. The blue smarties became white for a while when Nestlé switched from artificial to natural dyes.

In geometric terms, Smarties are what's known as 'oblate spheroids'. They have a minor axis of about 5 mm and a major axis of about 12 mm.

Of course, to mathematicians the *really* exciting thing about Smarties and M&Ms isn't their sugary deliciousness or the probability of getting 4 red ones in a row. No siree. It's all about something called 'packing density'.

The mathematical conundrum of 'packing density' goes way back to the 16th century when sailors had to work out the most efficient way to stow their cannonballs on board their ships. It took until 1998 for scientists to finally prove that the best way to do this is by using what we call a cubic or hexagonal close packing.

238

The 238th day of the year is August 26

The untouchables

238 is an 'untouchable' number. The untouchable numbers are those that are not the sum of the proper divisors of any number. For example, 2 and 5 are untouchable, but 4 is not because 4 = 1 + 3 and 1 and 3 are the proper divisors of 9.

The great mathematician Paul Erdös showed that there is an infinite number of untouchable numbers. Can you find the next untouchable number after 5?

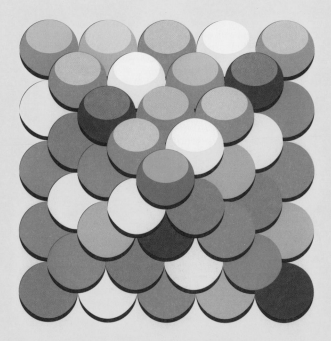

When stacked this way, the spheres (for example, gumballs) fill about $\pi \times (3/\sqrt{2}) \approx 74.05\%$ of the space. Nice work!

However, when spheres are dropped randomly into a space instead of packed precisely, they pack a lot less efficiently. While spheres pack randomly at about 64% efficiency, just a slight change to the shape of Smarties increases the density to 68%.

And even better: by tweaking the basic M&Ms shape you can get random packing that is very close to the 74% of ordered sphere packing. Fascinating ... and also delicious!

Nine cubes ...

When expressing 239 as a sum of square numbers, 4 squares are required, which is the maximum that any integer can require. It also needs the maximum number (9) of positive cubes.

The only other number that requires 9 cubes is 23 which is 2 cubed added twice followed by 1 cubed 7 times, but 239 can be expressed 2 different ways as the sum of 9 cubes ...

Can you work out how we express 239 as the sum of 9 cubes?

239

*The **239th** day of the year is August 27*

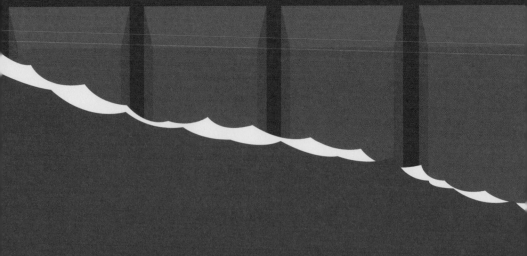

Have a break ...

The delicious chocolate-covered wafer biscuits known as KitKats were originally created by Rowntree's (makers of Smarties).

But these days they're made by ... you guessed it, Nestlé. KitKats come in a distinctive 4-finger structure. But it might not be distinctive for that much longer. In mid-2015 the latest blow was landed in a bitter battle between Nestlé and Cadbury. The feud started in 2004 when Cadbury tried to gain an exclusive patent over its purple colour – known numerically as Pantone 2865c. Despite some initial success, a series of courts around the world have since ruled against Cadbury. However, in 2015, Cadbury struck back, defeating Nestlé's argument before the European Court that the 4-finger structure was theirs alone. The dispute has nothing to do with the 1974 novel *The Chocolate War* by Robert Cormier. Just in case you were wondering.

240

*The **240th** day of the year is August 28*

Who boasts the most?

240 has more divisors (20 of them) than any previous number. What would be the next number with more?

Fearless Fibonacci

240 is the product of the first 6 Fibonacci numbers:

$240 = 1 \times 1 \times 2 \times 3 \times 5 \times 8$.

Sweet revenge?

Turns out there's a reason very few Shakespearean tragedies feature chocolate as the poison of choice.

Chocolate poisoning is an overdose reaction to theobromine, a substance found in chocolate, but also tea, cola beverages and some other foods. While it is possible for humans to die from chocolate poisoning, an 80 kg adult would need to eat in the vicinity of 5.7 kg of unsweetened dark chocolate or up to 40 kg of milk chocolate.

It's much more common for dogs to succumb to chocolate poisoning because they process the substance much more slowly and levels can build over a longer time. A 20 kg dog could die from as little as 500 g of milk chocolate. So next time you want to give your pooch a sweet treat ... don't!

Two forty-one

is the larger of a pair of twin primes. Except for 3 and 5, the larger of a pair of twin primes is always 1 more than a multiple of 6; the smaller is always 1 less than a multiple of 6.

And two for one

The band Reel Big Fish have a catchy little ska number called '241' – the only lyrics to which are 'two for one' repeated several times.

241

The **241st** day of the year is *August 29*

the Himalaya

Believe it or not, the Himalaya are growing each year.

You get a different answer about how much they're growing depending who you ask, but everyone agrees that it's happening.

Why? Well, it's because the 2 giant plates of Earth – the Indian Plate and the Eurasian Plate – continue to push against each other. They first came into contact some 40 to 50 million years ago after the Indian Plate had been pushing northwards at 20 cm a year for tens of millions of years. The Indian Plate is still moving north-east at about 5 cm a year, and the Eurasian Plate moves north, but only around 2 cm a year.

This combined impact sees the Himalaya 'grow' – estimates range from 40–61 mm each year.

242

The 242nd day of the year is August 30

If you need convincing

Can you convince yourself that 242, 243, 244 and 245 all have exactly 6 divisors? 242 is the smallest integer to begin a run of 4 consecutive integers all of which have the same number of divisors.

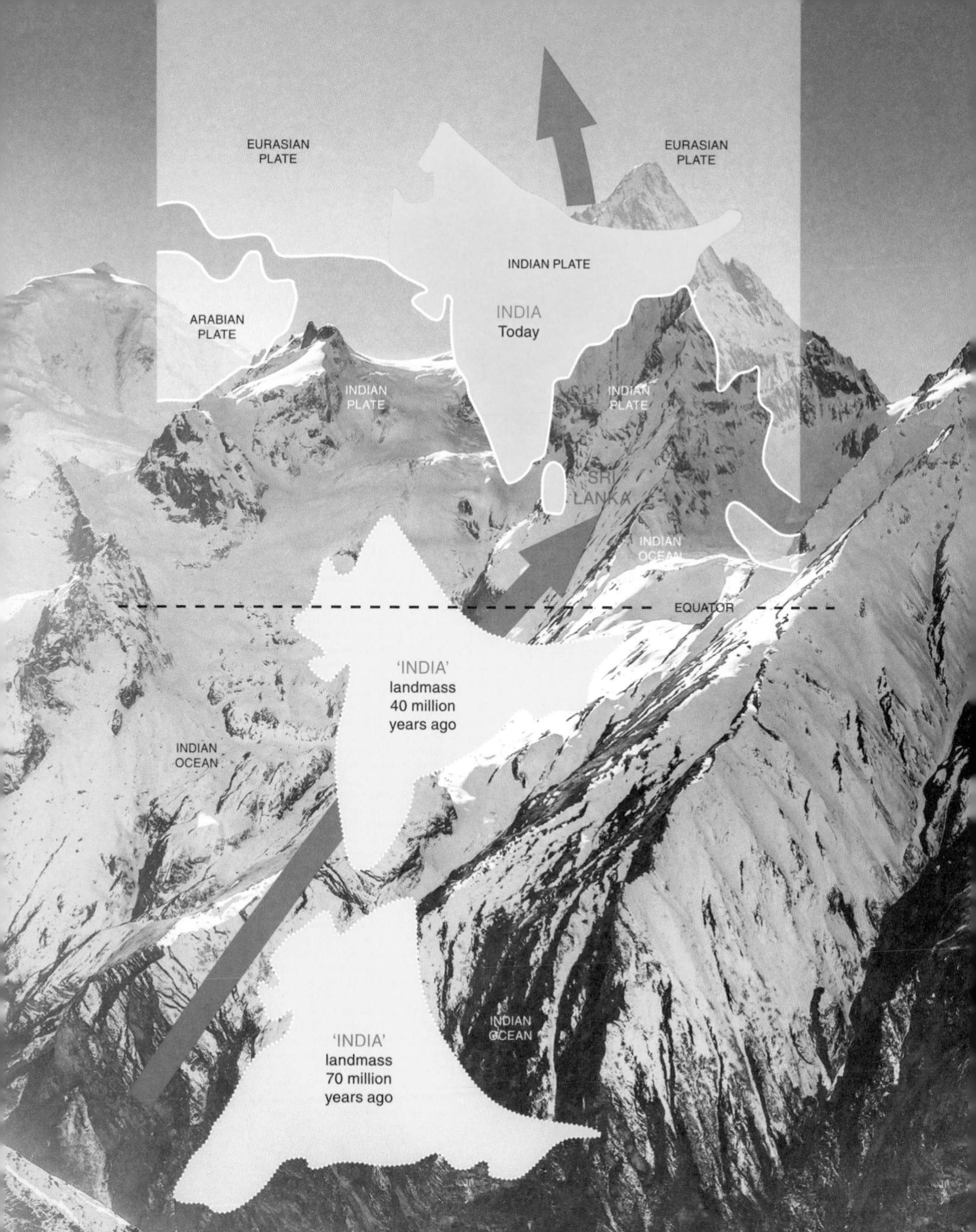

EURASIAN
PLATE

EURASIAN
PLATE

INDIAN PLATE

INDIA
Today

ARABIAN
PLATE

INDIAN
PLATE

INDIAN
PLATE

SRI
LANKA

INDIAN
OCEAN

EQUATOR

'INDIA'
landmass
40 million
years ago

INDIAN
OCEAN

'INDIA'
landmass
70 million
years ago

INDIAN
OCEAN

Pretty patterns

An interesting pattern
arises from the decimal
expansion of $1/243$. The first
few digits give us $1/243 =$
$0.004115226337448559...$

But the pattern of increasing
pairs of 0, 1, 2, 3 ... separated
by 4, 5, 6, 7 ... ends there. In
fact, $1/243 = 0.004115226337$
$448559670781893...$ repeating
endlessly.

243

The **243rd** day of the
year is **August 31**

As of 2015, 94% of the world's information is stored digitally.

But that's not all, 90% of all the data humans have ever created was produced in the last 2 years. That's an awful lot of cat videos.

244

*The **244th** day of the year is September 1*

108 days later

There is a cute relationship between 244 and 136 and the digits that make them up. It is this: $136 = 2^3 + 4^3 + 4^3$ and $244 = 1^3 + 3^3 + 6^3$.

If you've been scratching your head since May 16 trying to answer the quiz question without turning to the answers at the back of the book, I can end your pain after 108 days and say this is what we were getting at.

Viva la evolution

The very first 'computers' were actually people who 'computed' stuff (and were likely very good at maths!).

The first 'mechanised' computer – called the ENIAC – was invented in 1946 at Princeton University in the US. It was massive in every sense. It cost about US$6,000,000, was 24 m long, 2.5 m high, and a metre wide. It tipped the scales at about 30 tonnes (which equates to an entire school's worth of kids), got really hot and broke down all the time. The inventors would never have imagined most of us would today be carrying around tiny ENIACs in our pockets … At the time they were teased by their colleagues who thought the beast was a waste of time and 'this computing thing' would never work.

A basic smart phone mainboard is just a few centimetres wide and typically features not 1 but 2 tiny computers. If compared to the giant ENIAC, your smart phone:

- Costs 17,000 times less
- Is 40,000,000 times smaller
- Uses 400,000 times less power
- Is 120,000 times lighter

And the best thing: it's 1300 times more powerful!

Ta-da!

None of the numbers 245, 246, 247, 248 and 249 contain a 0, yet when you square them each of the squares does. If you've really got nothing better to do, why don't you convince yourself this is true. In fact, if you're really keen, note that except for 250 we can add 251, 252 and 253 to this sequence.

245

The **245th** day of the year is September 2

The thing about the pace of technological change is that it seems to accelerate as time goes on. So while the development of 'computing' in the 19th and early 20th centuries was 'methodical', in the 21st century it's 'exponential'. Read on and prepare to be amazed ...

Data storage

In 1981, some 45 years on from the ENIAC, the shiny new Apple III computer arrived on the scene. It was about the size of a couple of milk crates, boasted 5 megabytes (MB) of storage and cost a cool $3500. Back then, that was some serious coin, but in today's money – and you might want to be sitting down for this – it equates to $700,000 per gigabyte (GB) or $700 million per terabyte (TB)!

It's a bit harsh citing such an early figure, but even from the point where we began to master data storage, the prices have decreased at an astonishing rate.

The first 1 TB hard disk drive debuted in 2007. The 3.5 inch Deskstar 7K1000 cost $399 – thanks Hitachi. It was actually a drive composing 5 platters each of 200 GB. A mere 7 years later, it's not uncommon to see 3 TB drives for sale below $150 – a near tenfold reduction in price.

246

*The **246th** day of the year is September 3*

Jewellery maker

Just imagine one day you were making necklaces with 7 white beads and 7 black beads – we've all been there. Guess how many different necklaces you could make? Go on, guess ... 246. You're right? How did you possibly guess that?

IBM RAMAC 305 with a 350 disk storage unit
being unloaded. These babies leased for about
$200 per month back in 1957 (suffice to say, a lot
more than it sounds in today's terms) and held a
whopping ... 5 MB. That's about 1 pop song by One Direction
(audio only). Interestingly, I would find listening to said
song as painful as trying to lift an IBM RAMAC 305
onto a plane without mechanical assistance.

Differences aside

247 is the smallest number
which can be expressed as the
difference between 2 integers
such that together, they
contain all the digits 0 to 9.
Can you create the equation?
Hint: They are both 5-digit
numbers but their difference
is only 247 so think about

how the first couple of digits
of each number must be close
together and what the third
digits of each number must
be. Then think about the last
digit of each number.

247

*The **247th** day of the
year is September 4*

Data transmission

Of course, all that computing power would be next to useless if you weren't connected to anyone else, right? Thankfully, we have things like the SEA-ME-WE 3 (the name stands for South East Asia, Middle East, Western Europe) – the world's longest optical submarine telecommunications cable. It's truly mega: its basic length of 39,000 km means it would virtually run a full circuit of Earth around the equator!

SEA-ME-WE 3 is strong enough to withstand earthquakes and its twin fibre pairs can transport information at 480 gigabits per second – that's rather fast.

248

*The **248th** day of the year is September 5*

The power of 2

The powers of 2 are gorgeous and as a kid I used to sit around calculating them for fun. 2, 4, 8, 16, 32, 64, 128, 256 ...

But using only multiplication and powers, can you make all the above powers of 2 using the digits of 248 at most once each?

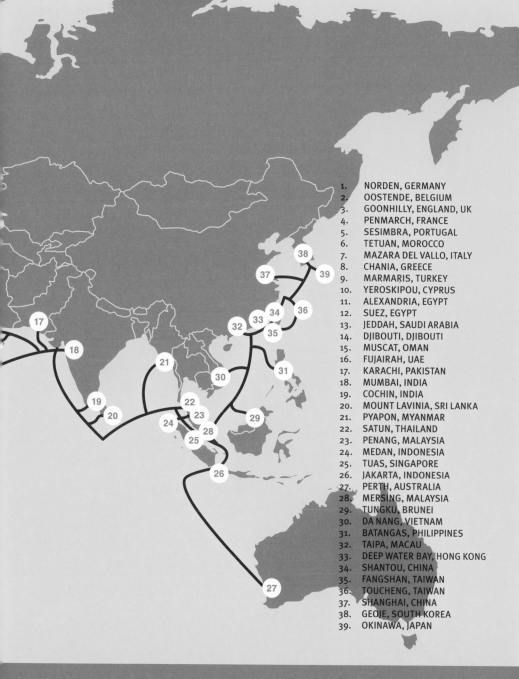

1. NORDEN, GERMANY
2. OOSTENDE, BELGIUM
3. GOONHILLY, ENGLAND, UK
4. PENMARCH, FRANCE
5. SESIMBRA, PORTUGAL
6. TETUAN, MOROCCO
7. MAZARA DEL VALLO, ITALY
8. CHANIA, GREECE
9. MARMARIS, TURKEY
10. YEROSKIPOU, CYPRUS
11. ALEXANDRIA, EGYPT
12. SUEZ, EGYPT
13. JEDDAH, SAUDI ARABIA
14. DJIBOUTI, DJIBOUTI
15. MUSCAT, OMAN
16. FUJAIRAH, UAE
17. KARACHI, PAKISTAN
18. MUMBAI, INDIA
19. COCHIN, INDIA
20. MOUNT LAVINIA, SRI LANKA
21. PYAPON, MYANMAR
22. SATUN, THAILAND
23. PENANG, MALAYSIA
24. MEDAN, INDONESIA
25. TUAS, SINGAPORE
26. JAKARTA, INDONESIA
27. PERTH, AUSTRALIA
28. MERSING, MALAYSIA
29. TUNGKU, BRUNEI
30. DA NANG, VIETNAM
31. BATANGAS, PHILIPPINES
32. TAIPA, MACAU
33. DEEP WATER BAY, HONG KONG
34. SHANTOU, CHINA
35. FANGSHAN, TAIWAN
36. TOUCHENG, TAIWAN
37. SHANGHAI, CHINA
38. GEOJE, SOUTH KOREA
39. OKINAWA, JAPAN

Prime wood

Back on June 8 we met the Woodall numbers; numbers of the form $W_n = n \times 2^n - 1$. The first few are 1, 7, 23, 63, 159, 383 ... The first few prime Woodall numbers are $W_2 = 7$, $W_3 = 23$ and $W_6 = 383$.

When we get to our 249th Woodall number we encounter:

W_{249} = 225251798594466661 4099154317747131957458142 6704487890973300733139 0393510002687 which is also prime. Perhaps you should just take my word for that.

249

*The **249th** day of the year is September 6*

On this day in 1766
Chemist/physicist John Dalton was born

This whole 'internet' thing ...

Believe it or not, back in the early 1990s, a lot of people viewed the internet as some geeky fringe type of fad that would just 'blow over'. And little wonder – in 1993, a mere 0.3% of the population were skulking about there.

In fact, it wasn't until around 1997 that we hit a whole number, and by the end of it, there were a whopping 70 million people (a little less than the current population of, say, Turkey), or about 1.7% of the population 'online'.

Suffice to say, since then, the web has grown in a *big* way. Nowadays, over 2,925,000,000 people are pottering about in the digital sphere, and few of us could imagine our world without it.

One of the web's more famous sites, Google (which, by the way, wasn't even founded until 1998), now processes over 40,000 search queries *per second*, which translates to roughly 1.2 trillion searches per year. I don't even want to guess how many of them are for cat videos.

And if that's not a sufficiently astonishing number, how about this: at the time of writing, there were an estimated 981,005,925 websites (by all means check again – it'll almost certainly have grown), which is barely a drop in the ocean compared to the number of emails sent and received: well over 100 billion.

For something that scarcely existed 20 years ago (at least not in its current form), you've got to admit the ol' interwebs has had a pretty good take-up rate!

250

The **250th** *day of the* *year is September 7*

Two fiddy

Can be expressed as the sum of 2 positive cubes and is also expressible as the sum of 2 (unique) positive squares in more than 1 way. That was quite a mouthful! Can you find all of these expressions?

3300: what's in a number?

Time stood still for chess lovers (and geeks in general) on 11 May 1997 when the greatest player of all time, Garry Kasparov, resigned without playing his 19th move of a match. Now, Kasparov doesn't win every single game, he's human, after all, but what made this a stunning moment wasn't that the world champion had gone down, but the fact that he had gone down ... to a computer!

The Beast of Baku was beaten by 'Deeper Blue', the unofficial name for IBM's chess computer program, which was an upgraded version of their Deep Blue machine, which Kasparov had actually beaten the previous year. In the rematch in New York, which was filmed for the doco *The Man vs. The Machine*, Kasparov won the first game, lost the second and drew the next 3 despite having strong positions. In game 6 he made a crucial mistake and ta-da, a machine beat the greatest-ever chess-playing human by $3\frac{1}{2} - 2\frac{1}{2}$!

We'll never have a number that quantifies Deep Blue's chess ability, because it didn't play sufficient official games against rated opponents, but what we do know is the following. The system used a parallel, RS/6000 SP Thin P2SC-based system with 30 nodes, with each node containing a 120 MHz P2SC microprocessor, enhanced with 480 special purpose VLSI chess chips. Its chess-playing program was written in C, ran under the AIX operating system and was capable of processing 200 million positions per second!

Ain't tellin' no fib

If I told you that the 251st Fibonacci number has the sum of its digits equal to 251, you could either calculate the Fibonacci numbers all the way up to F_{251} = 12776523572 9247325860370338946550318986595564473522249 or we could all just take Jim Wilder's word for it.

251

The 251st day of the year is September 8

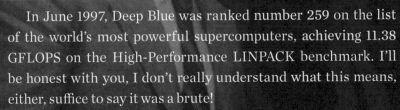

The Beast of Baku having immeasurably less trouble dispatching this hopeless *patzer* than he did Deep Blue.

In June 1997, Deep Blue was ranked number 259 on the list of the world's most powerful supercomputers, achieving 11.38 GFLOPS on the High-Performance LINPACK benchmark. I'll be honest with you, I don't really understand what this means, either, suffice to say it was a brute!

When I say we'll never have a 'number' for Deep Blue, chess Grandmasters are ranked by a points scale called their FIDE rating. This is based on something called the Elo rating scheme devised by the Hungarian born American physics professor Arpad Elo. Much like tennis pros and heaps of other athletes, chess players gain or lose points depending on their performances against other players and the ratings those players have. If you win a series of games against people ranked higher than you, your Elo will improve; perform badly, your rating will drop.

When he played Deep Blue, Garry Kasparov was rated around 2800 and had dominated world chess for years. His highest ever rating was 2851. The current world champ Magnus Carlsen has been rated as high as 2889.

In comparison, the 2014 computer chess world Champion, Komodo, was rated at over 3300 points. Massively higher than any human has ever achieved or most likely ever will!

252

The 252nd day of the year is September 9

Here's lookin' at you, 2-5-2

252 is the smallest number which is the product of 2 distinct numbers that are reverses of each other. Can you interpret what this is saying in an equation?

What's even more astounding is this – compared to Deep Blue and friends, the highest rating iPhone chess app, HIARCS, which has won tournaments against Grandmaster human opponents and boasts of being the world's best hand-held chess program, has played at 2900 and higher ... and costs only $9.99!

So in just 15 years we have gone from Deep Blue – an incredible arrangement of special purpose hardware and software inside an IBM RS/6000 SP2, 256 processors working in tandem, capable of examining 200 million moves per second and looking 12 positions deep – to a $9.99 iPhone app. Now, that's what I call progress.

Birthday twins

You may still be stunned by the paradox back on January 23 that a room of as few as 23 randomly selected people has a better than 50% chance of containing a shared birthday. We've also discussed that in a room of 187 people there's a better than even chance of 4 people sharing a birthday.

Well, if you want it to be all about you, and why not, you'll need 253 people, apart from yourself, in a room for there to be a better than even chance that someone has the same birthday as you.

253

*The **253rd** day of the year is September 10*

SMS? OMG!

Remember the good old fashioned text message (the sort we used to send in the Olden Days before WhatsApp and iMessage and all those things)? Their maximum size was 160 characters, which took 140 bytes, because there are only 7 bits per character in the text messaging system and 8 bits in a byte.

Consider an old 10c text message – and they often cost more than that. There are 1,048,576 bytes in a megabyte, so that's: 1,048,576 ÷ 140 = 7490 text messages to transmit 1 megabyte.

At 10c each, that's $749.00 *per megabyte*.

To put that into perspective, as space scientist of the University of Leicester Dr Nigel Bannister noted, that's anywhere up to 42 times more expensive than estimates for Hubble Space Telescope transmission costs.

Yeah, that's interesting but, OMG Adam, what about IRL? Well kids, at that rate, it'd cost you about $2247 to send a modest-sized (3 MB) selfie to your M8!

254

The 254th day of the year is September 11

Fat pizza

The maximum number of pieces that you can slice a pizza into (with standard straight cuts that don't slice the pizza parallel to the table or anything else weird) is closely related to the triangular numbers (see November 22 for a diagram).

254 is the maximum number of pieces a pizza could be cut into with how many straight lines?

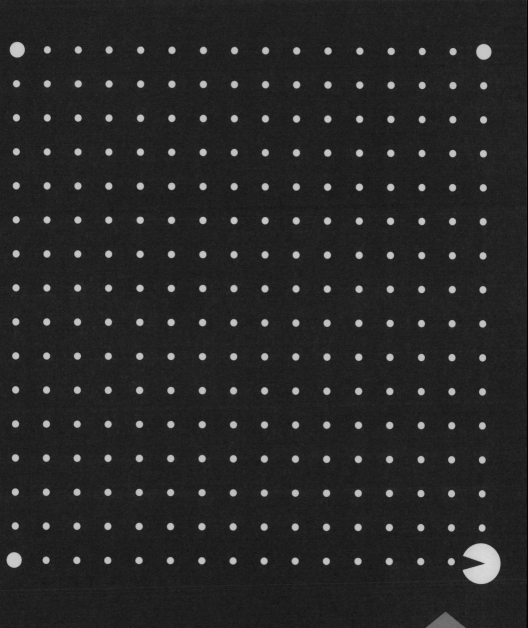

Pac-Man

Pac-Man was designed to continue indefinitely. A bug, however, prevents this from happening. When you've munched your way to level 255, the game freaks out. This is in part because Pac-Man stores your current level in a single byte (8 bits) and cannot 'count' to level 256. Instead of drawing 7 cute little bits of fruit in the bottom right of the screen for you to try and catch in the next level, Pac-Man draws 256 fruit and the chaos above ensues.

It becomes impossible to eat all the dots and move beyond this level which is known by Pac-Man enthusiasts as the 'kill screen'.

If you score every possible point up to this stage without losing a life, you acheive a 'perfect' Pac-Man score of 3,333,360 points. To find out more, watch the awesome arcade doco *King of Kong*.

255

*The **255th** day of the year is September 12*

Crypto might ...

Finally, a word on the delicate subject of money. At least something that resembles money, but is slightly different. Sort of. In 2009, our economy changed forever with the birth of the 'first decentralised digital currency' – the Bitcoin.

The traditional currencies of the world are issued by government authorities, with impressive names like 'central banks' and 'federal reserves'. Bitcoins are fundamentally different. They are disconnected from national agencies and instead are produced and monitored by a network of computers belonging to the people who own and use Bitcoins. This sounds a bit weird, but in some ways it's like the networks that allow torrent file sharing.

Generally speaking, national banks can produce more money or remove money from circulation if and when their economy needs it. Bitcoins are created quite differently. To make new Bitcoins, computers in the network have to perform massive number-crunching tasks. This is what's called 'Bitcoin mining'. Over time, the tasks become more demanding, thus making it harder to mine Bitcoins. In fact, the total number of Bitcoins that can ever be mined is limited to around 21 million. This makes it impossible for any bank or digital payer to devalue the currency by suddenly issuing lots more.

You buy Bitcoins, or little bits of Bitcoins called 'satoshis', with traditional dollars or pounds or yen or whatever. The amount you'll pay for a Bitcoin goes up and down depending on demand for Bitcoins at that moment in time, just like the daily exchange

256

The 256th day of the year is September 13

How to be perfect

We've spoken about perfect numbers before (January 6 and 28). Well, it turns out apart from the first perfect number 6, all perfect numbers are the sum of the first 2^n odd cubes for some n.

So $28 = 1^3 + 3^3$ is the sum of the first 2 odd cubes and $496 = 1^3 + 3^3 + 5^3 + 7^3$ (the first 4).

Well, the sum of the cubes of the first 256 odd cubes is a perfect number.

$$\sum_{k=1}^{256} (2k-1)^3 = 1^3 + 3^3 + \ldots + 511^3 = 8{,}589{,}869{,}056$$

the sixth perfect number.

rates between say US dollars and Philippine pesos changes. In the early days of Bitcoin their value fluctuated wildly.

Being part of a computer network, every time a Bitcoin is traded, the transaction is logged and the entire network is informed – so an individual computer crashing or losing its data does not bring the system down.

Because Bitcoins exist independently of central banks, trading in them avoids traditional bank charges and fees. It also means you can hide your money trail making these 'crypto currencies' attractive to 'dubious characters' who might wish to launder money.

Bitcoin is a radical development in the world of finance. But its overall geekiness, as well as it being such a novel concept, means it still plays a relatively small part in the world economy.

At least for now ...

Mersenn-ot

Mersenne thought $2^{257} - 1$ was a Mersenne prime; it later turned out to be composite. But you could forgive him for not knowing that $2^{257} - 1$ factorises into $53500613881435 9 \times 1155685395246619182673033 \times 3745505985018109365817 76630096313181393$ back in 1644, couldn't you?

257

The 257th day of the year is September 14

LONDON *by* numbers

1916
The year Harrods stopped selling cocaine and heroin over the counter.

1
The number of colours of London buses (red). Pre-1907, different routes had buses of different colours.

2
The number of London Tube stations – South Ealing and Mansion House – whose names contain all 5 vowels.

335 Hz
The frequency of the chime of the nominal note of Big Ben, the 13½ tonne, 2.3 m tall giant bell in the clock tower of the Palace of Westminster.

258
*The **258th** day of the year is **September 15***

Repeating primes

You can think of today as day 258 of the year or in Australia we'd write it as 15/9. Can you write 258 as the sum of 4 consecutive primes and 159 as the sum of 3 consecutive primes? Hint: One prime occurs in both sums.

26

The number of goldsmiths sworn in to weigh coins from the Royal Mint at an event called 'The trial of the Pyx', overseen by a dude known as the Queen's Remembrancer.

320

The number of basic routes a London cabbie must know to pass the famously gruelling test called 'the Knowledge', which covers 25,000 streets and 20,000 landmarks.

43 AD

The year in which the settlement (now known as London) was founded by the Romans.

1

The number of rifle ranges in the Palace of Westminster. There are also 8 bars, 6 restaurants, 1000 rooms, 100 staircases, 11 courtyards and a hair salon. Bizarrely, in 2008, the *Daily Mail* reported that it is still illegal to die in the Palace of Westminster. They did not mention the punishment!

Millionmillion

When you're a kid 'a million million' is about as big as it gets. My younger daughter Olivia certainly thinks it is impressively large. Well, 'a million million minus one' is almost as large. Convince yourself that 259 is a factor of 'a million million minus one'.

Now compared to 'a million million minus one' the amount 'a million minus one' seems almost small fry. But convince yourself using some good old long division that 259 also divides this amount.

259

The 259th day of the year is September 16

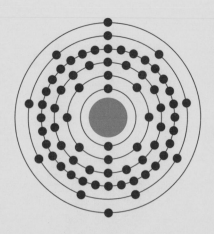

Lutetium

Lutetium was discovered by the French chemist, sculptor and painter, Georges Urbain, in 1907 while working at the Sorbonne University in Paris. The Austrian mineralogist Baron Carl Auer von Welsbach and American chemist Charles James also discovered it around the same time, but after a bit of to-ing and fro-ing it was agreed that Urbain had got in first. Its name derives from *Lutetia*, the Roman name for Paris.

Lutetium is the final and heaviest of those so-called 'rare Earth' elements.

260

The 260th day of the year is September 17

On this day in 1826 Mathematician Bernhard Riemann was born

Magic squares

260 is the constant for each row, column and diagonal of an 8 × 8 magic square. We calculate this by first adding $1 + 2 + 3 + ... + 64$, which is the same as $(1 + 64) + (2 + 63) + (3 + 62) + ... + (32 + 33)$ which is clearly 32 lots of 65. So all the 64 squares add up to 2080. If each of the 8 rows must add to the same, they must each add to $2080/8 = 260$.

52	61	4	13	20	29	36	45
14	3	62	51	46	35	30	19
53	60	5	12	21	28	37	44
11	6	59	54	43	38	27	22
55	58	7	10	23	26	39	42
9	8	57	56	41	40	25	24
50	63	2	15	18	31	34	47
16	1	64	49	48	33	32	17

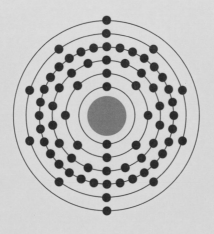

Hafnium

Hafnium loves sucking in neutrons, it doesn't corrode easily and has a very high melting point. As a result, hafnium and its alloys are used in nuclear reactors and submarines as 'control rods'. But if you're thinking about splashing out on some as gifts, the set of 50 or so you need for a decent sized nuke furnace will set you back over $1 million.

Some substances containing hafnium are extremely heat resistant so it's sometimes found in rocket engines and high temperature furnaces. Also, hafnium is used in flash bulbs ... remember them, kids? No ... okay ... go ask your folks.

Get some tesseraction

There are 11 ways you can 'unfold' a cube into shapes like these, which can in turn be folded back up into a cube. If you can picture a tesseract – that is, a cube in 4 dimensions (don't worry, I can't really either) – there are 261 possible ways of unfolding it into 8 cubes. Ow!

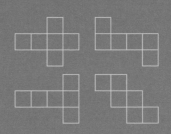

261

The 261st day of the year is September 18

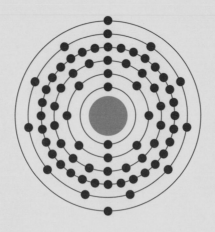

Tantalum

Tantalum is named after the Greek mythological figure Tantalus, the King of Sisyphus and father of Niobe (you'll remember him from the story on niobium). As a punishment for a dinner party faux pas (look it up, it's a cracker) Tantalus was sentenced to eternal torture with water and food just beyond his reach.

In 1802 the deaf Swedish chemist Anders Ekeberg named the hard, blue-grey metal 'tantalum' partly because of its refusal to become saturated even when dipped in acid.

262

The 262nd day of the year is September 19

Meandric numbers

If you had 6 bridges over a straight-line river, there are 8 different ways you could 'meander' over all 6 bridges, ending where you started without crossing over your path. For example ...

With 10 bridges, it is 262 'meanders' making 262 a 'meandric number'.

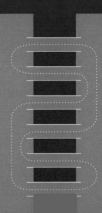

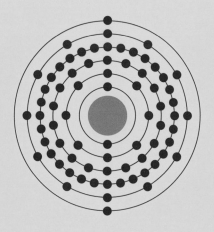

Tungsten W

The hard, rare metal known as tungsten comes in at number 74 on this parade of particles. Its name derives from the Swedish *tung sten*, which literally means 'heavy stone'. Tungsten's melting point of around 3400°C and boiling point of a whopping 5600°C are the highest of any known element. Some readers will remember that tungsten was widely used in light bulb filaments – before LED, halogen and other fancy-pants energy-saving bulbs came on the market.

Prime candidate

263 is a prime number, but it's also an example of lots of different types of prime numbers. In fact, 263 is an irregular prime, an Eisenstein prime, a long prime, a Chen prime, a Gaussian prime, a happy prime, a sexy prime, a safe prime, a balanced prime, a Ramunajan prime and a Higgs prime!

In case you're wondering how a prime can be sexy and safe at the same time, best you look up the various definitions.

263

*The **263rd** day of the year is September 20*

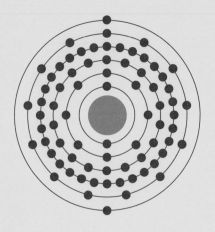

Rhenium

Rhenium is the only element named after a river. The Latin word *Rhenus* is the name of the Rhine, that great European river which starts in the Swiss Alps, winds its way through Germany and ends up in the Netherlands, finally flowing into the North Sea.

While you have probably never heard of rhenium, there's every chance you've got some around your house. Most likely it's in the filament of a lamp or an oven light. Because of its super-high melting point, it's also commonly used in jet, military and rocket engine construction.

264

The 264th day of the year is September 21

Two hundred and sixty-four

can be written as the sum of all the 2-digit numbers you can make from 2, 6 and 4; it can also be written as the sum of 10 consecutive primes.

Can you find these 2 ways of writing 264?

And if you're ever looking for another couple of cool ways to write 264, what about:

$264 = 77 + 88 + 99$ and
$264 = 33 = 55 + 77 + 99.$

Not bad, hey?

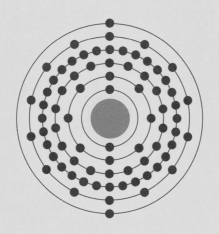

Osmium

Osmium stinks – literally. When an atom of osmium meets 4 atoms of oxygen, it creates osmium tetroxide, the odour of which is described as 'irritating and pungent'. Osmium gets its name from *osme*, the Greek word for 'smell'.

Not only that, when OsO_4 comes in contact with the oils that are present on a human finger, 2 oxygen molecules drop off and give us OsO_2 which leaves a black deposit. This is why old stinkypants osmium tetroxide was once used by forensic scientists to find human fingerprints.

Home on de-range

Back on February 13, I explained that the numbers 1, 2, 3, 4, 5 can be arranged in 44 ways such that no number is in its correct spot. These are called the 44 'derangements' of 5 objects and sometimes we write !5 = 44 calling it subfactorial 5.

Hello! My name is ____

If 6 people go to a meeting and decide 'let's fool everyone by swapping our name tags and all wearing a wrong name', they can do this !6 = 265 different ways. Pranksters!

265

The 265th day of the year is September 22

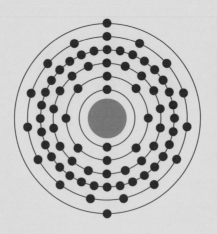

Iridium

Today we use extremely precise and high-tech science to define a metre. In ye olden days before we used things like a line in the atomic spectrum of krypton or the distance light travels in a vacuum, the standard measurement of a metre was given by the distance between 2 marks on a bar of 90% platinum, 10% iridium taken at the melting temperature of ice. Iridium was used because it's the most corrosion resistant of all known metals.

Iridium pairs up with osmium to form (not surprisingly) osmiridium, which, while it sounds like an Australian hippy lifestyle retreat, is actually to be found in the nibs of fountain pens and compass bearings.

266

The 266th day of the year is September 23

Drop the base

We count in a system known as 'base 10' which means the number 7563 really represents 3 ones plus 6 tens plus 5 ten times tens (hundreds) plus 7 ten times ten times tens (thousands). If we counted in base 11, we would think of 266 as $2 \times 11 \times 11 + 2 \times 11 + 2$ so we say that 266 is 222 base 11.

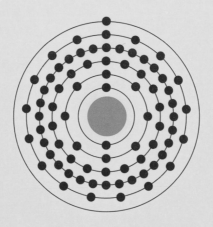

Platinum

The title 'platinum' is all the rage these days and is used to denote massive sales of CD or DVD sales, premium credit cards and top-shelf airline frequent flyer status. The actual element however was found in an ancient Egyptian burial casket from the 7th century BC which was unearthed at Thebes and made in honour of Queen Shapenapit. I've got no idea how good a queen old Shapenapit was, you'll have to ask an Egyptologist.

While Latin and Greek dominate the origins of the names of elements, platinum comes from the Spanish word *platina* meaning 'little silver'.

Googolly!

In 1920, 9-year-old Milton Sirotta coined the term 'googol' for the number written as 1 followed by 100 zeros. If you start counting at a googol, the first prime number you'll encounter is:

100000000000000000000000000000000000000000000000000000000000000000000000000000000000000000000000000000267.

267

The 267th day of the year is September 24

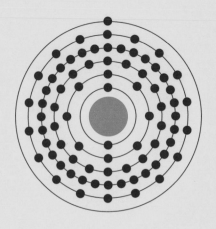

Gold Au

The biggest gold nugget ever found, The Welcome Stranger, weighed 109 kg and was so large it had to be broken into 3 pieces just to get it onto the scales. It was found a mere 3 cm below the surface in the town of Moliagul in Victoria, Australia, in 1869. Since then, all the gold we've found, extracted and gawked at has been surprisingly small. While estimates vary, the total amount would most probably fit into a cube with sides a mere 20 m.

Mount Erebus in Antarctica has been active since at least 1972 and spits out, among many other chemicals, gold dust!

268

The 268th day of the year is September 25

Go on, you can do it

Show that 268 is a number whose product of its digits is 6 times the sum of its digits. Once you've done that you can either go back and check for every number from 1 to 267 to see if it happens to them, or just take my word for it that 268 is the smallest such number.

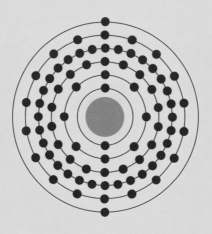

Mercury Hg

The chemical symbol for mercury is Hg, which comes from the Latin *hydrargyrum*, meaning 'liquid silver'. This refers to the fact that mercury (along with bromine) is one of only 2 elements that are liquid at room temperature.

Workers making felt hats years ago used to dip animal fur into mercury nitrate. This exposure often gave them various maladies including shaking and erratic behaviour otherwise known as 'hatter's shakes'. It's from such unfortunate conditions that we get the phrase 'mad as a hatter'.

4567891011121314151617181920212223242526272829303132333435363738394041424344454647484950515253
5556575859606162636465666768697071727374757677787980818283848586878889909192939495969798991001

All in the presentation

In Australian date notation, 26 September or 26/9 is the 269th day of the year. This is the only day of the year which presents itself in this way.

Fanged together

269 is the 'fang' of 2 different vampire numbers. If I told you the other fangs involved the numbers 1, 2, 4, 5, 8 and 8 can you work out the 2 vampire numbers and the 2 fangs that each partner with 269? Note, this is by no means a 'pleasant' question!

269

The 269th day of the year is September 26

On this day in 1905 Albert Einstein first published his paper on special relativity

Six new articles are produced on Wikipedia every second.

And $1/7$ of all time spent online is spent on Facebook.

270

The 270th day of the year is September 27

Harmonic mean

The harmonic mean of a set of numbers $x_1, x_2, x_3 \ldots x_n$ is given by the horrendous formula:

$$H = \frac{n}{\frac{1}{x_1} + \frac{1}{x_2} + \frac{1}{x_3} + \frac{1}{x_4} \cdots + \frac{1}{x_n}}$$

The factors of 6 are 1, 2, 3 and 6 and so the harmonic mean of the factors of 6 is $4/(1/1 + 1/2 + 1/3 + 1/6) = 4/2 = 2$.

It is rare for the harmonic mean of the factors of a whole number to itself be a whole number.

Well, it's hard to prove, but when you take the harmonic mean of the 16 factors of 270, you get H = 6.

Go on, I dare you.

Kids these days ...

In the first half of 2015, a funny little mathematical meme swept across the internet, televisions and newspapers of the world.

According to the posts, Asian schoolchildren of very young ages were answering incredibly hard maths questions in their school exams. The sites then challenged their poor, stupid western readers to try and complete them, stoking fires of cultural cringe and mathematical inferiority. I don't really care whether these questions were actually answered by Japanese children who were only 6 seconds old, but they are fun to try yourselves. Here's a sample of 3 and a much older classic.

You'll find the answers to all of them at the back of the book. But hey, you're smarter than an average 9-year-old Beijing schoolkid who kinda likes maths ... yeah?

Oh my, that's long

271 is prime and also the sum of 11 consecutive primes. Can you find the 11 consecutive primes that add to give 271?

271

The 271st day of the year is September 28

On this day in 1928 Biologist Alexander Fleming discovered penicillin

Allegedly set for 8-year-old Vietnamese kids in the high-lands town of Bao Loc

You need to fill in the gaps with the digits from 1 to 9 so that the equation makes sense, following the order of operations – multiply first, then division, addition and subtraction last.

		−			66
+		×		−	=
13		12		11	10
×		+		+	−
÷		+	×		÷

272

The 272nd day of the year is September 29

Pronic numbers

272 is a 'pronic' or 'hetero-mecic' number. This is a number that is the product of 2 consecutive integers, for example, 6 = 2 × 3 and 42 = 6 × 7 are both pronic.

Is 272 pronic? Of course it is ... convince yourself of this.

Pronic numbers are also called 'rectangular' numbers because when you draw a diagram they are very close but not quite square.

On this day in 1901
Physicist Enrico Fermi was born

Singaporean Year 5 students, (later upgraded to 14 year olds in an Olympiad test)

Albert and Bernard have just become friends with Cheryl and they want to know when her birthday is. Cheryl gives them a list of 10 possible dates:

May 15, May 16, May 19
June 17, June 18
July 14, July 16
August 14, August 15, August 17

Cheryl then tells Albert the month she is born and Bernard the numerical day she is born.

Albert says, 'I don't know when Cheryl's birthday is, but I know that Bernard doesn't know, either.'

Bernard replies, 'At first, I didn't know when Cheryl's birthday was, but I do know now.'

So Albert says, 'Well, now I also know when Cheryl's birthday is.'

So when is Cheryl's birthday?

Absolute zero

The temperature of just over 273°C below zero (absolute zero is specifically −273.15°C or −459.67°F) is so cold that it is considered impossible to actually reach because at this point atoms would, in theory, stop moving.

So when Australian Professor Andrea Morello cools a liquid mixture of 2 types of helium in his dilution fridge to just 0.007 degrees above absolute zero – a temperature significantly colder than the background temperature of the Universe – *that's* cool.

273

*The **273rd** day of the year is **September 30***

On this day in 1882 Physicist Hans Geiger was born

Hong Kong elementary school where first graders suppos-edly had 20 seconds to answer this one!

What parking spot number is the car parked in?
Don't forget – you have 20 seconds. Your time starts ... now!

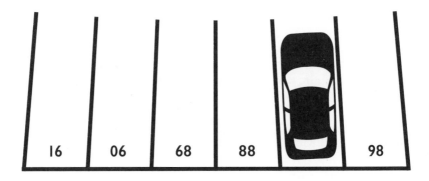

16   06   68   88   98

274

*The **274th** day of the
year is October 1*

Tribonacci

274 is a 'tribonacci' number.
The tribonacci numbers are
like the Fibonacci numbers,
but instead of starting with
2 predetermined terms,
the sequence starts with 3
predetermined terms and
each term afterwards is the
sum of the preceding 3 terms.

The first few tribonacci
numbers are 0, 0, 1, 1, 2, 4, 7 ...
The 7 for example comes from
1 + 2 + 4 = 7.

Calculate the tribonacci
numbers up to 274.

The Nine Schoolgirls Problem

Not all of these sorts of puzzles have come about just in the first half of 2015. Push your grey matter to try and solve this version of an 1850 classic called 'The Nine Schoolgirls Problem'.

Nine girls in a school walk out in groups of 3 for 4 days in a row. You, the teacher, must arrange the girls in walking groups so that no pair of girls ever walks in the same row (group of 3) more than once.

Answers at the back of the book, of course.

Partial partitions

The number 10 can be partitioned 42 different ways. Of these, some like 10 = 2 + 2 + 2 + 2 + 2 and 10 = 2 + 2 + 3 + 3 are partitions in which no part occurs only once, as opposed to 10 = 4 + 3 + 3 which has only one 4. There are 275 partitions of 28 in which no part occurs only once.

FANCI pants

$275 \times 719 = 197{,}725$ and $275/374 = 25/34$ thus making 275 a 'fang and anomalous numerator cancelling integer' or a 'FANCI' number. This is a term I just made up which will probably never catch on. By the way, there are 3 other 3-digit anomalous cancellations featuring 275. Can you find them?

275

*The **275th** day of the year is October 2*

In 2011, a polar
bear swam for
9 days and 687
kilometres

in search of sea ice around
the Beaufort Sea, North Alaska.

276

*The **276th** day of the
year is **October 3***

No turning back

If we let S(n) = the sum of the
proper divisors of n (so S(8) = 1
+ 2 + 4 = 7) and keep applying S
to the sums you get, eventually
you descend to 1, or get back to
a number you already had.

Some numbers (the perfect
numbers) start to cycle
immediately, for example,
S(6) = 6. The most common

cycles reached are of length
2 (the amicable or betrothed
numbers), for example, S(220) =
284 and S(284) = 220. We have
also found cycles of length 4 or
more, but every number will hit
a loop ... almost.

It seems 276 is a maverick
and just doesn't end in a cycle,
the first such number we
encounter.

Time ... to get yer geek on

I knew my kids truly saw me as a maths nerd a couple of Christmases ago when they gave me this clock as a present:

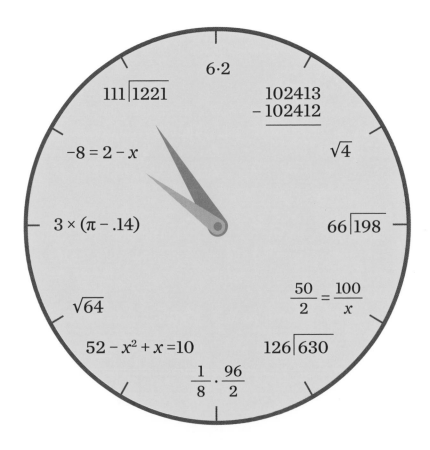

Be yourself

277 is the largest prime 'self' number we will encounter this year. A 'self' number is an integer which cannot be generated by any other integer added to the sum of that other integer's digits.

For example, 21 is *not* a self number, since it can be generated by the sum of 15 and the digits comprising 15,

that is, 21 = 15 + 1 + 5. No such sum will generate the integer 20, hence it is a self number. The next prime self number is 367, too large to be the number of a day of the year.

277

*The **277th** day of the year is October 4*

On this day in 1957 Sputnik 1 was launched into orbit

If you want to fly your geek flag above the kitchen door, it's available online, just search 'pop quiz clock'. Or at very least make your way around the clockface and convince yourself that the expressions match up to 1, 2, 3, ... 12.

But that's not the only nerdy clock going around – no way, José.

The clock opposite is labelled 'Easy as 1-2-3' because each of the points 1 to 12 on the dial are expressed mathematically using exactly one each of the digits 1, 2 and 3.

For example:

$12/3 = 4$ and $\sqrt{(1 + 2 + 3!)} = \sqrt{(1 + 2 + 3 \times 2 \times 1)} = \sqrt{9} = 3$

You might not be familiar with the bracket-like notations to either side of the $\sqrt{3}$ at 10 o'clock or the $\sqrt{123}$ at 11 o'clock.

At 10 o'clock, we see notation sometimes called the 'floor'; $\lfloor x \rfloor$ (pronounced 'floor x') which means the largest whole number less than or equal to x.

So $\lfloor 7.56 \rfloor = 7$.

Similarly, the notation at 11 o'clock is referred to as 'ceiling' and $\lceil x \rceil$, ceiling (x), means the smallest integer greater than or equal to.

So $\lceil 7.56 \rceil = 8$.

Given all that can you confirm that the clock face is accurate?

278

The 278th day of the year is October 5

278 =

$2 \times 2 \times 2 \times 2 \times 2 \times 2 \times 2 \times 2 + 22$

Convince yourself that 277^2 and 278^2 contain the digits 2, 7, 7 and 2, 7, 8 respectively.

On this day in 1958
Astrophysicist
Neil deGrasse Tyson was born

The clock face shows the following positions (clockwise from 12):

$1 \times 2 \times 3!$

1^{2^3}

$1-2+3$

$\sqrt{1+2+3!}$

$12\!\!\diagup\!\!3$

$1 \times 2 + 3$

$1 \times 2 \times 3$

$1 + 2 \times 3$

1×2^3

$1 + 2^3$

$12 - \lceil \sqrt{3} \rceil$

$\lfloor \sqrt{123} \rfloor$

Waring thin

I accept that it's unlikely that you're ever going to take a random whole number and try to express it as the sum of eighth powers. If however you choose to, I for one am certainly only going to encourage you. In fact, as a helpful guide, I'd remind you of Waring's problem and the result that every positive integer is the sum of at most 279 eighth powers.

279

*The **279th** day of the year is October 6*

And how about this beauty!

It's a clock face composed entirely of three 9s for each hour mark.

As long as you know that .9 (the .9 with the bar over it like at 7 o'clock) means 0.9999... which equals 1, you should be fine.

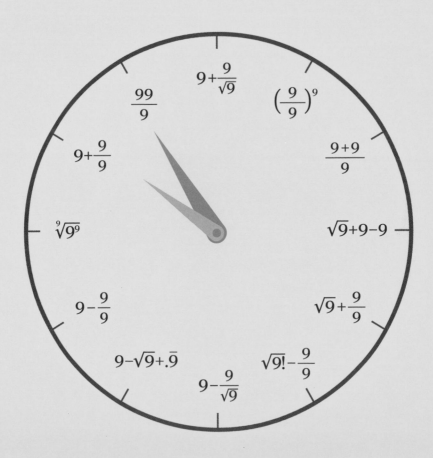

280

*The **280th** day of the year is October 7*

Harmonic numbers

The 'harmonic' numbers are defined by the sum:

$$H_n = \sum_{k=1}^{n} \frac{1}{k}$$

$H_1 = 1/1$, $H_2 = 1 + 1/2 = 3/2$,
$H_3 = 1 + 1/2 + 1/3 = 11/6$ ...

Convince yourself that the denominator of the eighth harmonic number, H_8 is 280.

But one of the heaviest clock faces I've seen sits in the office of a friend of mine who runs Mathletics worldwide. Not surprisingly, it's pretty hectic.

To understand this clock face, you need a fair bit of mathematical geekery.

Brace yourself ...

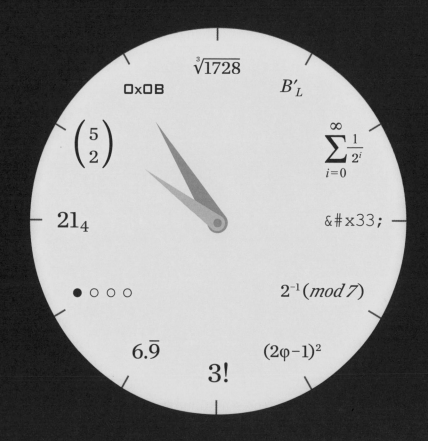

Party like it's prime

281 is prime and the sum of the first 14 prime numbers, that is $281 = 2 + 3 + 5 + 7 + 11 + 13 + 17 + 19 + 23 + 29 + 31 + 37 + 41 + 43$.

If the sum of the first k primes being a prime number has excited you, this is the sixth, and last, such day of the year so let's party.

281

*The **281st** day of the year is October 8*

Now, on the off chance you didn't immediately get all of these, here's the crib sheet for you.

1. B'_L. One of the toughest numbers on the dial, Legendre's constant gives us a description as to how spread out the prime numbers are once we get to very big numbers.

2. This statement is the same as $2 = 1/1 + 1/2 + 1/4 + 1/8 + 1/16 +$ ... which you can see by halving 2 into 1 and 1, then halving one of its halves into $1/2$ and $1/2$ and then halving one of the halves into $1/4$ and $1/4$ and going on forever!

3. 3 is the HTML character code for 3.

4. When counting in mod 7 when you get to 6 the next number is 0 and you start again. So in mod 7, the number 23 is just 2 because you've gotten to 0 three times in counting to 21 then you have 2 left over. 2^{-1} (mod 7) is the number, between 0 and 6, which when multiplied by 2 gives a number that equals 1 in mod 7. Clearly 4 works because $2 \times 4 = 8$, which is 1 in mod 7.

5. Here φ is the golden ratio, or $(1 + \sqrt{5})/2$. Check that $(2\varphi - 1)^2 = 5$.

6. $3! = 3 \times 2 \times 1 = 6$.

7. The bar over the 9 represents .9999... = 1 and 6.9999... = 7.

8. This is a representation of binary counting. In binary you only have 0s and 1s so the numbers 1, 2, 3, 4, 5, 6, 7, 8 become 1, 10, 11, 100, 101, 110, 111, 1000. So 8 = 1000 in binary and on the clockface ○ represents 0 and ● represents 1.

282

The 282nd day of the year is October 9

On this day in 1873
Physicist Karl Schwarzschild was born,
17 years before Clément Ader made the
first powered flight

Plane partitions

There are 282 plane partitions of 9 objects. (A plane partition is a 2-dimensional array of integers $n_{i,j}$ that are non-increasing both from left to right and top to bottom and that add up to a given number n.) That reads much harder than the idea; here is an image of a plane partition of 22 which, as they say, is worth a thousand words:

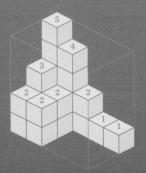

9. We count in base 10 so when we say 37 we really mean 3 × 10 + 7. If we are counting in base 4, the number 21 represents 2 × 4 + 1 = 9 in our more commonly used base 10.

10. This notation refers to how many ways can you pick 2 numbered balls out of a set of 5. There are 10 ways to pick a pair out of {1, 2, 3, 4, 5}. Maybe you'd like to write out all 10 pairs? Maybe not ;-)

11. This time we are in base 16; because 16 > 10 after we get to 9 we have to use other single figure notation so we use letters. So to count to 16 in base 16 you go 1, 2, 3, 4, 5, 6, 7, 8, 9, A, B, C, D, E, F after which you go 10, 11, 12, and so on. So in base 16, 0B = 11. The 0x tells us we are using hexadecimal when using computer code.

12. 12 × 12 × 12 = 1728 so the cube root of 1728 is 12.

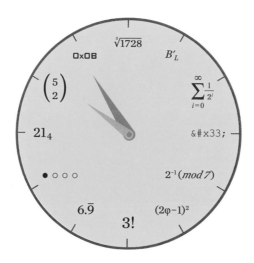

Ten numbers that make mathletes quiver ... but you've probably never heard of

First up, I need to stress these are not the universally agreed '10 most exciting' lesser known numbers. Get 10 mathematicians together for a dinner party (wouldn't that go off!) and you'll get 10 different arguments for what should be on that list, but these numbers are exceptional ... trust me.

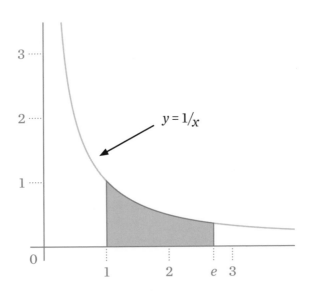

284

*The **284th** day of the year is October 11*

Never enough friends

284 is an amicable (or friendly) number paired with 220. The divisors of 220 add up to 284 and the proper divisors of 284 add up to 220. Amicable numbers were known to the Pythagoreans, who credited them with many mystical properties. A general formula by which some of these numbers could be derived was invented circa 850 by Thābit ibn Qurra (circa 830–901).

e = 2.718281828459 …

Check out the graph on the opposite page. The number *e* is the point on the number line where the area between the *x*-axis, the hyperbola $y = 1/x$, and the vertical lines $x = 1$ and $x = e$ is 1.

We've all heard of π, the ratio of the distance around a circle (circumference) to the distance across (diameter). Apart from π, *e* is the next most important number in all mathematics. If you remember *e* from high school, well done. For most people, it's a distant memory at best.

e is what's known as an 'irrational' number and the first few terms of its infinite decimal expansion are *e* = 2.718281828459...

For such a simple, innocent, even perhaps random-looking number, *e* occurs in myriad places in mathematics, especially in calculus. *e* you rock!

Some cool ways of calculating *e* include:

$$e = \sum_{n=0}^{\infty} 1/n! = 1 + 1 + 1/2 + 1/6 + 1/24 + 1/120 + \dots$$

and also $e = \lim_{n \to \infty} (1 + 1/n)^n$

So the series $(1 + 1/1)^1$, $(1 + 1/2)^2$, $(1 + 1/3)^3$ … gets closer and closer to *e*. Grab a calculator with a bit of grunt and check this for $(1 + 1/10,000)^{10,000}$ and so on.

Two eighty-five

is a square pyramidal number (like a stack of cannonballs, or oranges with the base in a square). A 9-layered square pyramid of oranges would contain 285 oranges. This is the same as saying that $285 = 1^2 + 2^2 + 3^2 + \dots + 8^2 + 9^2$, the sum of the first 9 squares.

285

*The **285th** day of the year is October 12*

1.644934066848226...

Sure, it looks like any other old stretch of numbers, but to the eye of a mathematician, it's special. 1.644934... is equal to $\pi^2/6$. So what, I hear you ask? Well, in 1735 a brilliant young mathematician by the name of Leonhard Euler shot to fame by proving that:

$$\pi^2/6 = \sum_{n=1}^{\infty} 1/n^2 = 1/1^2 + 1/2^2 + 1/3^2 + \ldots$$

In doing so, he solved what had been known as the Basel problem.

This infinite sum converges slowly. What we mean by this is that if you add up the first 10 terms of the sum, $1/1^2 + 1/2^2 + 1/3^2 + \ldots + 1/10^2$, you'll find you're still a long way from $\pi^2/6$. You have to take a lot of terms to get reasonably close.

1.618033989 – The Golden Ratio

$\varphi = (1+\sqrt{5})/2 = 1.618033989\ldots$

We say 2 numbers are in 'golden ration' if their ratio is the same as the ratio of their sum to the larger of the 2 quantities. Huh?

Well, if 2 numbers a and b are in golden ratio and $a > b$, it means that:

$(a + b)/a = a/b$ and in this case the ratio will equal φ (which is prounced 'phi', and is the 21st letter of the Greek alphabet).

286

The 286th day of the year is October 13

anoma/ly

286 is a bit special because it can be involved in anomalous cancellations both as a numerator *and* denominator. So we need to find 3-digit numbers here, three Xs and one Y. 286/X gives an anomalous cancellation for each X and Y/286 gives us another one.

They're pretty tough to find so prepare yourself for some serious fist-pumping if you can track these bad boys down.

A beautiful way to see this is in a 'golden rectangle'. If a and b are in golden ratio, then when you place a golden rectangle of side lengths a and b next to a square with sides a, the new rectangle with sides $a + b$ and a is also golden!

We can keep building this up, rectangle upon rectangle, and join the corresponding corners of these rectangles to get the beautiful 'golden spiral'.

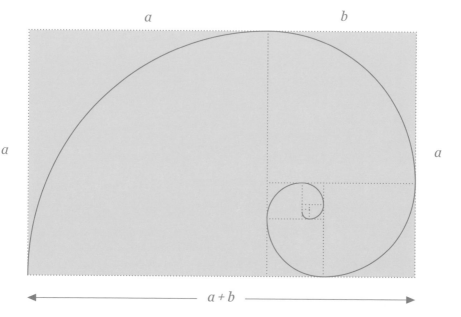

This curve keeps spiralling inwards forever. The small rectangle where the curve is about to enter can be thought of as a smaller scale copy of the larger original rectangle. Deep inside that smaller rectangle, lies another, smaller rectangle ... and so on.

Sometimes the golden ratio is overplayed with people claiming that every building in the ancient world, or the proportions of the human body, all conform to φ. This is certainly not the case but φ does appear in many places.

Remember the Fibonacci numbers? The ratio of consecutive Fibonacci numbers 1, 1, 2, 3, 5, 8, 13, 21, 34, 55 ... converges to φ. So the fractions:

$1/1 = 1$, $2/1 = 2$, $3/2 = 1.5$, $5/3 = 1.66...$, $8/5 = 1.6$, $13/8 = 1.675$, $21/13 = 1.615...$ and so on get ever closer to φ.

$\gamma = 0.5772156649$

Euler's constant, also known as the Euler-Mascheroni constant and written γ (the third letter of the Greek alphabet, pronounced 'gamma') is defined as the limit of the difference between the sum of the first n unit fractions and the natural log of n.

$$\gamma = \lim_{n \to \infty} \left(\sum_{k=1}^{n} 1/k - \ln(n) \right)$$

I'm the first to admit that unless you've done a reasonable amount of maths, this definition makes your stomach a little bit queasy.

But a simpler and more visual description of gamma is that it's the area between the hyperbola $y = 1/x$ and the steps formed by drawing rectangles of width 1 that cover the curve like this:

288

The 288th day of the year is October 15

Super gross

288 is the 'super-factorial' of 4. The 'super' here doesn't mean it's a factorial like some numbers we've already seen (for example 24) and just really good at being one.

No, a super-factorial is another thing altogether.

You should be able to work out that $1! \times 2! \times 3! \times 4! = 288$.

We can write this as $4\$ = 288$.

On another point, it is important that maths students learn not to say this number in public, as it is two gross. Get it, two gross – a gross is 12^2 or 144 ... and $2 \times 144 = 288$. Tough crowd.

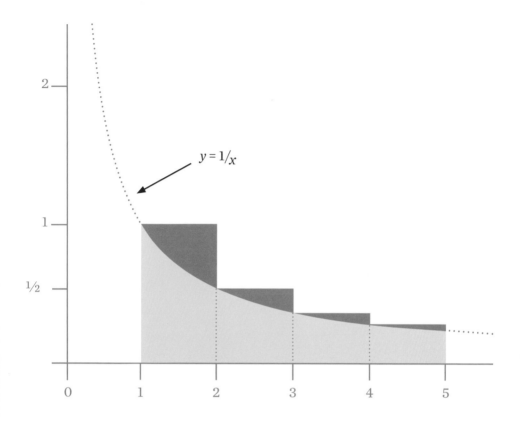

As this curve goes forever to the right, and the chunks of dark red get smaller and smaller, their total area adds up to γ.

It's approximately γ = 0.5772156649... and it pops up in all sorts of places in calculus. It's not known whether it's rational or irrational, that is whether we can write it as a fraction or if its decimal expansion just keeps going on forever without repeating, which is one of the main reasons it makes my list!

Friedman numbers

Using any of the basic operations, brackets and powers, if you can write a number using only its own digits, we call it a Friedman number. For example, $347 = 7^3 + 4$ is a Friedman number, as is $153 = 3 \times 51$ and $125 = 5^{(1+2)}$. Is 289 a Friedman number?

289

*The **289th** day of the year is October 16*

*808,017,424,794,512,875,886,459,904,961,710,757,005,
754,368,000,000,000 – The Monster group*

The size of |M|, the Monster group = 808,017,424,794,512,88
6,459,904,961,710,757,005,754,368,000,000,000.

The Monster group is one of the most amazing objects ever
discovered in mathematics. To understand it, we have to enter
the world of 'group theory'. Groups are things that arise when we
look at symmetry. Take a triangle, label its corners:

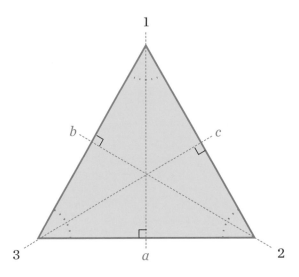

Notice that we can rotate the triangle clockwise 120°, 240° or
360° around its centre, or reflect it through its 'axes', *a, b* or *c*, and
we get the same shape. So these moves preserve the 'symmetry'
of the triangle.

290

*The **290th** day of the
year is October 17*

Two ninety

is a sphenic number, that
is, the product of 3 distinct
primes. It is also the sum of 4
consecutive primes. Can you
find how?

Do not touch!

290 is an 'untouchable'
number which, I remind
you, doesn't mean we think
it smells. It just means that
there is no other number for
which 290 is equal to the sum
of all its proper divisors.

Let's call these rotations R_{120}, R_{240} and R_{360}. But let's also rename R_{360} as 1 because a 360° rotation has the same effect as a not rotating at all, which is like 'multiplying' the triangle by 1. Also, let's name a reflection through the relevant dotted line just by the dotted line itself, that is *a*, *b* or *c*.

Play around with combinations of rotations and reflections and realise that doing any of these in order gives us symmetry; for example $R_{120} * a = b$.

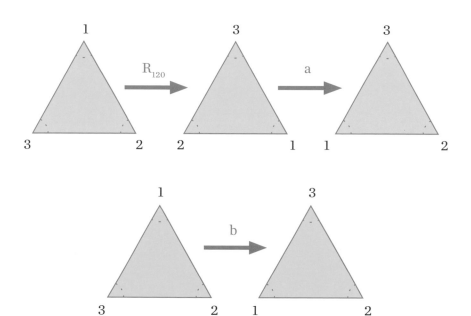

291

*The **291st** day of the year is October 18*

Trivial pursuit

Is 291 prime?

No it's not and we can tell almost instantly by using a lovely piece of mathematics.

It turns out that if the sum of the digits of a number is divisble by 3, then the original number was also divisible by 3.

So in the case of 291 we get 2 + 9 + 1 = 12 and 12 = 3 × 4. So 12 is divisible by 3 and therefore we know that 291 was divisble by 3.

A quick check gives us that 291 = 3 × 97.

The sets R = {1, R$_{120}$, and R$_{240}$} and S = {1, a} are called closed because if you do a combination of things in that set to the triangle you just get another thing in the set. For example, R$_{120}$ * R$_{240}$ * R$_{240}$ = R$_{240}$ and 1 * a * a * 1 * a = a. The full group of symmetries G = {1, R$_{120}$, R$_{240}$, a, b, c} can all be reached by doing one thing in R and one thing in S, so we can write G = RS.

R and S are called simple groups, sort of like factors of G. Different shapes have different symmetries. It's not hard to work out the corresponding set G if we had started with a square. For over a century mathematicians known as 'group theorists' have wanted to know all the types of symmetries that are out there and the further they looked the more complicated the shapes became. Eventually they found one absolute giant called, fittingly, the Monster. Its discovery is one of the great achievements of 20th century mathematics.

The group G, above, had 6 elements so we say it is of order 6. It was the symmetries of an equilateral triangle which lives in 2 dimensions.

The Monster contains 808,017,424,794,512,875,886,459,904, 961,710,757,005,754,368,000,000,000 symmetries and belongs to a mathematical structure in 196,883 dimensions!

292

The 292th day of the year is October 19

On this day in 1909
Physicist Marguerite Perey was born

Pieces of pi

If you simplify this fairly nasty continued fraction you get the excellent approximation for π of 103993/33102.

The involvement of a number as large as 292 means the previous approximation of 355/113 is extremely accurate for a fraction with a numerator and denominator less than 1000.

$$\pi \approx 3 + \cfrac{1}{7 + \cfrac{1}{15 + \cfrac{1}{1 + \cfrac{1}{292}}}}$$

i

No list of amazing numbers would be complete without *i* which mathematicians call the 'imaginary unit'. It has the awesome property that $i^2 = -1$.

For many people, finding out that some of their friends in school are studying a number that is 'the square root of minus 1!' is where high school maths truly becomes 'them' and 'us'.

A lovely way to think about *i* is this: pretend you're standing on the number line at 0, so a step forward takes you to 1, a step back takes you to –1. If you took 5 steps forward, then 3 back then another 8 forward, you would get to 10, and so on. If instead of stepping forward or back, you took a step to the left, you'd land on *i*.

Get it? Don't worry, that's a whole other book!

Onya, Soph!

293 is a Sophie Germain prime, that is, a prime number *p* such that $2p + 1$, in this case 587, is also prime. We think that there is an infinite number of these but as of yet we have not been able to prove it.

Sophie Germain used them in the early 1800s in her investigations of Fermat's Last Theorem and I'm sure she'd be stunned but excited to know that in the 21st century they are being used in public key cryptography and primality testing.

293

The 293th day of the year is October 20

$3^{3^{3^{3^{3 \cdot \cdot^{3}}}}}$ – *Graham's number*

Okay, prepare to hurt a bit, and you can blame it all on the little fellow ↑ called an 'up-arrow'. The up-arrow notation works this way:

$3 \uparrow 3 = 3^3$

$3 \uparrow \uparrow 3 = 3^{3^3} = 3^{27} = 7625597484987$

$3 \uparrow \uparrow \uparrow 3 = 3^{3^{3^{3 \cdot \cdot^{3}}}}$ (7625597484987 3s)

You might think you're seeing a pattern here and can get your head around $3\uparrow\uparrow\uparrow\uparrow3$. Don't get too excited yet.

Yes, $3\uparrow\uparrow\uparrow\uparrow3$ is another chain of 3s, but it's really hard to comprehend exactly how many 3s we're talking about. Bear with me because this is the last one we need to worry about.

$3\uparrow\uparrow\uparrow\uparrow3 = 3\uparrow\uparrow\uparrow (3\uparrow\uparrow\uparrow3)$

If you think about how massive the jump is from $3\uparrow\uparrow3$ to $3\uparrow\uparrow\uparrow3$ then you get some small insight into the size of the jump from $3\uparrow\uparrow\uparrow3$ to $3\uparrow\uparrow\uparrow\uparrow3$.

Wow. That hurts, yeah?

294

The 294th day of the year is October 21

Practical, as always

I'm sure you remember from April 22 – if you don't, I'll turn away for a second while you quickly go back and have a read – where was I ... oh that's right – I'm sure you remember the definition of a practical number. Well, 294 is also one.

On this day in 1833
Engineer/inventor Alfred Nobel was born

For Graham's number, think of that number we just really hurt calculating as $g_1 = 3\uparrow\uparrow\uparrow\uparrow3$

And think of g_2 as $3\uparrow\ ...\uparrow3$ with g_1 up-arrows

And g_3 as $3\uparrow\ ...\uparrow3$ with g_2 up-arrows

And on we go and on and on and on ...

Graham's number is ... g_{64}

I know, it hurts me to even type it!

Even g_1 is almost beyond imagination in its size. Massively beyond the number of fundamental particles in the Universe. And after we've worked out g_1, we've got another 63 iterations to go.

Graham's number came around as the upper bound (or highest possible value) of the answer to an actual problem in mathematics. For a long time its claim to fame was being the largest number that served any such practical purpose.

Despite it being beyond comprehension in its size, we do know that the last 12 digits of Graham's number are 262464195387. If this explanation has left you seeing spots before your eyes, don't be ashamed. It's pretty hectic.

Lychrel's second

295 is the second proposed Lychrel number. Recall from July 15 that a Lychrel number is a natural number that cannot form a palindrome by repeatedly reversing its digits and adding the resulting numbers. Well, like 196 before it, when we continue the process 295 + 592 = 887; 887 + 788 = 1675; 1675 + 5761 = 7436 and so on, we don't seem to get a palindrome. Unfortunately for 295, the number 196 came first so this game is called the 196-algorithm, much I'm sure to 295's chagrin.

Oh, and for you romantics out there: 'Lychrel' was coined by Wade VanLandingham and is a rough anagram of his girlfriend Cheryl's name.

295

The 295th day of the year is October 22

Avogadro's number

$6.0221415 \times 10^{23} = 602{,}214{,}150{,}000{,}000{,}000{,}000{,}000$

One for the chemists as much as the mathematicians, Avogadro's number is a crucial link between the mass of very small particles and larger things.

An atom of carbon in its most common form (carbon-12) contains 6 protons, 6 neutrons and 6 electrons. The protons and neutrons have roughly the same mass but the electrons have much, much less mass (only about $1/2000$th of the others). So the mass of 1 such carbon atom is about the same as that of 12 protons or 12 neutrons; another way to say this is that a proton and a neutron each have about $1/12$ of the carbon atom's mass.

But these masses are far too small to reliably measure, so instead we talk about 'atomic mass units'. It turns out that 12 grams of these carbon atoms has a mass of 6.0221415×10^{23} such units, which we call 1 mole.

6.0221415×10^{23} or $602{,}214{,}150{,}000{,}000{,}000{,}000{,}000$ is called Avogadro's number after the awesome Italian chemist of the same name.

296

The 296th day of the year is October 23

A distinct advantage

296 is the number of partitions of 30 with distinct parts. Now, even I'll admit that partitioning 30 in 296 different ways may be a bit tedious; perhaps you'd like to find the 10 ways 10 can be partitioned into distinct parts?

Happy mole day!

And for the chemists, today is 10/23 in the States so in honour of Avogadro's number, at about 6.02 (am or pm) you can sit down to a mole of molecules of your favourite compound. Happy mole day!

Fine-structure constant

$\alpha = 7.2973525698 \times 10^{-3} \approx 1/137$

One for the physicists, this fundamental physical constant sometimes called Sommerfield's constant, and denoted alpha, the first letter of the Greek alphabet, measures the strength of the electromagnetic interaction between elementary charged particles. This sounds a bit scary, but in essence, the 'fine-structure constant' is a measure of the strength with which atoms are held together.

If the fine-structure constant were slightly larger or smaller, many of the elements in the Universe would not be able to be produced and we probably wouldn't have life, or perhaps a Universe, at all. For example, some physicists have suggested that changing the fine-structure constant by just a couple of per cent could lead to a Universe full of carbon, *or* oxygen, but not both. That would make the whole 'life' thing reasonably challenging!

It should be noted that alpha doesn't exactly equal $1/137$, it's more like $1/137.0359992$ but it's very close and just the mention of $1/137$ is enough to send physicists' hearts all aflutter. Here's just one example, from Frank Close in his classic *The Infinity Puzzle: Quantum Field Theory and the Hunt for an Orderly Universe*:

'Alpha sets the scale of nature – the size of atoms and all things made of them, the intensity and colors of light, the strength of magnetism, and the metabolic rate of life itself. It controls everything that we see ... In 137, apparently, science had found Nature's PIN Code.'

Needs more Kaprekar

$297^2 = 88,209$ and $88 + 209 = 297$. This makes 297 a Kaprekar number. This is the only 3-digit Kaprekar number we'll see this year. Convince yourself that 703 and 999, the only other 3-digit Kaprekar numbers, also fit the criteria.

Also $297^3 = 26,198,073$ and $26 + 198 + 073 = 297$. Well, there you go!

297

The 297th day of the year is October 24

$\aleph_0$

Okay, now I'm going to freak you out. You might have eventually got your head around *i* being a number, but what is this thing?

It's actually the first letter of the Hebrew alphabet and it's called Aleph. But in mathematics we write $\aleph_0$, which we call aleph-null to describe the size of the infinity of counting numbers.

What do I mean by the size of the infinity of counting numbers? Surely that's just infinity? The important thing to understand is this: not all infinities are the same size. Some infinities are bigger than others! That's a pretty heavy concept the first time you hear it, but bear with me.

The set of counting numbers, {1, 2, 3, 4, ...} is clearly infinitely large. But you can write them in a logical order so that you know where any number will occur on the list: 'Where is 58?' you ask; 'Well, it's the 58th number on the list,' I reply.

Similarly, the set of even numbers {2, 4, 6, 8, ...} is countably infinite. 'Where is 58?' you ask; 'It's the 29th number on my list,' I reply. So even though there are numbers in the set {1, 2, 3, ...} that don't occur in the set {2, 4, 6, ...} these 2 sets are the same size. They are both countably infinite, or they have 'size' $\aleph_0$.

In fact, the set of all fractions, which we call the rational numbers, is also countably infinite. You can list the positive fractions using a table like the one over the page. List the fractions in the order that the yellow line goes through them ...

298

The 298th day of the year is October 25

Prime effort

298 = 2 × 149 so it is not prime, but semiprime. We mathematicians also call such a number biprime or a *pq* number. Look, I think you get the idea – it's not prime, but in this way it's closer than most.

Pick a palindrome

If you multiply 298 by (298 + 3) you get a palindromic number, 89,698.

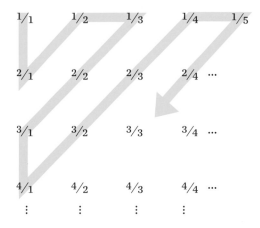

... and every fraction will appear. 'Where is $573/1296$?' you ask. 'It's in the 573rd row, 1296 columns along,' I reply, not getting at all bored because I love explaining countable and uncountable infinities.

This listing of the fractions was an observation of the genius mathematician Georg Cantor.

But when we get to the set of whole numbers, fractions and decimals that go on forever, like π, for example, things change. This set of numbers is called the 'real' numbers and it is *not* countably infinite.

We know this because if you try and produce a list of all the reals in a countable order I can always find a number that was not on your list.

Any way you slice it

If a cube-shaped cake was cut with 12 straight cuts, it can produce a maximum of 299 pieces. Good luck keeping the hordes of hungry 8 year olds back while you make that final cut. The last thing you want is to sever little Travis' finger in any dimension, but trust me, it is theoretically possible!

299

The 299th day of the year is October 26

Let's say you give me the following list of reals and claim it contains *every* real number:

0.023465757...
1.245364768...
1.594677786...
2.222222222...
3.123456789...

And so on ...

If I write a number that is different to the first digit of the first number and different to the second digit of the second number and different to the third digit of the third number, and so on, it can't be on your list because it is different to every number on the list by at least 1 digit.

0.023465757... change this 0 to a 1
1.**2**45364768... change this 2 to a 3
1.5**9**4677786... change this 9 to a 0
2.222**2**22222... change this 2 to a 3
3.123**4**56789... change this 4 to a 5 and so on down the list.

So choosing the number 1.3035... has to give me a new number that is not on your list.

300

*The **300th** day of the year is October 27*

Try, angles, try

300 is the 24th triangular number and hence the sum of the integers from 1 to 24.

On the topic of 300 as a sum, can you express 300 as the sum of a pair of twin primes? It is also the sum of 10 consecutive primes.

You can never write a countable list of the reals. The reals are not countably infinite. The size of this set is a larger infinity than $\aleph_0$.

Some mathematicians use $\aleph_1$ as the size of the infinity of real numbers.

In 2005, Paul Renteln and Alan Dundes gave the following humorous mathematical take on the '99 bottles of beer on the wall' drinking song: 'Aleph-null bottles of beer on the wall, Aleph-null bottles of beer, Take one down, and pass it around, There's still Aleph-null bottles of beer on the wall! Aleph-null bottles of beer on the wall, Aleph-null bottles of beer, Take one down, and pass it around, There's still Aleph-null bottles of beer on the wall! Aleph-null bottles of beer on the wall, Aleph-null bottles of beer, Take one down, and pass it around, There's still Aleph-null bottles of beer on the wall! Aleph-null bottles of beer on the wall, Aleph-null bottles of beer, Take one down, and pass it around, There's still Aleph-null bottles of beer on the wall! Aleph-null bottles of beer on the wall, Aleph-null bottles of beer, Take one down, and pass it around, There's still Aleph-null bottles of beer on the wall! Aleph-null bottles of beer on the wall, Aleph-null bottles of beer, Take one down, and pass it around, There's still Aleph-null bottles of beer on the wall! Aleph-null bottles of beer on the wall, Aleph-null bottles of beer, Take one down, and pass it around, There's still Aleph-null bottles of beer on the wall! Aleph-null bottles of beer on the wall, Aleph-null bottles of beer, Take one down, and pass it around, There's still Aleph-null bottles of beer on the wall! Aleph-null bottles of beer on the wall, Aleph-null bottles of beer, Take one down, and pass it around, There's still Aleph-null bottles of beer on the wall! Aleph-null

Check the tube

If you've ever posted something on YouTube and it's like really rocking – up to 298 views in a moment ... then it stalls at 301. What's going on?

Well, 300 is the point at which YouTube stops and takes a quick look (that is, it institutes a 'verification process') to check that you're not a weird bot or similar.

It will soon kick on to the millions of *Gangnam Style* views I'm sure you'll accrue.

301

The 301st day of the year is October 28

302

The 302nd day of the year is October 29

Checkered

There are 302 ways to play the first 3 moves in checkers. If you're a perfect player, or if you have at your disposal a handy little computer program that is effectively perfect, you will never lose a game again.

The game has been 'solved' and if 2 players both play 'perfectly' a draw will always ensue. Checkers, or draughts, is the 'largest' game that has been solved so far.

The final frontier

and that about sums it up!

Bipartite graphs

In mathematics, 'graph theory' is the study, not surprisingly, of graphs, which are collections of points (called vertices) joined by lines (edges).

A 'bipartite graph' is one in which the vertices can be split into 2 separate groups A and B such that every edge joins a vertex in A to one in B.

This bipartite graph has 8 vertices and there are indeed 303 such graphs.

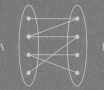

303

The 303rd day of the year is October 30

Twinkle, twinkle ...

Since the time of the Ancient Greeks (and probably the Babylonians before them), we have looked to the night sky, gazed in wonder at the stars and given them names.

Studying and identifying the constellations helped in everything from navigation to harvesting food. They were also regarded by many civilisations as objects of mythology and worship.

The constellations we recognise today were named more recently. Some have dropped of the list, like Felis (which resembled a cat), which was discovered by the French astronomer Jérôme Lalande in 1799. By the way, it wasn't named after the cartoon *Felix the Cat*, just in case you're wondering.

Since 1928, the International Astronomical Union have officially recognised 88 constellations – exactly the same number as keys on a piano. This is what mathematicians call ... a coincidence. The names of the constellations come from a variety of sources – 14 are men and women; 19 are land animals; 10 are water creatures; 9 are birds; 2 are insects; 2 are centaurs; 1 is a head of hair; 1 is a serpent; 1 is a dragon; 1 is a flying horse; 1 is a river and a further 29 are inanimate objects. The arithmetical among you would realise this totals more than 88 and that is because some constellations include more than 1 creature.

304

The 304th day of the year is October 31

A little Halloween joke

It's only fitting that on this day we share one of the all-time corniest mathematics jokes we know:

Why do mathematicians confuse Halloween and Christmas?

Because OCT 31 = DEC 25.

Get it?

The hilarity here rests on the fact that OCT 31 is an abbreviation of 31 in octal or base 8, while 31 base 8 is $3 \times 8 + 1 = 25$ in base 10 which we can write DEC 25 (25 in decimal). So OCT 31 = DEC 25.

Measuring constellations turns out to be tough going because there's no well-defined way of counting them. The clearest would be to count the number of named stars, but this is pretty arbitrary and results in a lot of underwhelming ties.

We instead measure constellations by area. When we do so, we get a top 5:

1302.844	Hydra
1294.428	Virgo
1279.66	Ursa Major
1231.411	Cetus
1225.148	Hercules, and
68.447	Crux, rounding out the list at 88th place.

What's interesting about this list is how 'area' is defined. The unit here is square degrees, which measures parts of the surface area of a sphere just as degrees measure parts of the perimeter of a circle.

Here the Earth is our centre and the surface area is taken from the sphere at (any) fixed distance around the Earth. So the larger the number the bigger the part of the night sky that this constellation takes up. Of course, if one constellation is a lot further away than another, it could have a smaller area in square degrees but be a lot larger than its closer constellatory cousin.

Three o five

has 2 representations as a sum of 2 squares: $305 = 4^2 + 17^2 = 7^2 + 16^2$. This means that these 2 triangles would have a longest side (hypotenuse) the same length. Check 'em out ...

305

The 305th day of the year is November 1

In all, the entire night sky has an area about 41,253 square degrees. The über-nerds will want to know that this is given by the formula for the surface area of a sphere:

$$A = 4\,\pi\,r^2 \text{ where } r = {}^{180}\!/_{\pi}.$$

Turning these areas into percentages, we get Hydra taking up ${}^{1302.844}\!/_{41,253} = 0.0316$, or just over 3% of the night sky. Poor little old Crux takes up a mere 0.17%. Although small, it's loved by Australians and many others because it contains the Southern Cross.

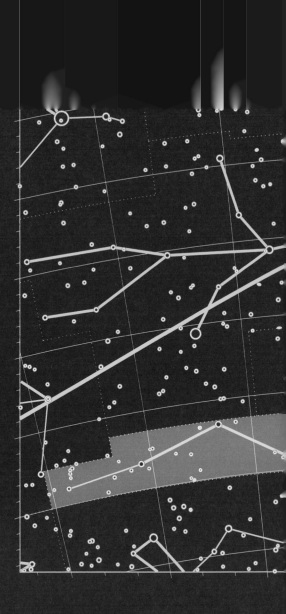

306

*The **306th** day of the year is November 2*

Wholesome goodness

When you put $n = 306$ into the following formula:

$$\frac{18n}{(18 + n)}$$

you get $18 \times {}^{306}\!/_{324} = 17$.

Woopdy doo, you might think, but hey … 306 is the largest number n for which this fraction is a whole number.

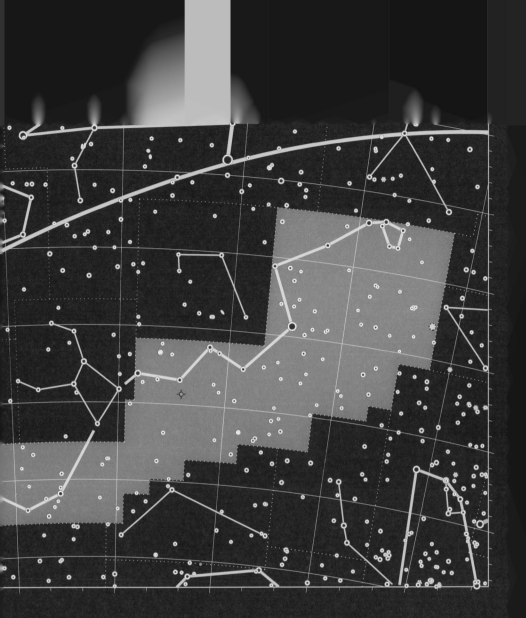

When measuring the size of constellations, these 'curved rectangles' are used to divide the night sky into a grid, and their area is measured in square degrees.

Hey, pal-indrome!

307 is the last day of the year whose square is a palindrome. Calculate 307^2 and convince yourself that 307^2 satisfies this quality.

While you're feeling frisky, why don't you take a good long look at the number 307 and add up the sum of the cubes of its digits. You don't quite get 307, do you – but you come very close! Just wanted to show you that during the year ;-)

You'd get the same for cubing the digits of 370, making 370 an Armstrong, or narcissistic number just like 371, 407 and 153.

307

The 307th day of th *year is* **November**

On this day in 195 *Laika, on* Sputnik 2, *became t* *first animal to enter Earth's ort*

A circular argument

308

*The **308th** day of the year is **January 4***

Four circles can be drawn on the plane in a way to separate it into 14 regions as you can see here, including the area outside the circles.

More generally, n circles can divide the plane into, at most, $n^2 - n + 2$ regions. So if 18 circles are drawn in the plane, they can separate the plane into at most $18^2 - 18 + 2 = 308$ regions.

Now *that's* a number

Now, some of these estimates vary significantly in each direction, but you get the idea – they're big. Really big.

How big, you ask? Well, here's one to start things off. Light – you know, the sort that allows us to see – travels 9.46 *trillion* km in a single year. Easy to say, but think about that figure just for a second, it's:

$$9.46 \times 10^{15} = 9,460,000,000,000,000 \text{ metres}$$

... which is 236,500,000,000 laps of the Earth. Or over 30 million trips to the Sun *and* back.

We write 10^{15} for one followed by 15 zeros to save time ... and space. You encounter this notation a lot when you're talking about very big – or very small – numbers.

Read on for a few more mind-bendingly big 'uns ...

High five three o nine

$309^5 = 2,817,036,000,549$. It is the smallest number whose fifth power contains all the digits 0 to 9. Good on you, 309.

Now, taking the fifth power of every integer from 1 to 308 is probably a bit too much of an ask, but if you're feeling really eager you might want to try a handful of examples so that you can fully appreciate what 309 has achieved here.

309

The 309th day of the year is November 5

86,000,000,000

THE NUMBER of neurons in the human brain.

400,000,000,000

STARS in the Milky Way.

3,000,000,000,000

ESTIMATED OPTICAL DIAMETER in metres of VY Canis Majoris, one of the largest known stars – a red hypergiant, about 1500 times the size of our Sun. It's in the Canis Major constellation, in the southern celestial hemisphere: just head to quadrant SQ2 and trust me, you can't miss it.

10,000,000,000,000

DIAMETER IN METRES of the solar system.

$3.72 \times 10^{13} =$ 37,200,000,000,000

CELLS in a human body.

10^{14}

BACTERIA in a human body.

1.5×10^{14}

NEURAL CONNECTIONS in your cerebral cortex

9.46×10^{15}

DISTANCE IN METRES that light travels in a single year, called unimaginatively, a light year. That's 9.46 trillion km, if you're trying to figure out the Uber fare.

1.5×10^{15}

AMOUNT OF DATA created each day in 2015 (in bytes).

3.991×10^{16}

DISTANCE TO PROXIMA Centauri, the nearest star after the Sun, in metres.

4.355×10^{17}

AGE OF the Universe in seconds.

7.5×10^{18}

GRAINS OF sand on Earth.

10^{19}

NUMBER OF insects on Earth (no, not just the number of mosquitos at your summer BBQ).

310

*The **310th** day of the year is November 6*

Told you to trust me ...

$(1!)^2 + (2!)^2 + ... + (310!)^2$ is prime. Again this falls into the 'best to trust me on this' category.

To convince yourself you've got your head around converting different bases to base 10 and back (see May 26, June 18 or September 23 for a refresher), write out 310 in base 6. It's a pretty cool result.

4.3252×10^{19}

NUMBER OF positions in a Rubik's Cube: 43,252,003, 274,489,856,000, to be exact.

6×10^{24}

MASS IN kilograms of the Earth.

9.2×10^{26}

APPROXIMATE DIAMETER in metres of the visible Universe.

5×10^{30}

NUMBER OF bacteria on Earth.

1.417×10^{32}

TEMPERATURE in degrees Celsius right after the Big Bang.

10^{46}

NUMBER OF possible chess positions.

3×10^{52}

ESTIMATED MASS in kilograms of the entire observable Universe.

8.066×10^{67}

WAYS OF arranging a deck of cards. Remember this one? Remember how else we can notate it? Yep: 52! (52 factorial).

10^{80} to 10^{97}

ESTIMATES OF THE NUMBER of fundamental particles in the observable Universe. (Hey, feel free to let me know if you reckon you can figure it out exactly!)

10^{100}

A GOOGOL, named by 9-year-old Milton Sirotta in 1920 for the number 1 followed by 100 zeros.

1.2×10^{100}

NUMBER OF ways of arranging 70 people in a line – aka 70! (70 factorial).

$10^{10^{100}}$

ONE FOLLOWED by a googol zeros, called a googolplex. Originally Milton Sirotta wanted a googolplex to be 1 followed by as many zeros as you could write before your arm got tired. His uncle Edward Kasner went for this more formal and much more massive definition. Forget your arms – the Universe itself does not have enough room for you to write all of the zeros needed for a googolplex.

Who's prime anyway?

311 is not only prime, but is a prime under any permutation of its digits (113, 131, 311).

If I wrote down the list of numbers with this property, which number would appear either side of 311?

311

*The **311th** day of the year is November 7*

The super-giant star Deneb in the Cygnus constellation can be seen with the unaided eye, especially in winter.

So what, I hear you ask? Well, Deneb is at least 1500 light years away, or 14,000,000,000,000,000 km – an amazing distance to be able to see with the naked eye.

312

The 312th day of the year is November 8

Here's a cracker

$$312 = 0! \times 5! + 1! \times 4! + 2! \times 3! + 3! \times 2! + 4! \times 1! + 5! \times 0!$$

Now, if you haven't been paying attention so far, you will need to know that $0! = 1$ after which this expression, despite looking like it has crawled out of the bowels of evil itself, isn't all that hard. Go on, have a crack.

The 30-gon

A 30-sided figure is called, unimaginatively, a 30-gon and has a glorious 16,801 interior intersection points.

When we join up all the vertices of this pentagon we find 5 internal intersections and another 5 external meeting points at the vertices.

As the number of vertices increases, the number of internal intersections increases rapidly, as well. If you draw all the diagonals of a regular dodecagon, it has 313 intersections – at the 12 vertices of the dodecagon as well as 301 interior intersections.

313

*The **313th** day of the year is November 9*

*On this day in 1914
Astronomer Carl Sagan was born*

ANTARCTICA
by numbers

295 km

The length of the gigantic iceberg that broke free from the Ross Ice Shelf in 2000. 37 kms wide and with a surface area of 11,000 km^2 above the water, it was of course 10 times bigger below.

50–100,000 years

How long it can take snow falling at the South Pole to 'flow' to Antarctica's coast, at which point it falls of the edge to become part of an iceberg.

10,000,000

The tonnage of a swarm of krill spotted by scientists in 1981. This would weigh as much as 140 million people. Scientists are concerned at the possible impacts upon the marine food chain of harvesting krill for fish foods and health supplements.

−13.6°C

The warmest temperature ever recorded at the South Pole ... positively balmy.

314

The 314th day of the year is November 10

Small but powerful

314 is the smallest number that can be written as the sum of 3 positive distinct squares in 6 ways. I'll give you $314 = 5^2 + 8^2 + 15^2 = 3^3 + 4^2 + 17^2$ to start. Find the other 4.

Celebratory pi

Being the 314th day of the year and 3.14 being π to the second decimal place, November 10 joins March 14 (3/14 in the US) and July 22 (22/7 in Australia) as the third π day of the year. In my humble opinion you can't have enough π days!

300°C

On days below –100 degrees Fahrenheit (–73°C), freezing funsters at Amundsen-Scott South Pole Station set the sauna to 200 degrees Fahrenheit (93°C), sit in the sauna for 10 minutes, then run naked around the South Pole and back to the sauna – a total temperature change of 300°C.

4

The number of the 17 species of penguin found in Antarctica that actually breed there – the Adelie, Chinstrap, Emporer and Gentoo. The others breed elsewhere.

60–65 m

The height by which the world's oceans would rise if Anatrctica's ice sheets melted entirely.

Do it by hand!

315² can be written as the sum of the cubes of 5 consecutive integers. Find them.

Ow, Adam, that's tough.

I know, but I'm backing my readers to be able to work out 315² by hand, divide that roughly by 5 and ask, 'How big is a typical number whose cube is around the size of this amount?' and go from there.

Wow, Adam, your readers must be awesome.

315 is also divisible by both its digit sum (3 + 1 + 5 = 9 and 315 = 9 × 35) and its digit product (3 × 1 × 5 = 15 and 315 = 15 × 21). Lucky old 315.

315

*The **315th** day of the year is November 11*

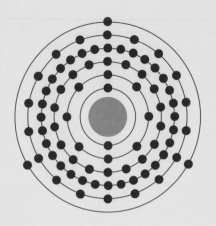

Thallium

The element with an atomic number of 81 is a post-transition metal that doesn't exist on its own in nature. Fans of crime writer Agatha Christie might remember thallium being used as a poison in her novel *The Pale Horse*. In fact, when a 1972 autopsy found elevated levels of thallium in the remains of a man who had been cremated, it proved that he had been poisoned and provided a landmark moment in modern forensics. Thallium was also used in insecticides and rat poisons but has been since superseded because it didn't discriminate enough – it basically just poisoned everything!

316

The *316th* day of the year is *November 12*

Three's a crowd

316 can be written as the sum of 3 consecutive triangular numbers. Can you find them? Hint: Again divide 316 into thirds and this should guide you towards one of the triangular numbers that you require.

Sub prime ...

$316^{23} + 316^{21} + 316^{19} + 316^{17} + 316^{15} + 316^{13} + 316^{11} + 316^9 + 316^7 + 316^5 + 316^3 + 316^1 + 316^0$ is prime.

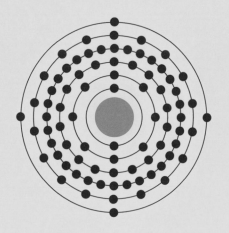

Lead Pb

The soft, malleable transition metal known as lead will be familiar to most of you. But not because you find it in 'lead' pencils. That's actually just an urban myth. The chemical symbol for lead is Pb which derives from *plumbum*, its Latin name. In turn, the word plumbum gives us the English word 'plumbing'. Because of its high density and resistance to corrosion, lead is often used for ballast in the keels of sailboats. Beethoven's hair was found to contain 100 times the usual level of lead, which may explain the great composer's volatile moods and perhaps even his deafness.

456789101112131415161718192021222324252627282930313233343536373839404142434445464748495051525365657585960616263646566676869707172737475767778798081**82**83848586878889909192939495969798991001

317 me

The number 317 is prime. It is the concatenation of the primes 3 and 17 and also of the primes 31 and 7.

You can remove any digit from the number 317 and the 2-digit number you're left with is prime.

And just in case you need another prime fact about the number 317 to push you over the edge and into nerd heaven, have a look at this.

The product of the primes up to and including 317, less 1, that is, the number given by:

$2 \times 3 \times 5 \times 7 \times ... \times 317 - 1$

is prime. Yeah!

317

The **317th** *day of the* *year is* November 13

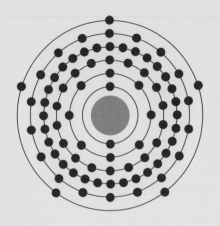

Bismuth

Thanks to the Nobel Prize winning work of Australians Barry Marshall and Robin Warren, we now know that peptic and duodenal ulcers aren't caused by stress or spicy food but by the bacteria Helicobacter pylori – a particularly hardy sucker that can survive exposure to the acidic environment of gastric juices. Bismuth, in the form of 'colloidal bismuth subcitrate', can be used to take care of Helicobacter.

While I know a bit about a few things, I know diddly-squat about make-up. But I do know that the 'pearlescent' effect in nail varnish and face powders and the like is often produced with bismuth.

318

The 318th day of the year is November 14

Partition mission

If 22 is partitioned into distinct positive integer parts in all possible ways, there will be 318 parts used in total.

318 is also the number of partitions of 18 into at most 9 parts and the number of partitions of 70 into exactly 8 primes.

'This is Wiggum, reporting a 318! Waking a police officer!'

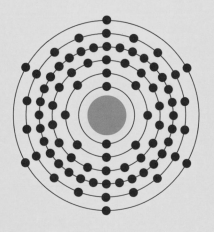

Polonium

Polonium has 3 oxides. When 1 atom of polonium bonds with 1 of oxygen we get polonium monoxide; similarly, if it bonds with 2 or 3 atoms of oxygen we get polonium dioxide and polonium trioxide respectively. These oxides don't seem to have any massively important chemical or industrial applications at the moment, so why am I telling you about them? Polonium is named after Poland, birthplace of Marie Curie who discovered the element in 1898. The brilliant scientist teamed with her husband Pierre to extract polonium from uranium pitchblende, explaining why this substance emitted 4 times the radioactivity you would expect to see from uranium alone.

456789101112131415161718192021222324252627282930313233343536373839404142434445464748495051525356575859606162636465666768697071727374757677787980818283**84**8586878889909192939495969798991100

No calculator zone

Calculate 319^3 (with pen and paper). What do you notice about it? Sure, it'll take a bit of effort, but if you get it right, imagine the sense of reward!

Back on November 6 we noted that 310 in base 6 was 1234. Cute. Well, calculate 319 in base 2 (which we also call binary) and check it out.

319

The 319th day of the year is November 15

On this day in 1738 Astronomer William Herschel was born

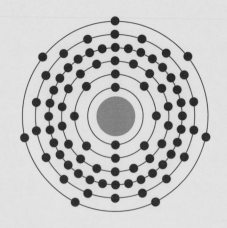

Astatine

At number 85 on the atomic hottest 100 is the super rare and radioactive chemical element astatine. In all of human endeavour, we've produced less than a millionth of a gram of the stuff and almost all of it has since decayed away. It's unlikely we'll ever make enough for it to be seen with the naked eye and even if we did it's so radioactive it would disintegrate almost immediately.

In the entire Earth's crust there is thought to be only about 30 g of astatine. In Australia, the technical term for this amount is 'two thirds of bugger all'. Not that I'm suggesting 45 g = bugger all. It's just a turn of phrase.

1 2 3 4 5 6 7 8 9 10 11 12 13 14 15 16 17 18 19 20 21 22 23 24 25 26 27 28 29 30 31 32 33 34 35 36 37 38 39 40 41 42 43 44 45 46 47 48 49 50 51 52 53 54 55 56 57 58 59 60 61 62 63 64 65 66 67 68 69 70 71 72 73 74 75 76 77 78 79 80 81 82 83 84 **85** 86 87 88 89 90 91 92 93 94 95 96 97 98 99

320

The 320th day of the year is November 16

Chess minus

There are 320 moves that a queen could make on a 5 × 5 chessboard. I'll be the first to admit that's not the most relevant piece of information, even for chess players, given the whole chessboard is 8 × 8 and the like. But hey, what can you do?

A no-so-little tidbit ...

$320^6 + 320^5 + 320^4 + 320^3 + 320^2 + 320^1 + 320^0 =$ 1,077,107,785,830,721 and is prime.

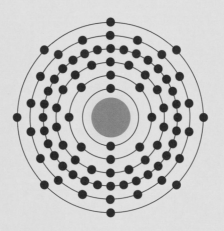

Radon

Sitting at 86 on the Periodic Table, the intensely radioactive radon is the heaviest known elemental gas. It's an elusive element as it's colourless, odourless and tasteless. If you're ever in the French spa town of Le-Mont-Dore you might want to pop in for a relaxing hot bath containing radon, arsenic and iron from the local thermal springs, or even have some 'nasal irrigation' consisting of a carbon dioxide–radon mix. Then again, you might not.

4 5 6 7 8 9 10 11 12 13 14 15 16 17 18 19 20 21 22 23 24 25 26 27 28 29 30 31 32 33 34 35 36 37 38 39 40 41 42 43 44 45 46 47 48 49 50 51 52 53 54 55 56 57 58 59 60 61 62 63 64 65 66 67 68 69 70 71 72 73 74 75 76 77 78 79 80 81 82 83 84 85 **86** 87 88 89 90 91 92 93 94 95 96 97 98 99 100

Delannoy numbers

The lines in these diagrams are called 'lattice paths', and we've limited ourselves to being able to take steps only east $(1, 0)$, north $(0, 1)$, and northeast $(1, 1)$.

If the grid gets expanded, we know that $D(4, 4) = 321$.

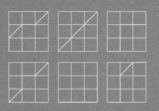

In a 3×3 grid there are 63 such 'Delannoy paths' so we write the Delannoy number $D(3, 3) = 63$.

321

*The **321st** day of the year is November 17*

On this day in 1790 Mathematician A.F. Möbius was born, 134 years before Benoit Mandelbrot

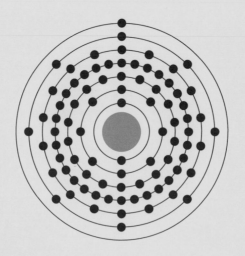

Francium

Of the first 100 elements, francium has the distinction of being the single element keenest to 'get up and go'. Of all the different forms of francium, the longest-lived has a half-life of a mere 22 minutes. This is the shortest of any element's half-life. As a result, no amount of francium that could be weighed has ever been made.

A massive word-up to Marguerite Perey who discovered francium. Perhaps not surprisingly, she was a student of the momentously talented Marie Curie. Tragically, like Curie, she died from cancer caused by her close study of radioactive materials.

322

The 322nd day of the year is November 18

Lucas sequence

322 is the 12th Lucas number. The Lucas sequence is similar to the Fibonacci sequence with $L_1 = 1$ and $L_2 = 3$ and each term is the sum of the 2 previous terms. Writing the Lucas numbers as L_n and the Fibonacci numbers as F_n, there are some beautiful relationships between the two:

$$L_n = F_{n-1} + F_{n+1}$$

$$L_{n+1} = \frac{1}{2}(5 F_n + L_n)$$

$$F_{2n} = L_n \times F_n \text{ for example.}$$

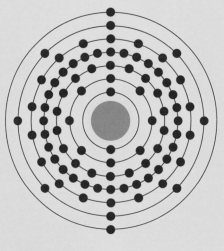

Radium

Radium poisoning caused the deaths of many workers who used to lick the paintbrushes with which they were applying the radioactive element to make luminous alarm clocks and watches. Before we understood its radioactivity, there were many health crazes based on its supposed 'rejuvenating properties'. In the early 1900s, thousands of radium ore 'Revigators' were sold. These were ceramic crocks lined with radium out of which you were advised to drink a cup of water each morning. Well, turns out it was a crock in more ways than one – it contained low levels of radiation, arsenic, lead, vanadium and uranium. Yum!

456789101112131415161718192021222324252627282930313233343536373839404142434445464748495051525355657585960616263646566676869707172737475767778798081828384858687**88**8990919293949596979899100

Motzkin up and down

We spoke about the Motzkin numbers back on February 20. Well, if you drew every possible path from (0, 0) to (8, 0) that never dropped below the x-axis using only moves between lattice points with slopes of 1, 0, or –1, there are 323 possible paths, making 323 the eighth Motzkin number.

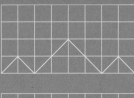

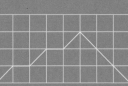

323

*The **323rd** day of the year is November 19*

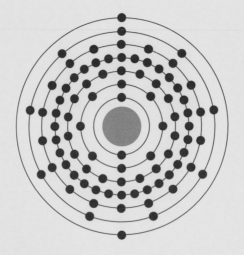

Actinium

In 1899, the famous French chemist, André-Louis Debierne, announced the discovery of a new element. He separated it from pitchblende residues left by Marie and Pierre Curie after they had extracted radium. He named the soft, silvery-white metal actinium, which comes from the Greek word *aktis*, meaning 'beam'. Actinium is the first element in the radioactive series known as 'actinides'. It glows in the dark because it is so radioactive it excites the air around it. Other actinides include uranium, thorium and the synthetically produced plutonium. They're commonly used in nuclear reactors and weapons.

324

The 324th day of the year is November 20

Grab a pen ...

If I take 5 numbers that add together to give 16 and instead multiply them together I might get $2 \times 2 \times 2 \times 5 \times 5 = 200$ or $2 \times 2 \times 3 \times 3 \times 6 = 216$.

Well, 324 is the largest possible product I can get. Can you find the integers?

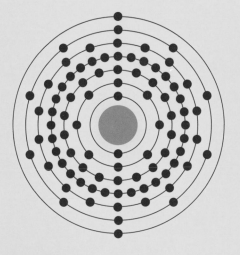

Thorium

A radioactive actinide metal, thorium is one of only 4 radioactive elements that can occur naturally in nature (the other 3 are bismuth, plutonium and uranium). Thorium was discovered in 1828 by the Norwegian mineralogist Morten Thrane Esmark and identified by the Swedish chemist Jöns Jakob Berzelius, who named it after Thor, the Norse god of thunder. It is thought that about half of the heat given off by the Earth – a staggering 20 terawatts – comes from the radioactive decay of thorium, uranium and potassium.

Or a pencil

By the time we've gotten this far into the year we've already passed 14 numbers that could be written as the sum of 2 distinct positive squares in 2 ways.

But now on November 21, we meet 325, which is the smallest number that can be written as the sum of 2 distinct positive squares in 3 ways. What a great way to spend November 25 finding these 3 ways!

325

The 325th day of the year is November 21

On this day in 1783
The Montgolfiers launched the first free-flying, manned, hot air balloon

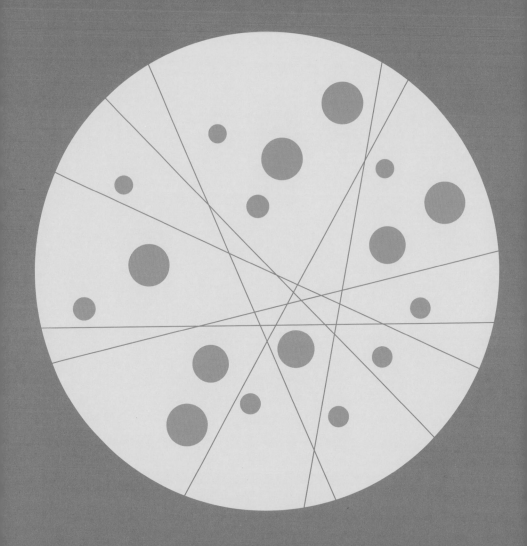

Pizza cutter

326

*The **326th** day of the year is April 2*

326 is the maximum number of pieces that can be produced from a pizza with 25 straight cuts. These are sometimes called 'lazy caterer numbers' or, more generally, central polygonal numbers.

It's really hard to draw the 25 cuts so that you can see all the pieces, so here's an exampe with 7 cuts. As you can see, some pieces are absolutely miniscule.

326 is also the sum of the first 14 consecutive odd primes: 326 = 3 + 5 + 7 + 11 + 13 + 17 + 19 + 23 + 29 + 31 + 37 + 41 + 43 + 47.

At any given time around the world, 45,000,000 people are drunk.

This rises considerably on New Year's Eve.

Can you dig it?

327 is the largest number *n* so that *n*, 2*n*, and 3*n* together contain every digit from 1 to 9 exactly once. Show this for 327 and try to find any other number less than 327 with this property.

327

*The **327th** day of the year is November 23*

SHANGHAI *by* numbers

50,000 m^2

The size of the roof of the world's first circular railway station, Shanghai South.

90 minutes

How long it takes for the limited number of 10,000 new driver's licences released each month by authorities to sell out.

100 years

Since the death of Russian poet Alexander Pushkin. The Shanghai Russian community erected a statue to him on the corner of Dongping Lu and Fenyang Lu. It's the only surviving statue from before the People's Republic.

9

The number of dragons on the Nine Dragon Pillar which is actually a critical central steel pillar supporting the city's merging highways. Local lore says it was built to appease a sleeping dragon who had been woken by the roadworks, though it really serves a structural purpose.

328

*The **328th** day of the year is November 24*

Tau numbers

328 is a 'refactorable' or 'tau' number since it is divisible by its number of divisors. We know that there cannot be 3 consecutive integers that are refactorable and that no perfect number can be refactorable.

Can you work out the divisors of 328 and confirm that it is refactorable?

650 m

The height of Shanghai Tower, the world's second tallest building. So many skyscrapers have been built in Shanghai over the last decade or more that the city is feared to be slowly sinking.

The number of plays (*Private Lives*) Noël Coward wrote in Shanghai while convalescing from influenza.

88

The number of storeys that the laundry chute runs in the Grand Hyatt hotel – it has internal buffers to slow the speed of your descending underpants!

24 million

Shanghai's population – the biggest city on Earth (depending on how you measure 'city' which is a whole other discussion).

Con-man

The concatenation of the consecutive numbers 328 and 329 gives 328,329 which is a square number (328,329 = 573²).

We haven't seen this phenomenon since July 2 introduced us to 183,184 and we won't see it again in the year. Let's make the most of it!

329

The 329th day of the year is November 25

Winter on Uranus lasts 42 years.

Brrrrrr!

330

Inside a hendecagon

You might remember the awesome diagram of a 30-gon on November 9 and discussed the fact that a 12-sided figure has 301 interior intersections.

Well, perhaps surprisingly, an 11-sided regular polygon has more, namely 330 internal intersections. But if you think about the 11-sided figure and how it has fewer 'repeating' internal intersections where multiple diagonals meet, it should become clearer.

Cosmos-logical

You don't need me to tell you that the Universe is an amazing place. Its size, its content, what we know about how it came into existence and how it might end, the suggestion that maybe it's not the only Universe but one of many ... each one of these topics is mind-blowing and could command an entire book in and of itself.

When I started to stargaze, my first port of call was Bryan Gaensler's great work *Extreme Cosmos*. This excellent book walks you through the biggest, fastest, hottest things that we knew of back in 2011. Bryan openly admits that things are rapidly changing in his field and records are constantly being broken. Indeed, many of the record holders in *Extreme Cosmos* have been displaced, but the broader explanation of how the cosmos works is in itself so simple and elegant that the book is still highly recommended.

This is such an exciting time for cosmologists, not least because the tools they use to examine the Universe are becoming more and more sophisticated. We've gone from the discovery of the first planet outside our solar system in 1992 to learning about 2000+ planets in just 23 years. Exquisite images from deep space are now almost commonplace. And when the Square Kilometre Array radio telescope fires up in Western Australia and South Africa ... well, hold onto your asteroids!

The Three's Knees

31, 331, 3331, 33331, 333331, 3333331 and 33333331 are all prime. Is 333333331?

Semi-remembered

Now, be honest, you've forgotten what a semiprime is, haven't you? Go back to October 25 (happy birthday to my sister Leisha by the way) and check it out. Then convince yourself that 331 is the sum of the first 15 semiprimes.

331

The **331st** *day of the year is* November 27

Twinkle, twinkle ...

225,300

THE NUMBER OF stars counted by the Henry Draper Catalogue in 1924.

500,000,000

THE NUMBER OF stars, galaxies and other objects catalogued by the Sloan Digital Sky Survey in 2014. If you want to see something truly amazing, hop online and search for the 'Flight Through the Universe' by the good people at Sloan.

100,000,000,000

THE NUMBER OF stars in the Milky Way galaxy alone.

300,000,000,000,000,000,000,000

A 2011 ESTIMATE of the number of stars in the observable Universe. That's 300 sextillion, by the way.

100,000,000,000,000,000,000,000,000

A 2014 ESTIMATE of the number of stars in the observable Universe (courtesy of Cornell University's David Kornreich aka 'Ask An Astronomer').

We're not suggesting the Universe has had lots of cute little babies in between 2011 and 2014. These number vary greatly because this is an inexact science and our methods of measurement are still evolving.

Suffice to say, there are *heaps* of stars in the observable Universe.

332

*The **332nd** day of the year is November 28*

Canny combos

332 is the number of ways to partition 47 into non-zero triangular numbers. (36 + 10 + 1 would be one; 36 + 1 + 1 + 1 + 1 + 1 + 1 + 1 + 1 + 1 + 1 + 1 another.)

The other 330 ways all use combinations of numbers in the series 1, 3, 6, 10, 15, 21, 28, 36 and 45.

Hot spots

5500°C

THE SURFACE TEMPERATURE of the Sun (about 5 times hotter than a candle flame).

10,000°C

THE SURFACE TEMPERATURE of Sirius, the brightest star in our night sky.

300,000°C

THE TEMPERATURE of the 'white dwarf' star at the centre of the Red Spider Nebula (NGC 6537), 20 trillion km away in the Sagittarius constellation.

15,000,000°C

THE TEMPERATURE at the Sun's core.

100,000,000°C

THE TEMPERATURE at the core of 'red giant' stars that have exhausted their heat source and collapsed under gravity, becoming smaller, denser and hotter.

3,000,000,000°C

THE TEMPERATURE at the core of much bigger stars than our Sun as they burn up their basic gases and produce heavier elements like silicon and iron.

5,000,000,000°C

THE TEMPERATURE in the largely iron core of these larger stars as they collapse into neutron stars and undergo supernova explosion.

10,000,000,000°C

THE TEMPERATURE of the Universe 1 second after the Big Bang.

10,000,000,000,000,000°C

THE TEMPERATURE of the Universe one 100 millionth of a second after the Big Bang.

100,000,000,000,000,000,000,000,000°C

THE TEMPERATURE 0.000000000000 00000000000000000000000 0000001 seconds after the Big Bang ... beyond which we're in the dark. Get it ... in the dark!

Super subsections

$166^3 + 500^3 + 333^3 =$ 166,500,333 making 166,500,333 a type of 'narcissistic' number. But to be honest, if I was the sum of the cubes of my 3 subsections like 166,500,333 is, I'd probably steal a glance at myself in the mirror occasionally – it's pretty hot. What do you notice about 165,033?

333

The 333rd day of the year is November 29

The big chill

−273.15°C

THIS IS WHAT'S KNOWN as 'absolute zero', how cold it can theoretically get before atoms stop moving.

−270.42°C

THE CURRENT AVERAGE temperature of the Universe – the 'Cosmic Microwave Background' or CMB. This is down from 2700°C 380,000 years after the Big Bang when the Universe cooled enough for hydrogen atoms to form.

−272°C

THE TEMPERATURE IN the Boomerang Nebula due to 1500 years of 600,000 km/h winds shifting 60,000,000,000,000,000 tonnes of star material per second and dropping the temperature below the background temperature of the rest of the Universe.

0.00000000005°

IN APRIL 2015, a group of scientists from Stanford University announced they had cooled an arrangement of rubidium molecules to just 0.00000000005 of a degree above absolute zero. Australian quantum computing guru Andrea Morello does something similar in his 'dilution fridge' at the University of New South Wales using a liquid mixture of different types of helium atoms. When a student of his first engages the dilution fridge successfully, Andrea loves telling them, 'Congratulations, you've just created the coldest place in the Universe'! You cannot beat a science gag.

334

The **334th** day of the year is November 30

But wait, there's more

334 is semiprime because 334 = 2 × 167 with 2 and 167 both prime.

We've already talked about semiprimes, that is numbers with just 2 prime factors.

When 2 consecutive numbers are semiprime, we say they form a semiprime pair.

Looking at the number after 334 we see that 335 = 5 × 67 so 334 and 335 form a semiprime pair.

There will be one more semiprime pair this year, can you find it?

Light

GRB 080319B

WE ALL LOVE looking at the night sky, seeing a bright and beautiful light and wondering, 'How far away is that?'. Well, the brightest electromagnetic events in the Universe that we know about are called 'gamma ray bursts'. They occur when a high mass star collapses to form a neutron star or a black hole.

How bright is that? For about half a minute on 19 March 2008, the gamma rays of the high mass star known as GRB 080319B were visible to the naked eye. These rays travelled 7.5 billion years to reach the Earth and were the brightest object we'd ever seen.

Deadly 'ASASSN'

IN JULY 2015 astronomers based at the gorgeously named All Sky Automated Survey for SuperNovae project in Chile reported what is thought to be the brightest supernova ever discovered.

The positively blingy ASASSN-15lh is thought to shine brighter than 500 billion suns and its light has taken over 2.8 billion years to reach us.

Heart of darkness

N 2014, NASA's Spitzer Space Telescope is believed to have discovered the darkest place ever recorded in space. Spitzer spied a clumpy cloud of gas and dust so massive and dense it cast a cosmic shadow ... which was this darkest ever place.

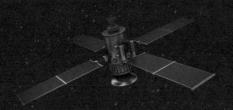

Prove it, y'all

$2^{335} = (2^{333} - 741) + (2^{333} - 483) + (2^{333} + 285) + (2^{333} + 939)$ making 2^{335} the smallest power of 2 which equals the sum of 4 consecutive primes.

We've spent a lot of time talking about the sum of consecutive primes in this book and you might think I have some bias against consecutive composite numbers.

How dare you! In fact, in penance for this vile smear why don't you prove that 335 is the sum of the first 19 composite numbers?

335

*The **335th** day of the year is December 1*

4,600,000,000

THE AGE IN YEARS of the Sun and the Earth.

13,820,000,000

THE BEST 'guess' for the age of the Universe, in years.

13,000,000,000

THE AGE OF SMSS 0313, perhaps the oldest star we've discovered thanks to Australia's Coonabarabran Sky-Mapper wide-field survey telescope. It's 6000 light years from Earth in the Hydrus constellation.

86,400

THE NUMBER OF rotations per day of a standard type of neutron star called a 'pulsar'. This is about 1 rotation per second. Feeling dizzy? You might want to sit down then.

5,000,000

THE NUMBER OF daily rotations (62 per second) of a pulsar in the Dorado constellation identified in 1998.

58,000,000

THE NUMBER OF daily rotations (716 times per second) of the pulsar PSR J1748 – 2446ad.

36 hours, 48 minutes, 10.032524 seconds

THE TIME OF the orbit of pulsar PSR J 1909-3744 to within 1 microsecond. This pulsar rotates 340 times per second and its 3,500,000 km orbit is the most perfect circle in the known Universe.

As Bryan Gaensler puts it, 'Instead of shrinking in and out by a sizeable amount over the course of one circuit as is the case for Earth, over 36 hours the size of the pulsar's orbit changes by about ten millionths of a metre, less than the width of a human hair. That we can make such exquisite measurements on a tiny object so far away is nothing short of astonishing.' Hear, hear!

336

The 336th day of the year is December 2

Bringing the prime to the party

Next time you're throwing a 'partition into primes party', which is the *coolest* kind of party you can have, remember that there are 336 ways to partition 41 into primes, for example {37, 2, 2}, {19, 7, 7, 5, 3} and so on.

On this day in 1942
The first artificial nuclear reactor,
Chicago Pile-1, successfully went critical

6700 years

HOW LONG IT WOULD TAKE,
at the speed of light, to get to the
Little Gem Nebula (NGC 6818).

It was discovered by William
Herschel in 1787, six years after
old Billy H. had discovered the
planet Uranus.

Sure, it'd be a long trip, but you'd
habe to agree – a cracking view
once you got there!

Pythagorean primes

337 is a Pythagorean prime.
This is a prime number of
the form $4n + 1$. Pythagorean
primes are exactly the primes
(except for 2) that are the sum
of 2 squares.

In this case we see that 337
is prime; $337 = 4 \times 84 + 1$
and $337 = 9^2 + 16^2$.

337

*The **337th** day of the
year is December 3*

Big boppers: you call that a star ... now *that's* a star

1,400,000

THE DIAMETER OF the Sun in kilo-metres (big enough to fit over 1 million Earths). We call the distance 695,500 km one *solar radius* and when we measure another star we compare its radius to our Sun.

1180 solar radii – Betelgeuse

THE NINTH brightest star in the night sky despite being 642 light years away.

UY Scuti

IN A FIELD FULL of controversy and 'margins of error', 'the Scut' may well be the largest star we've ever seen. Its radius is over 1700 times that of the Sun, yet it has only about 30 times its mass. Any of the 10 largest stars we've found – if substi-tuted for our Sun – would crowd out beyond Mercury and Venus, bump us for six, push out Mars and go way past the orbit of Jupiter!

These images below (left to right) show the relative sizes of planets to UY Scuti (Source: Wikipedia; adapted from an image by Jcpag2012; background changed)

Jupiter < Proxima Centauri < Sun < Sirius

Sirius < Pollux < Arcturus < Aldebaran

338

*The **338th** day of the year is December 4*

Hyped up

$17^2 + 7^2 = 338$ and $338 = 2 \times 13^2$. So these 2 triangles both have hypotenuse $\sqrt{338} = 13\sqrt{2}$.

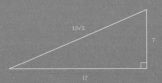

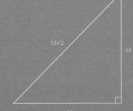

Mini-marvels

25 km

THE PRESUMED DIAMETER of neutron stars, the remnants of the explosions of stars much larger than our Sun.

50–100 cm

THE DIAMETER OF asteroid 2008 TS26. This is about the size of a large beach ball (or a bean bag if you're an indoors type). TS26 is the smallest known object that orbits the Sun. It does so every 32 months and is a candidate to one day smash into Earth – or at least burn up in our atmosphere upon entry.

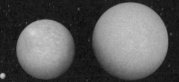

Aldebaran < Rigel < Antares < Betelgeuse

Betelgeuse < VY Canis Majoris < NML Cygni < UY Scuti

Mighty fine 3-3-9

If you've ever sat around adding consecutive powers of the number 339, this next fact will come as no surprise to you.

For the remaining 100% of the human population, you *will* be surprised to learn that:

$339^{10} + 339^9 + 339^8 + 339^7 + 339^6 + 339^5 + 339^4 + 339^3 + 339^2 + 339^1 + 339^0$ is prime.

339

*The **339th** day of the year is December 5*

Live fast, die young

28,000 km/h

THE SPEED OF the International Space Station in orbit.

39,000 km/h

THE SPEED AT which the *Apollo 10* astronauts returned from orbiting the Moon in May 1969.

107,000 km/h

THE SPEED YOU'RE going at right now! Strictly speaking, it's the speed the Earth maintains in its orbit around the Sun.

170,000 km/h

THE SPEED OF MERCURY. Until about 20 years ago, Mercury was the bees-very-rapidly-moving-knees as far as planets went. But since then there has been an explosion in space observation technology and a resulting increase in what we can see. We've now checked out nearly 2000 'exoplanets' (extra-solar planets, orbiting a star other than our Sun) and the list just gets longer.

340

*The **340th** day of the year is December 6*

Don't drag the queens

If you had a 6 × 6 chessboard and 2 queens, there are 340 ways you could place the queens safely on the board, that is, so they can't capture each other in a single move.

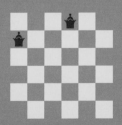

863,000 km/h

IN 2008 we spotted a gas giant exoplanet called Wasp-12b, almost twice the diameter of Jupiter that positively bangs through space at 863,000 km/h – that's around 240 kilometres every second or a lap of the Earth in just under 3 minutes. To add to the thrill, some scientists believe the surface and core of Wasp-12b is made of carbon ... perhaps in the form of diamonds! Bling *and* speed – what a combination.

But if you're thinking of moving to Wasp-12b to enjoy the ride, I should point out it has a surface temperature of 2250°C (nearly half that of the Sun and perhaps the hottest planet temperature we've ever discovered). Not only that, it's so close to its host star it's being stretched into the shape of a football and torn apart. Sadly, the ol' Waspy has only 10 million years to live.

914,000 km/h

THE SPEED OF THE SUN as it orbits the Milky Way.

5,700,000 km/h

THE SPEED OF the neutron star RX J0822.0-4300, spat out of an exploding supernova around 3700 years ago. RX J0822 could travel from Sydney to Perth every 2 seconds, could orbit Earth in under half a minute and could get from Earth to the Moon in 4 minutes.

That's an incredible speed for something so large but, not surprisingly, really small things can move faster than really large things. And when we say faster, we mean *much* faster.

1,079,252,850 km/h

THE FASTEST SPEED that anything has ever been clocked in the Universe happened back in 1991 in Utah in the US when a cosmic ray (which was probably a proton or an iron atom nucleus) was measured hitting the Earth's atmosphere at 99.99999999999999999996% of the speed of light. It so shocked physicists that they call it the 'Oh My God' particle.

Lucas the legendary

In the US, they write December 7 as 12/7 which is a chance for me to shoehorn in the fact that $127 = 2^7 - 1$ is a Mersenne prime.

Now $2^M - 1$ is not usually prime for M a Mersenne prime, but in the case of $M = 127$ we get $2^{127} - 1$ which is indeed a Mersenne prime.

Not just any old prime either, it's the largest Mersenne prime ever calculated by hand.

Well done, Édouard Lucas, who in 1876 proved that the 39-digit beast:

170,141,183,460,469,231,731, 687,303,715,884,105,727 is prime.

341

The 341st day of the year is December 7

Hey bro, that's heavy

330,000,000,000, 000,000,000 tonnes

THE MASS of Mercury.

6,000,000,000, 000,000,000,000 tonnes

THE MASS of Earth.

2,000,000,000, 000,000,000,000, 000 tonnes

THE MASS of Jupiter, which is double the mass of every other planet in our solar system combined!

2,000,000,000, 000,000,000,000, 000,000 tonnes

THE MASS of our Sun. Now, if I just keep adding zeros we'll run out of space pretty quickly, so let's call the mass of our Sun 1 'Solar Mass', or $1\,M_\odot$.

ONCE THINGS START getting really heavy, things also get really complicated. Working out the mass of a distant star is not as simple as dropping a bag of potatoes on the checkout scale. The mass of many huge stars is known only to within a factor of 4 or so, so take these entries with a grain, or perhaps a few trillion trillion tonnes, of salt.

The heaviest star we can currently see unaided is the large blue supergiant Alnilam, the middle star in the belt of Orion coming in at 40 $M_\odot$. But even old Alni is on the slight side compared to the Wolf-Rayet class star in the Large Magellanic Cloud which we know by the romantic name of RMC 136a1. As of mid-2015, it had the highest confirmed mass of any star, a staggering 265 $M_\odot$. I can't imagine where it buys its pants.

However, even these big stars aren't the heaviest 'objects' that we know about. Sagittarius A*, the massive black hole at the centre of the Milky Way galaxy, has a mass 4.3 million times that of our Sun. That's incredible but it's highly likely there are even *heavier* black holes out there.

342

The 342nd day of the year is December 8

Onya, oblong!

342 is an 'oblong' (or pronic, or heteromecic) number, the product of 2 consecutive integers.

And for fans of heteromecics, there will be no more of them this year.

Let's send them off in style by calculating the 2 consecutive integers that multiply to give 342.

AND THIS HASN'T even raised the thorny question of whether you can count the mass of an entire galaxy as a single 'object' and therefore clusters of galaxies which would allow me to tell you about things like Abell 2163, a galaxy cluster with mass something like 4,000,000,000,000,000 $M_\odot$ ...

These images below (left to right) show the relative sizes of planets to Earth (Source: Wikipedia; adapted from an image by Jcpag2012; background changed)

Mercury < Mars < Venus < Earth

Earth < Neptune < Uranus < Saturn < Jupiter

The final Friedman?

As we mentioned back on October 16, a Friedman number is a number that can be made up of arithmetical operations of its digits. So December 13, a few days from now, is the last Friedman number day of the year, with $347 = 7^3 + 4$.

Can you show that 343 is also a Friedman number?

343

The *343rd day of the year is December 9*

Here comes the (our) Sun

4,600,000,000 years

THAT BIG BALL of yellow in the sky is about 4,600,000,000 years old.

5500°C

THE SURFACE TEMPERATURE of the Sun (about 5 times hotter than a candle flame).

15,000,000°C

THE TEMPERATURE at the Sun's core.

2,000,000,000, 000,000,000,000, 000,000 tonnes

THE MASS of the Sun (about 330,000 Earths).

1,400,000 km

THE DIAMETER of the Sun.

39% hydrogen, 60% helium, 1% carbon, oxygen, silicon, iron and minute traces of just about every other element ever identified

THE CURRENT COMPOSITION of the Sun. Its original composition was 72% hydrogen, 27% helium, 1% others – the change is due to 4.6 billion years of 'nuclear fusion' turning hydrogen into helium.

3.86×10^{26} joules per second

THE ENERGY OUTPUT of the Sun. This equates to about 6 trillion Hiroshima explosions every single second. That's 386,000,000,000,000, 000,000,000,000 joules, by the way.

344

The **344th** day of the year is December 10

Give me more, 344!

344 is the sum of 2 positive cubes. There will only be 1 more day for the rest of the year with that property. Can you express 344 as the sum of 2 cubes and find the remaining day for this year?

Lazy n circles ...

If you understood what I told you back on November 4 about the n circles dividing the plane into at most $n^2 - n + 2$ regions, it should be a doddle to work out that 19 circles can divide the plane into at most 344 regions.

*On this day in 1815
Mathematician Ada Lovelace was born,
86 years before the first Nobel Prize*

4,000,000 tonnes

THE MASS OF the Sun that is burnt each and every second.

490–507 seconds

THE TIME IT TAKES light to travel the 149,600,000 km or so from the Sun to the Earth, depending on where we are in our orbit.

9,000,000,000 years

THE LIFE EXPECTANCY of the Sun.

1,000,000, 000,000 years

THE LIFE EXPECTANCY of some red dwarf stars.

This incredible background image shows a long filament of solar material that had been hovering in the Sun's atmosphere, the corona, erupting out into space on 31 August 2012. Although it didn't travel directly toward Earth, it did connect with Earth's magnetosphere, creating an aurora. Source: NASA Goddard Space Flight Center (cropped and inverted)

Hidden cuteness

Work out 345 × 3523 (by hand, lazy bones!) and what do you see? There are a couple of 'cute' facts hidden away in here.

Udderly amazing

345 is the average number of squirts from a cow's udder needed to yield a US gallon of milk. Hey, I know this isn't particularly mathematical but it's almost Christmas and I'm keen to mix it up a bit!

345

*The **345th** day of the year is December 11*

50

MIGHT SOUND LIKE A SMALL NUMBER in the scheme of these monsters, however it represents an massive leap forward in our technology.

This is the number of times *more* sensitive than *any* other radio instrument we've ever built that the Square Kilometre Array, or SKA, will be, once completed in Australia and South Africa.

But if that number's not enough for you, how about this one: it's been estimated that the array could generate an exabyte (or 1 quintillion bytes) of raw uncompressed data … *per day.*

As the cracking Australian astrophycisit and project scientist Lisa Harvey-Smith puts it, we're essentially building a new internet in Western Australia and South Africa.

Behind is artist impression of all four SKA components together – the SKA dishes (MeerKAT and ASKAP in the background, for you dish-watchers out there), along with a station of the low frequency aperture array in the bottom right corner and a station of the mid frequency aperture array in the bottom left corner. The left half of the image represents the antennas in Africa and the right half the ones in Australia. Source: SKA Organisation (Cropped)

346

*The **346th** day of the year is December 12*

Smithereens

Can you prove that 346 is a Smith number? Well, you'd need me to tell you what a Smith number is first, wouldn't you? If the sum of a number's digits equals the sum of the digits of its prime factors it is a Smith number.

Safety in numbers

347 is a safe prime, 1 more than twice a Sophie Germain prime, 173. There is only 1 more safe prime this year.

There is a 1-digit number that you can add to any of the digits of 347 and all 3 different answers you get will still be prime. Can you work out that number?

347

*The **347th** day of the year is December 13*

This amazing photo ...

... shows the International Space Station passing the Moon.

It was shot by Dylan O'Donnell with a digital SLR camera and a telescope in June 2015 as the ISS whizzed over Australia. Now, when I say 'whizzed by', I mean it – the ISS took a mere 0.33 seconds to travel past the moon, as seen from Earth!

Sure, the ISS is 109 × 73 × 20 m, so it would sit on about an entire football field, but the exercise required such precision that Dylan had been waiting 12 months before firing a burst of exposures (at 1/1650th of a second) at the exact moment, crossing his fingers and hoping it would show up in review.

It did, Dylan ... you legend!

Image source: http://deography.com/international-space-station-over-australia

348

*The **348th** day of the year is December 14*

Secret geekiness

$348^5 = 5103830227968$ and $381^5 = 8028323765901$ making 348 the smallest number whose fifth power contains exactly the same digits as another fifth power.

Who would have known 348 and 381 shared this geeky little secret?

Palindromic numbers

If you like your palindromic numbers, and hey, who doesn't, 348 is a great springboard from which we can reach $348 + 3 \times 4 \times 8 = 444$; $348 - 3 \times 4 \times 8 = 252$; $348 + (3 + 4 + 8) = 363$ and $348 - (3 + 4 + 8) = 333$ all of which are palindromes.

Productive prime

349 is a prime, the sum of 3 consecutive primes and the last number of the year that will be a member of a twin prime pair.

349 is also the largest year date that is a prime p such that p minus the product of its digits and p plus the product of its digits are both also prime; that means that 349 along with $349 + 3 \times 4 \times 9 = 457$ and $349 - 3 \times 4 \times 9 = 241$ are all prime.

349

*The **349th** day of the year is December 15*

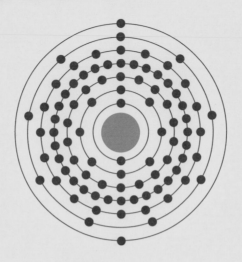

Protactinium

Radioactive elements decay until they reach what's known as a 'steady state'. When the radioactive isotope uranium-238 decays to lead it creates quite a family: uranium-238 begets thorium-234, which begets protactinium, then back to uranium-234, thorium-230 then radium, radon, polonium and finally good old lead. Measuring levels of protactinium is a way to accurately date geological sediments up to 175,000 years old.

A massive shout-out to the awesome Scottish chemist Ada Florence Remfry Hitchins who was the principal research assistant to Nobel Prize-winning chemist Fred Soddy. She played a crucial role in the discovery of protactinium.

350

The 350th day of the year is December 16

Stirling numbers of the second kind

350 is S(7, 4), a Stirling number of the second kind. This doesn't mean 350 is a fine, upstanding number as much as there are 350 ways of partitioning 7 elements into 4 non-empty subsets. So you can arrange A, B, C, D, E, F and G into 4 alphabetical groups like {(AD), (CF), (G), (BE)} 350 different ways.

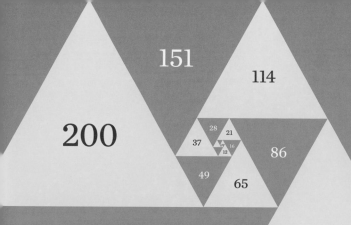

151

114

200

28
21
37
16
12

86

49

65

265

351

Still da man, Padovan!

351 has the distinction of being the 23rd number in the Padovan sequence, which you've probably never heard of (unless you bought my previous *Big Book of Numbers*).

The Padovan numbers are given by the lengths of the sides of the series of equilateral triangles that spiral outwards, as shown in the diagram above.

The sequence starts 1, 1, 1, 2, 3, 4, 5, 7, 9, 12, 16, 21 ... and the nth term of the sequence, P_n, is given by $P_n = P_{n-2} + P_{n-3}$.

351

*The **351st** day of the year is December 17*

On this day in 1903 Orville Wright successfully made the first controlled, powered flight

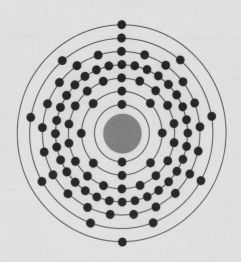

Uranium

On 26 February 1896, the famous French chemist Henri Becquerel noticed that a uranium sample left overnight on an unexposed photographic plate had caused an image to burn into the plate – even though it hadn't been exposed to sunlight. He correctly deduced that the uranium itself was spontaneously giving off invisible rays. Marie Curie later christened this phenomenon 'radioactivity' but it was back on 26 February 1896 that science changed forever.

352

The 352nd day of the year is December 18

Chess plus

There are 352 ways to arrange 9 queens on a 9 × 9 chessboard so that none are attacking another. The 'generalised queens problem' was worked on by, among others, the great mathematician Carl Friedrich Gauss, but we don't yet have any formula to give us the answer for any $n × n$ board.

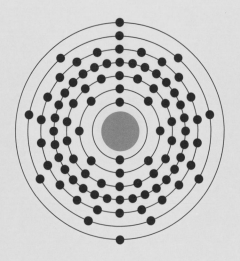

Neptunium

Why would you name an element after the planet Neptune? Well, if you'd just created something out of uranium, that would go next to uranium on the Periodic Table and uranium was named after Uranus, so you'd just look at the planet next to Uranus in the solar system and see that it was Neptune and ... Ta-da!

The sturdiest type of neptunium is called neptunium-237 which has a half-life of 2.14 million years. That's a long time. But get this: even if there had been a trillion tonnes of neptunium back in the original crust of the Earth 4.6 billion years ago, it would all have disappeared ... billions of years ago.

456789101112131415161718192021222324252627282930313233343536373839404142434445464748495051525355657585960616263646566676869707172737475767778798081828384858687888990919293949596979899100

353

The **353rd** *day of the year is* December 19

Palindromic primes

If you have a passion for palindromic primes, then today is the day for you, my friend. You see, 353 is the last day of the year that is a palindromic prime and is the first multi-digit palindromic prime with all prime digits.

Norrie and the fourth power

353 is also the smallest number whose fourth power is equal to the sum of 4 other fourth powers, as discovered by R. Norrie in 1911:

$$353^4 = 30^4 + 120^4 + 272^4 + 315^4.$$

Well done, Nozza.

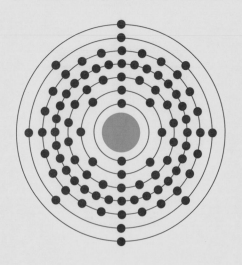

Plutonium

Uranium is named after the planet Uranus; neptunium after Neptune; plutonium after ... you guessed it ... the *former* planet of our solar system, Pluto. Say what? Yep, in 2006 the International Astronomical Union downgraded Pluto from planet to 'dwarf planet' status – but that's another story for another book.

If the 94th element is called plutonium, why is its chemical symbol Pu? According to John Emsley who wrote the bible on this subject, the discoverers of plutonium – Glenn Seaborg, Arthur Wahl and Joseph Kennedy – liked the letters Pu because it sounded a little bit rude. And they say geeks have no sense of humour!

1234567891011121314151617181920212223242526272829303132333435363738394041424344454647484950515
545556575859606162636465666768697071727374757677787980818283848586878889909192939495969798 99

354

The **354th** *day of the year is December 20*

Prime cuts

The number 121,339,693,967 is prime, but dropping 1 digit off at a time from the left, the numbers 21339693967, 1339693967, 339693967, 39693967, 9693967, 693967, 93967, 3967, 967, 67 and 7 are also all prime. This makes 121339693967 a 12-digit, left-truncatable prime. There are 354 of them.

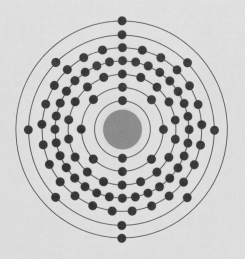

Americium

Though you may never have heard of americium, you'll find it in smoke alarms in millions of homes and buildings around the world. Your average smoke detector contains about 150 micrograms of americium oxide.

Americium is the only element whose discovery was announced on a children's radio show. On 11 November 1945, American chemist Glenn Seaborg was a guest on 'Quiz Kids'. He revealed that the US World War II secret weapons program had produced americium and curium. Now that's geek radio gold!

3456789101112131415161718192021222324252627282930313233343536373839404142434445464748495051525 555657585960616263646566676869707172737475767778798081828384858687888990919293949596979899100

The best pi in town

355 is almost exactly 113π. 'How close?' I hear you ask. Well, actually very close:

113π = 354.9999699...

No year day is closer. In fact, $355/113$ is such a good approximation of π that to do any better you have to jump all the way out to $52163/16604$.

Other cute but less accurate approximations of π include:

$9/5 + \sqrt{9/5} = 3.14164...$ and $7^{7/4^9} = 3.14157...$

355

The 355th day of the year is December 21

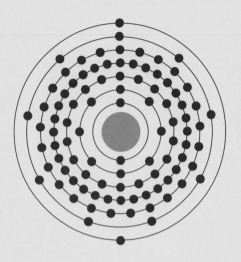

Curium

With 96 protons in its nucleus, meet curium, named after the legendary husband and wife team, Marie and Pierre Curie. Polish born Marie was the first woman to win a Nobel Peace Prize, the first person to win 2, and the only person to win Nobel prizes in different fields (chemistry *and* physics). She was a total gun.

One way to reduce the world's reserves of the dangerous and highly radioactive element plutonium is to bombard it with neutrons turning it into the much less nasty and more useful curium.

1234567891011121314151617181920212223242526272829303132333435363738394041424344454647484950515253
5455565758596061626364656667686970717273747576777879808182838485868788899091929394959697989991

356

*The **356th** day of the year is December 22*

One last selfie

There are 356 ways to partition the number 36 into distinct parts without any part being the number 1.

We spoke about self numbers back on October 4. Well, 356 is also a self number and is in fact the last one we'll encounter this year.

On this day in 1887 Mathematician Srinivasa Ramanujan was born

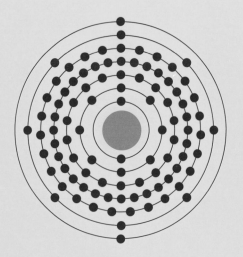

Berkelium

Some 2 billion years ago in what is now Gabon in central Africa, up to 20 natural nuclear reactors were in action. They ran on uranium for fuel and used a local water supply for moderation. These reactors functioned for up to a billion years and while berkelium is today only produced in labs and facilities, it was quite likely produced in the Gabon reactors all those years ago.

By the way, berkelium gets its name from Berkeley, California, the location of the University of California Radiation Laboratory where it was discovered in December 1949.

Pascal's triangle

There are 357 odd numbers in the first 46 rows of Pascal's arithmetic triangle. The left and right edges are all 1s and we get any internal entry by adding the 2 numbers above it together.

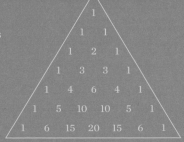

357

The **357th** day of the year is December 23

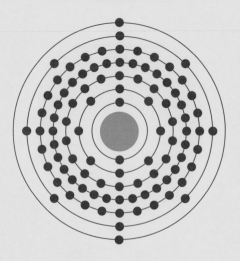

Californium

Despite being extremely rare and only ever found today when synthesised in laboratories or reactors, you can pick up a microgram of californium for the comparatively cheap price of $10. When I say 'you can pick up' I strongly recommend you don't pick it up, or even attempt to buy it in the first place.

When a small amount of californium is injected into cervical cancer tumours, the eruption of neutrons from the californium devastates the tumour, shrinking it in size and often extending the lives of patients for 10 years or more.

358

The 358th day of the year is December 24

Three five eight

is twice a prime, hence a semiprime, and is also the sum of 6 consecutive primes starting at 47. See, I didn't even get you to work that out yourself, I just told you where the sequence started. I'm getting soft as we approach Christmas!

A prime addition

The sum of the first 358 prime numbers is 398,771 which is itself a prime number.

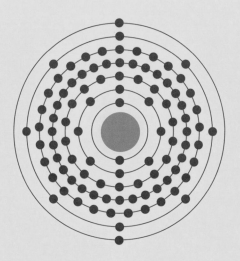

Einsteinium

Einsteinium was discovered in the debris of the first thermonuclear explosion which took place on 1 November 1952 on the Pacific island of Eniwetok. The explosion, codenamed 'Mike', was the forerunner of the development of the hydrogen bomb. After the blast, less than 200 atoms of the new element were found on a neighbouring atoll, but that was enough to identify einsteinium. Although the new element was detected in 1952, the military project was so sensitive the discovery was not announced until 3 years later.

4 5 6 7 8 9 10 11 12 13 14 15 16 17 18 19 20 21 22 23 24 25 26 27 28 29 30 31 32 33 34 35 36 37 38 39 40 41 42 43 44 45 46 47 48 49 50 51 52 53 54 55 56 57 58 59 60 61 62 63 64 65 66 67 68 69 70 71 72 73 74 75 76 77 78 79 80 81 82 83 84 85 86 87 88 89 90 91 92 93 94 95 96 97 98 99 100

Three five nine

is a Sophie Germain prime and the last safe prime for the year. If you start with $n = 89$ and iterate $2n + 1$ you will get a string of primes that includes 359, namely 89, 179, 359, 719, 1439 and 2879. The next number on this list is 5759 but can you show this is composite?

359

The 359th day of the year is December 25

On this day in 1642
Isaac Newton was born

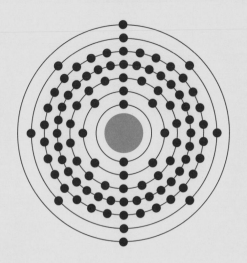

Fermium

Finally, meet fermium. Also discovered following 'Mike', the fallout of the nuclear tests on Eniwetok in 1952, it's the element furthest up the Periodic Table that can be produced in a nuclear reactor. But it's a bugger to pin down. Recall, isotopes of an element have the same number of protons, but a different number of neutrons in their centre (nucleus). Well, when you create 1 type of fermium (fermium-257) it almost immediately grabs a neutron and becomes a different isotope, fermium-258. Now while fermium-257 is pretty stable, fermium-258 has a half-life of only 0.37 milliseconds and so vanishes almost instantly. Have your selfie sticks ready, and smile with me as we wave goodbye to the first 100 elements!

360

The 360th day of the year is December 26

On this day in 1791 Mathematician/inventor Charles Babbage was born

Explementary!

360 is the number of degrees in a circle, and there is a (rather new) word for 2 angles that sum to 360 degrees. They are called 'explementary'.

360 is a highly composite number: it has 24 divisors, more than any number less than 360; no number has more divisors until we get to 720, which has 30.

★★★★★★★★★

360 is the smallest number that is divisible by 9 of the 10 numbers 1 to 10. Can you tell which number from 1 to 10 inclusive is not a factor of 360?

Under perfect conditions, the most stars that you can see is about 2500.

'Perfect conditions' means far from contaminating light and with no Moon in the sky, too. This 2500 is a long way from the 'million' often mentioned in songs or phrases.

What makes a square?

$361 = 19^2$ and happens to be the sum of consecutive triangular numbers: $361 = 171 + 190 = T_{18} + T_{19}$.

In fact, you can see from the diagram here that the sum of 2 consecutive triangular numbers has to be a square; for example, $T_3 + T_4 = 6 + 10 = 16 = 4^2$. In general, $T_n + T_{n+1} = (n+1)^2$.

361

*The **361st** day of the year is December 27*

MADRID
by numbers

US$3.5 billion
The approximate value of the
Real Madrid Football Club.

250
The average number of 'cloud free' days in Madrid – making it Europe's sunniest capital.

1 per 192
There is around 1 bar per every 192 people in Madrid, making it one very relaxed city!

362
The 362nd day of the year is December 28

Big wood

Back on September 6 we met the 78-digit prime Woodall number W_{249}.

Well, $W_{362} = 362 \times 2^{362} - 1$ is also prime. While it's big, with over 100 digits, it's nowhere near the biggest prime Woodall number we know. That is currently $W_{3752948}$ which has 1,129,757 digits!

25,000

The capacity of Toros de Las Ventas, Madrid's most famous bullfighting ring.

1725

The year in which the world's oldest restaurant, Restaurante Sobrino de Botín, (according to *Guinness World Records*), was founded.

650 m

Madrid's elevation above sea level. As such, it is Europe's highest capital.

12 midnight

The time lots of people feel Madrid really starts to come alive – many locals still take a brief siesta and some shops close to recharge their batteries.

0 km

The centre of Puerta del Sol in Madrid is the point from which all Spanish road distances are officially measured. Similar to the sandstone obelisk in Sydney's Macquarie Place Park just near Circular Quay.

Ask your mother

363 is the sum of 9 consecutive primes and is also the sum of the first 5 positive powers of 3. If you'd like to get that as a tattoo, well, I'd check with Mum first, but make sure you show the tattooist this:

$363 = 23 + 29 + 31 + 37 + 41 + 43 + 47 + 53 + 59 = 3^5 + 3^4 + 3^3 + 3^2 + 3^1$

Heavenly harmonies

363 is the numerator of the seventh harmonic number, which is a fancy way of saying it's the number on the top of the fraction $1/1 + 1/2 + 1/3 + 1/4 + 1/5 + 1/6 + 1/7 = 363/140$.

363

The *363rd day of the year is December 29*

Knight tours

If you put a standard 64-square 8 × 8 chessboard on each face of a cube, there would be 384 squares. What's this got to do with 364, you ask? Well, not a lot – but there aren't 384 days in a year and I just love this puzzle!

The great British puzzlist Henry Dudeney once set himself the task of devising a complete 'knight's tour' of a cube, each of whose sides is a chessboard. Starting at the golden knight, a successful

tour would take you through the labelled path and onwards, landing on every square exactly once before returning to its starting position.

364 *is* the total number of gifts in the *Twelve Days of Christmas* song: 1 + (2 + 1) + (3 + 2 + 1) ... which is a series of triangular numbers. We can work this out using the formula for the sum of the first n triangular numbers $S_n = n \times (n + 1) \times (n + 2) / 6$, for $n = 12$.

In 1972, American astronaut Eugene Cernan wrote his daughter's initials on the surface of the Moon.

Those initials will still be visible in 50,000 years.

Is this the end?

We've reached the final day of the year and what better way to celebrate such an occasion than with some squares and arithmetic?

365 is the sum of 2 squares in 2 ways. It can also be expressed as the sum of 3 consecutive squares.

Can you work out the 3 ways of expressing 365?

Once you've done that, that's all for the mathematical calendar. Happy New Year!

365

*The **365th** day of the year is December 31*

Answers!

Page 6
1 + 2 + 4 + 7 + 14 = 28, making January 28 a 'perfect' day.

Page 7
7! = 7 × 6 × 5 × 4 × 3 × 2 × 1 = 5040 so 2 × 7! = 10,080. The number of minutes in a week = 7 × 24 × 60 = 10,080. Similarly, there are 10! = 10 × 9 × 8 × 7 × 6 × 5 × 4 × 3 × 2 × 1 = 3,628,800 seconds in 6 weeks.

Page 10
Adding up the digits of any of these pandigital numbers we get 0 + 1 + 2 + ... + 8 + 9 = 45. But a branch of mathematics called 'number theory' tells us that if the sum of the digits of a number is divisible by 9, then the original number is also divisible by 9. Now 45 is divisible by 9 so we know that the original number, containing 0, 1, 2, 3, 4, 5, 6, 7, 8 and 9 in any order is divisible by 9. None of these pandigitals is prime.

Page 14
To work these out, notice that 1 + 2 + 3 + 4 + 5 + 6 + 7 + 8 = 36 so to land on 0 you are just breaking the numbers 1, 2, 3, 4, 5, 6, 7 and 8 into groups that both add up to 18. For example, (4, 6, 8) and (1, 2, 3, 5, 7) so we can put plus signs in front of 1 group and minus signs in front of the other to get + 1 + 2 + 3 − 4 + 5 − 6 + 7 − 8 = 0 as does − 1 − 2 − 3 + 4 − 5 + 6 − 7 + 8.

Page 25
$10^2 = 6^2 + 8^2$ and $13^2 = 12^2 + 5^2$.

Page 27
0, 1, 8, 17, 18 and 26.

Page 28
1 + 2 + 4 + 8 + 16 + 31 + 62 + 124 + 248 = 496 and $1^3 + 3^3 + 5^3 + 7^3 = 496$.

Page 32
$32 = 2^4 + 4^2$

Page 41
41 = 2 + 3 + 5 + 7 + 11 + 13

Page 48
1, 2, 3, 4, 6, 8, 12, 16, 24 and 48.

Page 51
ANSWER: 3 × 50c, 4 × 20c, 1 × 5c and 4 × 2c is $2.43 from which I can't give you exactly $2.00.

ANSWER: 3 × $1, 1 × 50c, 4 × 20c and 1 × 5c is one of the many ways you could make $4.35 but can't create exactly $4.00.

Page 54
$54 = 2^2 + 5^2 + 5^2 = 1^2 + 2^2 + 7^2 = 3^2 + 3^2 + 6^2$

Page 56
1 2 3 4
2 1 4 3
3 4 1 2
4 3 2 1

1 2 3 4
2 4 1 3
3 1 4 2
4 3 2 1

1 2 3 4
2 3 4 1
3 4 1 2
4 1 2 3

1 2 3 4
2 1 4 3
3 4 2 1
4 3 1 2

Page 58
7 which generates 49, 97, 130, 10, 1, 1 ...

Page 59
101 5 71
29 59 89
47 113 17

Page 62
$62 = 2^2 + 3^2 + 7^2 = 1^2 + 5^2 + 6^2$

Page 71
$71^3 = 357{,}911$ which is the odd numbers 3, 5, 7, 9 and 11 joined together or 'concatenated'.

366

*The **366th** day of the year happens ... sometimes.*

The end

Now, a year doesn't usually have a 366th day, but this book will be read most often in 2016 – a leap year – so in the spirit of generosity I have one last number fact.

366 is the number of days in a leap year. They occur every 4 years, so if the year is divisble by 4, say 2016, 2020, 2024 and so on, it is a leap year.

But did you know the centuries, 1700, 1800, 1900 and so on, are *not* leap years?

And to fully complicate things, this rule about centuries does not apply to every 4th century. So 2000, 2400 and so on, *are* leap years. Not that we're likely to make the next one.

Page 76
$25^2 = 625$

Page 78
$78 = 1^2 + 2^2 + 3^2 + 8^2 = 1^2 + 4^2 + 5^2 + 6^2 = 2^2 + 3^2 + 4^2 + 7^2$

Page 80
1117 and 9767.

Page 85
$93 = 3 \times 31, 94 = 2 \times 47, 95 = 5 \times 19$

Page 90
$90^3 = 729,000$ and $728,{}^{999}/_{89} = 8191 = 2^{13} - 1$ so because 13 and 8191 are both prime, 8191 is Mersenne.

Page 96
$14^2 - 10^2 = 196 - 100 = 96$ and the real tough one, $25^2 - 23^2 = 96$.

Page 98
${}^{49}/_{98} = {}^4/_8 = {}^1/_2$

Page 102
$102 = 19 + 23 + 29 + 31$

Page 103
$103^2 = 10,609$ and $301^2 = 90,601$.

Page 108
$108 = 3^3 + 9^2 = 2^3 + 10^2$

Page 109
109 has 3 distinct digits, whereas $109^2 = 11,881$ has only 2.

Page 115
The only other 2 examples you need to look at are $2! - 2 = 0$ and $3! - 3 = 3$.

Page 117
ANSWER: $117 = 11^2 - 2^2 = 5^3 - 2^3$

ANSWER: $999,999 = 3^3 \times 7 \times 11 \times 13 \times 37$

Page 119
ANSWER: $5! - 1 = 119 = 7 \times 17$

ANSWER: $119 = 17 + 19 + 23 + 29 + 31$

Page 121
$n = 3$

Page 124
$124 = 5 + 7 + 11 + 13 + 17 + 19 + 23 + 29$

Page 125
$125 = 11^2 + 2^2 = 10^2 + 5^2$

Page 127
$211 - 1 = 2047 = 23 \times 89$ so it is not a Mersenne prime.

Page 128
$128 = 109 + 19 = 97 + 31 = 67 + 61$

Page 129
$129 = 12 + 82 + 82 = 22 + 22 + 112 = 22 + 52 + 102 = 42 + 72 + 82$

Page 132
$12 + 13 + 21 + 23 + 31 + 32 = 132$

Page 133
'Unhappy' numbers get caught in the loop 89, 145, 42, 20, 4, 16, 37, 58, 89.

Page 135
$\$1.35 = 1 \times 50c + 4 \times 20c + 1 \times 5c$
$(50 + 4 \times 20 + 5)$

Page 136
Starting with 136 we get the sum of the cubes of its digits is $1^3 + 3^3 + 6^3 = 244$. Now, summing the cubes of those digits we get $2^3 + 4^3 + 4^3 = 136$.

Page 139
ANSWER: 181 and 191

ANSWER: ${}^{139}/_{973} = {}^1/_7$

Page 145
${}^{145}/_{435} = {}^1/_3$

Page 148
$125,433 = 231 \times 543$; $378,450 = 435 \times 870$; $567,648 = 657 \times 864$

Page 149
$149 = 6^2 + 7^2 + 8^2$

Page 152
$152 = 3 + 149 = 43 + 109 = 73 + 79 = 13 + 139$

Page 153
370, 371 and 407.

Page 159
ANSWER: $159 = 47 + 53 + 59$

ANSWER: Using the formula $W_n = n \times 2^n - 1$ we get $W_1 = 1, W_2 = 7, W_3 = 23, W_4 = 63$ and $W_5 = 5 \times 2^5 - 1 = 5 \times 32 - 1 = 159$.

Page 162
Writing $12^2 + 4^2 + 1^2 + 1^2$ as (12, 4, 1, 1) the other answers are (11, 6, 2, 1), (11, 4, 4, 3), (10, 7, 3, 2), (10, 6, 5, 1), (9, 8, 4, 1), (9, 7, 4, 4), (9, 6, 6, 3) and (8, 8, 5, 3).

Page 164
$16 + 3 = 19, 16 - 3 = 13, 14 + 3 = 17, 14 - 3 = 11, 64 + 3 = 67, 64 - 3 = 61$, all of which are prime.

Page 165
$165 \times 951 = 156,915$

Page 166
$166/664 = 1/4$

Page 167
$167 = 5^3 + 2^3 + 2^3 + 2^3 + 2^3 + 2^3 + 1^3 + 1^3 = 4^3 + 4^3 + 3^3 + 2^3 + 1^3 + 1^3 + 1^3 + 1^3$

Page 178
$178^5 = 178{,}689{,}902{,}368$ – well done if you got this out!

Page 179
$179 \times 725 = 129{,}775$

Page 182
$182/819 = 2/9$

Page 183
328 and 329 concatenate to form $328{,}329 = 573^2$.

Page 185
$185 = 4^2 + 13^2 = 8^2 + 11^2$

Page 186
$7 \times 5 \times 3 \times 2 - 4 \times 3 \times 2 \times 1 = 186$

Page 187
$187 / 286 = 17/26$, $187/385 = 17/35$, $187/748 = 1/4$, $187/484 = 17/44$, $187/583 = 17/53$, $187/682 = 17/62$, and $187/880 = 17/80$.

Page 188
$188 = 7 + 181 = 31 + 157 = 37 + 151 = 61 + 127 = 79 + 109$

Page 189
$11 \times 13 \times 17 \times 19 = 46{,}189$

Page 192
219, 273, 327

Page 194
ANSWER: $194 = 13^2 + 4^2 + 3^2 = 12^2 + 7^2 + 1^2 = 12^2 + 5^2 + 5^2 = 11^2 + 8^2 + 3^2 = 9^2 + 8^2 + 7^2$

ANSWER: $194 = 13^2 + 5^2$

Page 197
$17 + 19 + 23 + 29 + 31 + 37 + 41 = 197$

Page 199
ANSWER: $199 = 61 + 67 + 71 = 31 + 37 + 41 + 43 + 47$

ANSWER: $199/995 = 1/5$

Page 200
204 is also unprimeable. The first odd unprimeable number is 325.

Page 201
209, 210

Page 204
$125{,}460 = 246 \times 510$

Page 206
5000 fIvE thOUsAnd.

Page 207
$89 + 67 + 41 + 5 + 3 + 2 = 89 + 61 + 47 + 5 + 3 + 2 = 207$

Page 208
$2^2 + 3^2 + 5^2 + 7^2 + 11^2 = 4 + 9 + 25 + 49 + 121 = 208$

Page 209
No it won't because $1^7 + 2^6 + 3^5 + 4^4 + 5^3 + 6^2 + 7^1 = 732$ which is greater than 365.

Page 215
The denominators in each sum are (2, 3, 7, 42), (2, 3, 8, 24), (2, 3, 9, 18), (2, 3, 10, 15), (2, 3, 12, 12), (2, 4, 5, 20), (2, 4, 6, 12), (2, 4, 8, 8), (2, 5, 5 10), (2, 6, 6, 6), (3, 3, 4, 12), (3, 3, 6, 6), (3, 4, 4, 6) and (4, 4, 4, 4) but the fractions can be written in various orders hence the 215 sequences.

Page 216
I thought that if $3^2 + 4^2 = 5^2$ and $3^3 + 4^3 + 5^3 = 6^3$, then $3^4 + 4^4 + 5^4 + 6^4$ will equal 7^4 and we can just keep going on up through the powers. It took me about 5 minutes to confirm that $3^4 + 4^4 + 5^4 + 6^4 = 2258$ and $7^4 = 2401$. Still hurts today ;-)

Page 217
ANSWER: $217 = 6^3 + 1^3 = 9^3 - 8^3$

ANSWER: $237 = 3 \times 79$

Page 220
For 220, $1 + 2 + 4 + 5 + 10 + 11 + 20 + 22 + 44 + 55 + 110 = 284$ and for 284 we get $1 + 2 + 4 + 71 + 142 = 220$.

Page 221
ANSWER: $221 = 37 + 41 + 43 + 47 + 53 = 11 + 13 + 17 + 19 + 23 + 29 + 31 + 37 + 41$

ANSWER: $221 = 5^2 + 14^2 = 102 + 11^2$

Page 223
$223 = 71 + 73 + 79 = 19 + 23 + 29 + 31 + 37 + 41 + 43$

Page 225
$1^3 + 2^3 + 3^3 + 4^3 + 5^3 + 6^3 = 441 = 21^2 = (1 + 2 + 3 + 4 + 5 + 6)^2$

Page 226
$3!^3 + 2!^3 + 1!^3 + 0!^3 = 6^3 + 2^3 + 1^3 + 1^3 = 216 + 8 + 1 + 1 = 226$

Page 227
$227 = (5 + 37) + 5 \times 37$ with 5 and 37 prime.

Page 229
239 gives us $239 + 932 = 1171$ which is prime.

Page 230
230 = 2 × 5 × 23 and 231 = 3 × 7 × 11.

Page 231
$231 = 2^2 + 3^2 + 7^2 + 13^2$

Page 232
The proper divisors of 945 add up to 1 + 3 + 5 + 7 + 9 + 15 + 21 + 27 + 35 + 45 + 63 + 105 + 135 + 189 + 315 = 975 > 945. Well done! You can see why Nicomachus didn't spot this one!

Page 233
The sequence 1, 1, 2, 3, 5, 8, 13, 21, 34, 55, 89, 144, 233 ... contains 233 as its 13th term. Now, some people start the sequence 0, 1, 1 labelling 0 the 0th term and this doesn't affect 233 as 13th.

Page 234
234 + (2 + 3 + 4) = 243 = 3^5 and 234 − (2 + 3 + 4) = 225 = 15^2.

Page 238
52 – don't worry if you gave up, that's just about the hardest question I've asked in the book. If you got it, you're a calculating gun with impressive focus and concentration.

Page 239
$239 = 5^3 + 3^3 + 3^3 + 3^3 + 2^3 + 2^3 + 2^3 + 2^3 + 1^3 = 4^3 + 4^3 + 3^3 + 3^3 + 3^3 + 3^3 + 1^3 + 1^3 + 1^3$

Page 240
360 has 24 divisors.

Page 242
The divisors of 242 are 1, 2, 11, 22, 121 and 242. For 243 we get 1, 3, 9, 27, 81 and 243; for 244 we have 1, 2, 4, 61, 122 and 244 and finally 245 also with 6 divisors, namely 1, 5, 7, 35, 49 and 245.

Page 247
247 = 50,123 − 49,876

Page 248
2, 4, 8, 2^4, 4 × 8, 8^2, 2^4 × 8, 2^8

Page 250
$250 = 5^3 + 5^3 = 15^2 + 5^2 = 13^2 + 9^2$

Page 252
252 = 12 × 21

Page 254
The 22nd triangular number is 253 so 22 slices of a pizza will yield at most 254 pieces.

Page 258
258 = 59 + 61 + 67 + 71 and 159 = 47 + 53 + 59.

Page 259
'One million million' is 1,000,000,000,000 (which used to be called a billion by some but is now called a trillion by pretty much everyone). What they all agree on is that 999,999,999,999 = 259 × 3,861,003,861. Also 999,999 = 259 × 3861.

Page 264
264 = 24 + 42 + 26 + 62 + 46 + 64 = 11 + 13 + 17 + 19 + 23 + 29 + 31 + 37 + 41 + 43

Page 268
For the digits of 268: 2 × 6 × 8 = 96 = 6 × 16 = 6 × (2 + 6 + 8).

Page 269
269 × 581 = 156,289 and 269 × 842 = 226,498. Well done if you got this!

Page 271
271 = 7 + 11 + 13 + 17 + 19 + 23 + 29 + 37 + 41 + 43

Page 272
ANSWER (Snake problem, solution given by Alex Bellos in theguardian.com):
Rewrite the snake as an equation:
a + (13b/c) + d + 12e − f − 11 + (gh/i) − 10 = 66
We are trying to find a, b, c, d, e, f, g, h and i, which we know are some combination of the digits 1, 2, 3, 4, 5, 6, 7, 8 and 9.
There are 362,880 possible combinations of the digits 1 to 9 placed in 9 slots.
We can tidy the equation to:
a + (13b/c) + d + 12e − f +(gh/i) = 66 + 11 + 10 = 87
or
a + d − f + (13b/c) + 12e + (gh/i) = 87
From here we can assume that b/c and gh/i will be whole numbers, and also that we don't want 13b/c to be too big. Knowing this, we start plugging numbers in and seeing how we go.
There is more than one solution, so there are many difference guesses that will lead to the right number.
To keep the term 13b/c as small as we can, let b = 2 and c = 1.
Which gets us to
a + d − f + 26 + 12e + (gh/i) = 87
or
a + d − f + 12e + (gh/i) = 61
The numbers remaining are the digits from 3 to 9. They include the prime numbers 3, 5 and 7. Let's get rid of them so they don't complicate the other terms.
Let a = 3, d = 5 and f = 7.
Which leaves us with
3 + 5 − 7 + 12e +(gh/i) = 61
or
12e +(gh/i) = 60
The numbers remaining are 4, 6, 8, 9.
Playing around with these gets us
e = 4, g = 9, h = 8, i = 6
48 + (72/6) = 48 + 12 = 60

ANSWER (Pronic numbers):
272 = 16 × 17

Page 273

ANSWER (Birthday problem):
Albert is told the month, so either May, June, July or August. Bernard is told the day, so either 14, 15, 16, 17, 18 or 19.

Albert says I don't know when Cheryl's birthday is, but I know that Bernard doesn't know too.

It's obvious after just being told the month that Albert doesn't know when her birthday is. We can ignore that bit. But the rest of the statement is important.

If Bernard was told 18 or 19, he would know the birthday, because these numbers only appear once. This could only happen if Albert was told May or June.

So for Albert to know that Bernard does not know, Albert must therefore have been told July or August (because this rules out Bernard being told 18 or 19).

Line 2) Bernard: At first I don't know when Cheryl's birthday is, but now I know.

From Albert's statement, Bernard now knows Albert has been told July or August.

If Bernard was told 14 he would not know if it was July 14 or August 14. But if he was told 15, 16 or 17 he would know which date was Cheryl's birthday.

So Bernard must have been told 15, 16 or 17.

Line 3) Albert: Then I also know when Cheryl's birthday is.

So after Bernard's statement, Albert knows that the possible dates are July 16, August 15 and August 17. If Albert now knows the date he must have been told July. If he had been told August, he would not know if August 15 or 17 is the birthday.

Cheryl's Birthday is July 16.

Page 274

ANSWER (Parking problem): 87 (the numbers are upside down).

ANSWER: 0, 0, 1, 1, 2, 4, 7, 13, 24, 44, 81, 149, 274

Page 275

ANSWER (Nine Schoolgirls Problem):
Draw the girls in a grid like this:
A B C
D E F
G H I
On day 1 (A, B, C) walk together as do (D, E, F) and (G, H, I).

To make sure B doesn't walk with A on day 2, slide the second column down 1 spot each and bring the H around to the top. With the third column do the same but slide it 'up' to make sure that B and C separate.

On day 2 you get:
A H F
D B I
G E C
On day 3, slide the columns again to get a new set of combinations.

On day 4, take the original columns as your groups.

ANSWER: $176/275 = 16/25$; $275/473 = 25/43$; $275/671 = 25/61$

Page 278

$277^2 = 76{,}729$ and $278^2 = 77{,}284$.

Page 280

$H_8 = 1 + 1/2 + 1/3 + 1/4 + 1/5 + 1/6 + 1/7 + 1/8 = 761/280$

Page 283

ANSWER: Twin primes differ by 2 so it's either 281 or 285 but 285 is obviously divisible by 5, so 281 and 283 are twin primes.

ANSWER: $283 = 2^5 + 8^1 + 3^5$

Page 286

$286/385 = 26/35$; $286/583 = 26/53$; $286/781 = 26/71$ and $187/286 = 17/26$.

Page 287

$287 = 89 + 97 + 101 = 47 + 53 + 59 + 61 + 67 = 17 + 19 + 23 + 29 + 31 + 37 + 41 + 43 + 47$

Page 289

Yes, $289 = (8 + 9)^2$ so 289 is a Friedman number.

Page 290

$290 = 2 \times 5 \times 29 = 67 + 71 + 73 + 79$

Page 296

(10), (9, 1), (8, 2), (7, 3), (6, 4), (7, 2, 1), (6, 3, 1), (5, 4, 1), (5, 3, 2), (4, 3, 2, 1)

Page 297

$703^2 = 494{,}209$ and $494 + 209 = 703$; $999^2 = 998{,}001$ and $998 + 001 = 999$, indeed all strings 9 ... are Kaprekar.

Page 300

$300 = 149 + 151 = 13 + 17 + 19 + 23 + 29 + 31 + 37 + 41 + 43 + 47$

Page 307
$307^2 = 94,249$

Page 310
Written in terms of powers of 6, we get
$310 = 216 + 2 \times 36 + 3 \times 6 + 4 = 1234$ base 6.

Page 311
199 and 337, the only other such digit triples there are.

Page 314
$314 = 16^2 + 7^2 + 3^2 = 13^2 + 12^2 + 1^2 = 13^2 + 9^2 + 8^2 = 12^2 + 11^2 + 7^2$

Page 315
$315^2 = 25^3 + 26^3 + 27^3 + 28^3 + 29^3$

Page 316
$316 = 91 + 105 + 120 = T_{13} + T_{14} + T_{15}$

Page 319
ANSWER: $319^3 = 32,461,759$. You can proudly tell your friends that 319 is the largest number whose cube has no repeated digits.

ANSWER: In base 2, 319 is written as 100,111,111 with 6 consecutive 1s. Neat, hey?

Page 324
$16 = 3 + 3 + 3 + 3 + 4$ and $3 \times 3 \times 3 \times 3 \times 4 = 324$.

Page 325
$325 = 1^2 + 18^2 = 6^2 + 17^2 = 10^2 + 15^2$

Page 327
327, $2 \times 327 = 654$ and $3 \times 327 = 981$. This property also holds for 192 (384, 576), 219 (438, 657) and 273 (546, 819). Interestingly, 192 and 219 are 'anagrams' of each other, as are 273 and 327 and their respective doubles and triples also match up.

Page 328
The 8 divisors of 328 are 1, 2, 4, 8, 41, 82, 164, 328 and $328 = 8 \times 41$.

Page 331
ANSWER: No, $333333331 = 17 \times 19607843$.

ANSWER: Using the prime numbers 2, 3, 5, 7, 11, 13, 17 and 19 we get the first 15 semiprimes 4, 6, 9, 10, 14, 15, 21, 22, 25, 26, 33, 34, 35, 38 and 39. Add them up and you'll get 331.

Page 333
$16^3 + 50^3 + 33^3 = 165,033$

Page 334
$361 = 19 \times 19$ and $362 = 2 \times 181$.

Page 335
$335 = 4 + 6 + 8 + 9 + 10 + 12 + 14 + 15 + 16 + 18 + 20 + 21 + 22 + 24 + 25 + 26 + 27 + 28 + 30$

Page 342
$342 = 18 \times 19$

Page 343
$(3 + 4)^3 = 343$

Page 344
$344 = 7^3 + 1^3$ and $351 = 7^3 + 2^3$ so it's December 17.

Page 345
$345 \times 3523 = 1,215,435$ and the equation only uses the numbers 1, 2, 3, 4 and 5. But did you also spot that $345 = 3 \times 5 \times 23$?

Page 346
$346 = 2 \times 173$ and $3 + 4 + 6 = 2 + 1 + 7 + 3$ so 346 is a Smith number.

Page 347
Adding 2 to any digit of 347 keeps it prime (547, 367 and 349 are prime).

Page 359
$5759 = 13 \times 443$

Page 360
7

Page 365
$365 = 13^2 + 14^2 = 19^2 + 2^2 = 10^2 + 11^2 + 12^2$

Index

38,000

The number of manmade objects that have orbited the Earth since the launch of *Sputnik* in 1957.

9.2×10^{26}

The approximate diameter in metres of the visible Universe.

3.8 cm

The distance the Moon is moving away from the Earth each year.

4.5 billion years

The approximate age of the Moon.

26 days

The length of time it would take a regular passenger airliner to reach the Moon (or 130 days in a car!).

59%

The percentage of the Moon which is visible from Earth.

12

The number of people who have been to the Moon: the astronauts on the *Apollo* missions from 1969 to 1972.